MICHAEL P. McINTYRE, Ph.D., The Ohio State University, is Professor and Chairman of the Department of Geography at San Jose State College. He has also taught at the University of Washington, and The Ohio State, Kent State, and Wayne State Universities. Dr. McIntyre is a member of the Association of American Geographers, California Council of Geography Teachers, and the Association of Pacific Coast Geographers.

PHYSICAL GEOGRAPHY

MICHAEL P. McINTYRE
San Jose State College

THE RONALD PRESS COMPANY · NEW YORK

Library of Congress Catalog Card Number: 66–16851

PRINTED IN THE UNITED STATES OF AMERICA

This volume is respectfully dedicated to

HOWARD H. MARTIN

Emeritus Professor of Geography
University of Washington

Scholar — extraordinary

Mentor — inspirational

Friend — incomparable

Preface

The study of geography involves a great deal more than merely the familiar locating places and coloring maps. Its ultimate aim might properly be described as area analysis. And among those elements that the geographer classifies, locates, describes, and explains in his analysis are two basics: *man* and his *physical environment,* each intimately interwoven one with the other and mutually reciprocal in their relationship.

While recognizing this relationship as the heart of modern geography, we have nonetheless followed the established practice of isolating the physical environment for purposes of pedagogical simplicity, and this book, then, becomes a study of the physical environment in its totality. It is intended to be a one-semester or one-quarter text and is aimed at the typical lower-division student who, more often than not, suffers from a paucity of organized scientific training. Basic principles and broad generalizations are emphasized, for with the entire physical world as the scope of operation and the beginning student with no previous geography background, the gross image becomes of primary significance. The method employed is systematic; the discussion is analytical-descriptive with emphasis on the concept of nature's inherent ecological unity. A special group of eight world maps, in color, located in the back of the book, provides effective visual presentations of this ecological unity with regard to world climates, natural vegetation, topography, population, and the like.

Although maps are not, strictly speaking, a part of physical geography, a chapter dealing with them has been included. It has been placed deliberately near the beginning, for this basic tool of the geographer is a means of communication fully as important as the printed word as he attempts to classify material and present its distributional pattern. The student, constantly utilizing maps as part of his basic equipment, should be fully aware of their variety, advantages, and, too, their limitations. And he should be initiated into the mysteries of map use at an early stage of his geographic education.

Hopefully, this generalized non-technical presentation will, rather than plunge the average lower-division student into a morass of specialized detail, bring to him a fresh unencumbered awareness and a fuller appreciation of those familiar things about him which, in the past, he has observed only casually.

It is a distinct pleasure to acknowledge those who have assisted me in so many ways. The color maps and a number of the black-and-white world maps which appear in this book have been modified from similar maps in the Goode Base Map Series copyright by the University of Chicago. My thanks to the Department of Geography, The University of Chicago, for such use of their maps. To the following go my sincere thanks: Mildred Howell and her colleagues who typed the manuscript—Alice DeLisle, Louise Elsner, Arpra Rivers, Bonnie Rix; the many agencies who so generously made available photographs, maps, and other illustrative materials and who are identified by specific credit lines; my colleagues whose comments, suggestions, and, above all, encouragement have been invaluable to me; and, of course, my students over years who acted unknowingly as a sounding board, alternately complaining and applauding, but always asking searching questions.

MICHAEL P. MCINTYRE

San Jose, California
    January, 1966

Contents

APPENDIXES

PHYSICAL GEOGRAPHY

The Earth in Space

THE SHAPE OF THE EARTH

For most normal purposes, the earth may be regarded properly as a perfect sphere. It is true that geodesists and navigators, with their finite measurements, must take into consideration the slight flattening at the poles and bulging at the equator as a result of rotation, but neither this 27-mile difference in diameter nor the 29,000-foot height of Mt. Everest vs. the 36,000-foot depth of the Marianas Trench marking the maximum crustal relief are of sufficient magnitude when balanced against the total size of the earth to disturb its general sphericity. For our purposes in the following discussions, we may legitimately regard the earth as an absolute sphere.

EARTH MOTIONS

The earth is constantly in motion in two separate and distinct circulations at the same time. We as inhabitants are not immediately aware of this, since we do not stagger about on our moving platform but are held securely through gravity; nor does the wind whistle through our ears, since the atmosphere, also held to the earth by gravity, moves with us. There are, however, a number of readily observable phenomena that are the direct result of these motions. Alternating day and night, the progression of the seasons, and the differing length of day during the year are among them. Also, the rising and setting sun and the movements of many of the heavenly bodies are *apparent* motions rather than actual; these stationary objects appear to migrate as they are observed from a moving planet.

Rotation vs. Revolution

In common parlance, the words "rotation" and "revolution" are exact synonyms, but when used to describe earth motions, they have separate meanings and must be applied properly. "Rotation" is the earth's movement about its axis; "revolution" is its movement about the sun.

Day and night are the result of rotation, as any location will first be turned toward the sun and then away as the earth spins on its axis. This is a constant and steady movement of about 1,000 miles per hour at the equator; this movement is so constant that our system of time is geared to it and reckoned on a 24-hour basis (one rotation). The sun, appearing to wheel around the earth once in every 24 hours, rising in the east and setting in the west, is actually not moving at all. This is an apparent motion viewed from a moving earth and, therefore, the earth must rotate in the *opposite* direction from the sun's apparent motion, or from *west to east*. (Fig. 1–1.)

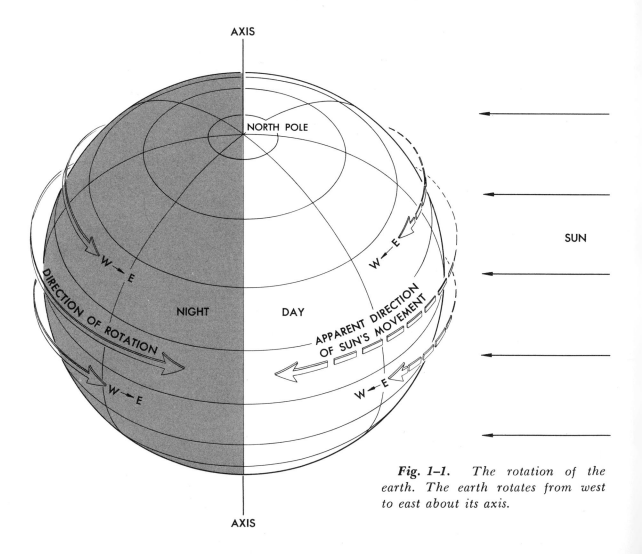

Fig. 1–1. *The rotation of the earth. The earth rotates from west to east about its axis.*

Revolution is a different matter—variations are the rule. The earth's orbit does not describe a perfect circle about the sun, but an ellipse, and the sun is not in the center of the ellipse. Thus, the earth is constantly at different distances from the sun, and the 93,000,000 miles that is so frequently cited as the distance from earth to sun is merely a mean or average.[1] The speed at which the earth follows its orbit varies also, its most rapid advance being in January and its minimal speed in July. Despite these variations, the earth manages to go around the sun in about the same length of time each circuit, but this period does not come out even with our 24-hour days (determined by rotation). It actually measures about 365¼ days and necessitates the familiar leap year every fourth year when we add up the accumulated quarters and splice them onto the tag end of February.

An important resultant of revolution is the seasons; however, revolution is not the complete explanation. There is another factor that, in conjunction with revolution, causes the progression of seasons—the inclination of the earth's axis. The standard statement is that the earth's axis is inclined very close to 23½° from the vertical. This is true, but the following questions may well arise: "How can the vertical be determined when we are dealing with a turning sphere in space?" "Vertical to what?" Obviously, we need a plane of reference from which to determine the vertical before a 23½° variation can be reckoned. There is such a plane. It is called the *ecliptic* and is the plane of the earth's orbit about the sun. The axis then is inclined 23½° from the vertical to this plane and maintains its inclination always pointing in the same direction (parallelism) throughout each revolution. (Fig. 1–2.)

Every year about June 21, the earth is in a position where the inclined axis points directly toward the sun and the Northern Hemisphere is presented so as to receive a maximum of sunlight, while the Southern Hemisphere is tilted away. This results in the shortest and most direct rays of the sun striking a point well north of the equator, but the Southern Hemisphere experiences only low-angle rays that are capable of much less efficient heating. This is our Northern Hemisphere summer.

Three months later, September 21, revolution has carried the earth through a quarter of its orbit, and although the axis continues to be inclined the same amount, this inclination is now at right angles to the sun and both hemispheres receive equal sunlight. In this position, the most direct rays strike the equator, concentrating the greatest heating here midway between the poles. This season is fall.

---

[1] As it happens, the earth is nearest the sun in January and farthest away in July. Obviously, a couple of million miles more or less have no appreciable effect on the temperature of the earth, or our Northern Hemisphere summer would be in January.

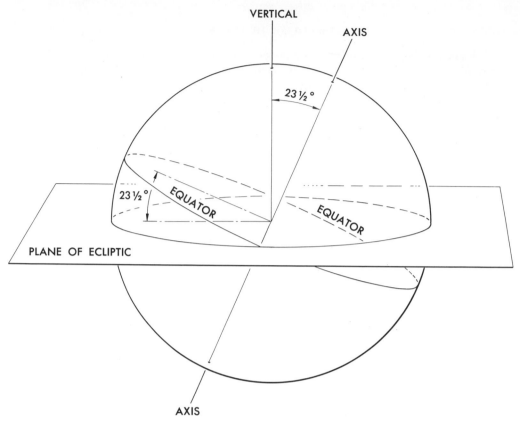

VERTICAL

AXIS

23½°

23½°

EQUATOR

EQUATOR

PLANE OF ECLIPTIC

AXIS

Fig. 1–2. Inclination of the earth's axis. The earth's axis maintains a constant inclination of 23½° from a line vertical to the plane of the ecliptic.

After three more months of revolution, December 21, the earth has reversed its June position. The Southern Hemisphere is now tilted directly toward the sun, and summer prevails as the direct rays strike at a point south of the equator, but only weak, low-angle rays affect the Northern Hemisphere. This is, of course, our winter.

On March 21, after still another quarter-revolution, the earth reaches a point where the axis is once again lined up at right angles to the sun's rays, and both hemispheres receive the same amount of sun as they did in the fall. Now spring has arrived.

Finally, after three more months, the earth returns to its original position of June 21 [2] and it is summer again. (Fig. 1–3.)

Revolution could not accomplish this familiar seasonal sequence alone; revolution plus the earth's axial inclination are required.

[2] These exact dates, the 21st of June, September, December, and March, may vary from the 20th to the 23rd as a result of the speed variations in revolution. However, for our purposes here, we will be consistent and use the 21st.

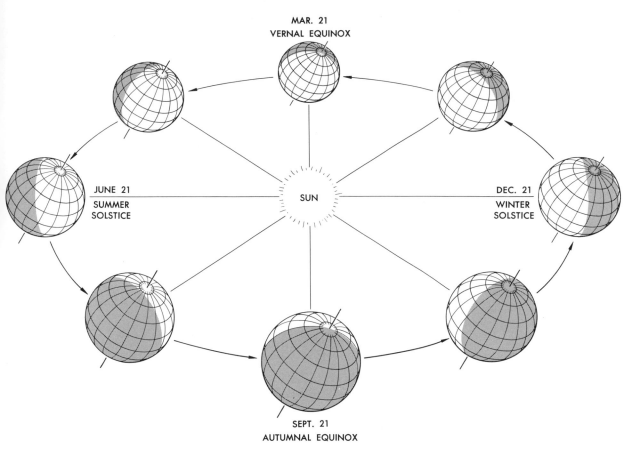

Fig. 1-3. *The revolution of the earth.*

THE TROPICS—CANCER AND CAPRICORN

On every world map and globe, there appears a pair of dashed lines, one in each hemisphere, parallel to the equator and not far from it. Everyone has carefully memorized at one time or another that the northern line is called the Tropic of Cancer and the southern one the Tropic of Capricorn. It is well to know the names, but of more importance is the recognition of why these lines exist in their particular positions. A clue is found in their latitude of $23\frac{1}{2}°$ north and south. (Latitude is numbered in both directions from the equator through a quarter of a 360° circle, with the equator being 0° and each pole 90°. See pp. 11–17 for an explanation of latitude.) This points to a direct relationship between the Tropics and the axial inclination, and in turn the seasons. The Tropic of Cancer may be defined as *the northernmost point on the earth that ever experiences the sun directly overhead at noon.* This only occurs on one day each year—June 21. Conversely, the Tropic of Capricorn is *the southernmost point on the earth that ever experiences the sun directly overhead at noon*—December 21.

These Tropics are the outer limits of the particular phenomenon of the noon overhead sun at least once each year. Only between Cancer and Capricorn does this ever occur. Although these Tropic lines experience the overhead sun only once each year, the entire region between them finds the sun overhead on two dates during the year. The equator, halfway between Cancer and Capricorn, has these two dates equally spaced between June 21 and December 21—September 21 and March 21—but the overhead sun dates of all other locations are unevenly spaced, depending on how close they are to the equator. To us on the earth, it *appears* that the overhead sun migrates from Cancer to Capricorn and back in one year, thus passing over each spot in between twice—once as it moves south and again as it moves north. (Fig. 1–4.)

June 21, when the most direct rays of the sun strike the earth 23½° north of the equator, is called the *summer solstice,* and December 21, when the reverse obtains, is the *winter solstice.* The two midway points between these extremes, when both hemispheres receive equal sunlight and the direct sun's rays are overhead at the equator, are the equinoxes—September 21 the *autumnal equinox,* and March 21 the *vernal equinox.*

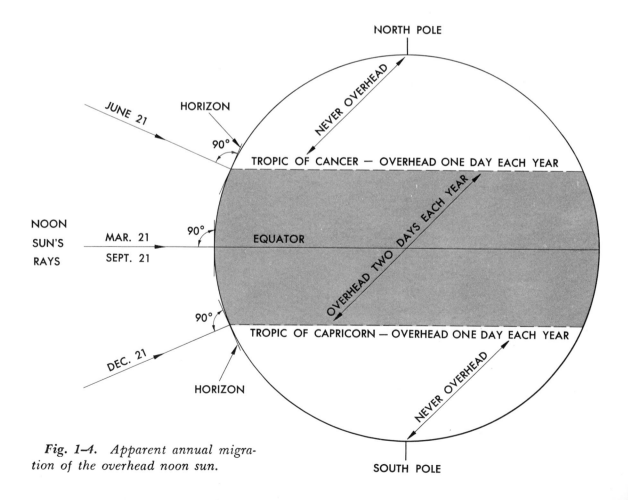

Fig. 1–4. *Apparent annual migration of the overhead noon sun.*

THE ARCTIC AND ANTARCTIC CIRCLES

Also seen on world maps and globes are the dashed lines in each hemisphere some little distance away from the poles. These are, of course, the Arctic and Antarctic Circles and, like the Tropics, mark the outer limits of a special phenomenon peculiar to the polar regions. Again we find a relationship with axial inclination when we discover that the Arctic and Antarctic Circles are 23½° from their respective poles or 66½° from the equator (66½° north or south latitude). These are *the farthest points from each pole that experience at least one day when the sun never sets and at least one day when it never rises each year.* At the Arctic Circle, the day when the sun fails to set is June 21, the summer solstice when the noon sun is overhead at the Tropic of Cancer; the one day when the sun does not rise is December 21, the winter solstice when the noon sun is overhead at the Tropic of Capricorn. The situation is identical at the Antarctic Circle except that the dates are reversed. Within the polar regions enclosed by the Arctic and Antarctic Circles, more than one 24-hour period of light and of dark during each year are the rule. The number of these days increases with the distance traveled toward the poles, culminating in six months of light and six months of dark at the poles themselves.

These peculiarities are brought about by the alternating presentation of each hemisphere, first toward the sun and then away as the earth travels its orbit. During the Northern Hemisphere summer when this hemisphere is tilted toward the sun, the rays of the sun strike beyond the North Pole and, at the same time, fall short of the South Pole. Rotation which causes day and night over the earth is ineffective in the polar areas during this period, for regardless of time of day, the north polar regions remain exposed to continuous sunlight while those areas near the South Pole receive none at all. The distance that the sun's rays reach beyond the North Pole and fall short of the South Pole is at its maximum on June 21 and measures 23½°. On December 21, the sun's rays fall short of the North Pole and strike beyond the South Pole by this same amount. (Fig. 1–5.)

Thus, it can be seen that the middle latitudes, the Northern Hemisphere zone between the Arctic Circle and the Tropic of Cancer, and the Southern Hemisphere zone between the Antarctic Circle and the Tropic of Capricorn, experience neither of these two special phenomena. Those who live near the Arctic or Antarctic Circle will be familiar with extremely long summer days and winter nights. But in each 24-hour period of the year, the sun will set and rise if only for a short time. And even on the margins of the Tropics, although the sun will appear very high in the sky at noon in the summer, it will never be directly overhead.

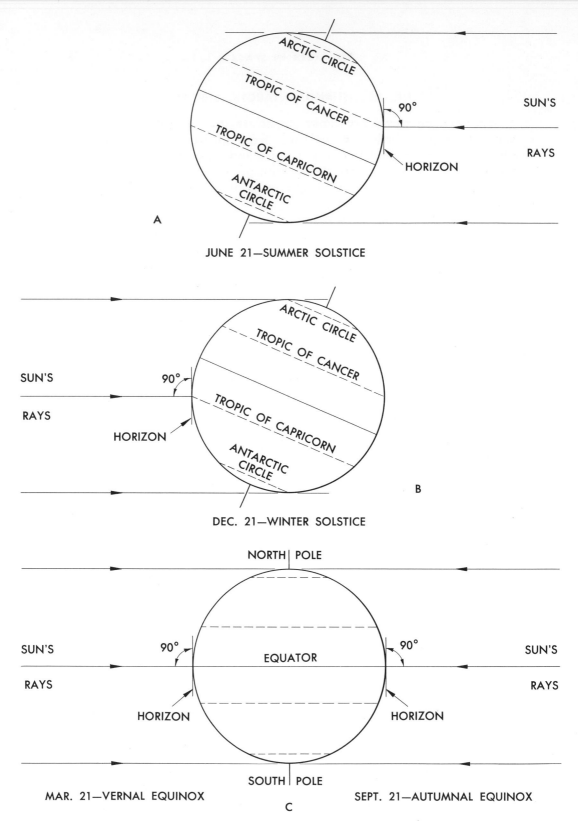

Fig. 1–5. *Earth and sun at the solstices and equinoxes.*

LENGTH OF DAY

Only at the equator are day and night of equal length every day of the year. Elsewhere on the earth, day and night are always of unequal duration, *except for the equinoxes.* On these two critical dates, day and night are each 12 hours long everywhere. Near the equator, the variations of length of day are so small that they are not readily apparent, but as one moves poleward, the differences become striking over a period of a year, until at the poles the extreme of six months of light and six months of dark is reached. Yet even here on September 21, the sun, which has been above the horizon at the North Pole for six months, finally sets. During the first 12 hours of that equinoctial day, the sun has been up, and for the last 12 hours, it has been down, and day and night are of equal length. And on March 21 at the North Pole, the sun, which has not risen for six months, suddenly appears, and the day is equally divided into dark and light. So, even at the poles, day and night are of equal length on the equinoxes, as they are everywhere else on the earth. (Fig. 1–6.)

LATITUDE AND LONGITUDE

In order to measure accurately the position of any place on the surface of the earth, a system of grid coordinates has been established. This system, although man-made, is tied to two fixed points established by nature—the poles, which are the ends of the earth's axis. One group of coordinates, lines of longitude or meridians, are great circles passing through both poles, and thus their planes are parallel to the axis.[3] (Figs. 1–7 and 1–8.) The second series of lines, latitude or parallels, are circles drawn at right angles to the meridians and thus the axis. Of these, only the equator is a great circle, as it is the largest latitude circle and the only one that divides the earth into two equal halves—hence, the name equator. (Fig. 1–9.)

There are an infinite number of these latitude and longitude lines, as *every* place on the earth is at the intersection of a particular latitude and longitude line. Since maps and globes normally show only certain selected latitudes and longitudes actually drawn on them, the impression sometimes prevails that these are all there are. In reality, the map-makers put on just enough to be used as general reference lines, for obviously if they drew all of the infinite number that are possible, the maps and globes would be solid black and useless for the purpose for which they are intended.

[3] Assuming, as we are, that the earth is a perfect sphere, a great circle may be defined as *the largest circle that can be drawn on the surface of the earth* or *a circle that divides the earth into two equal halves.*

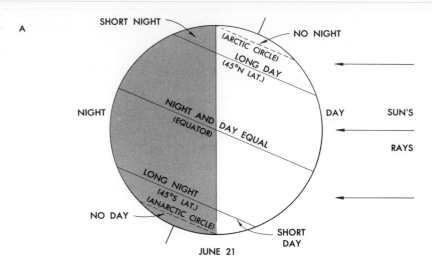

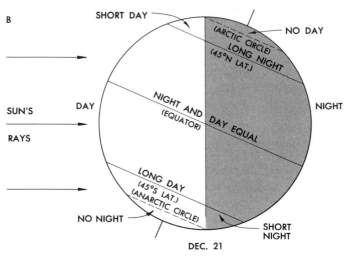

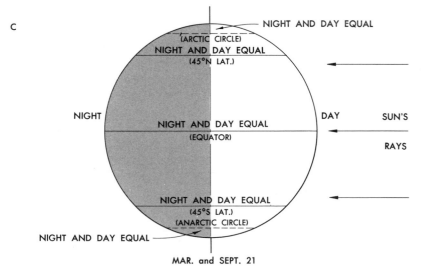

Fig. 1–6. Length of day.

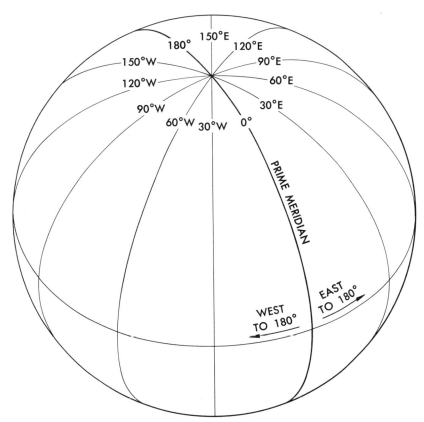

Fig. 1–7. *Longitude. All lines of longitude are great circles passing through both poles; thus, their planes are parallel to the axis.*

Latitude

All latitude is reckoned from the equator, and the latitude of any given place is its distance north or south of the equator. So the east-west trending circles of latitude, parallel to the equator, measure distance from the equator, and knowing your latitude tells you which one of the circles you are on; just where you are on that circle remains to be pinned down by longitude. Since latitude is reckoned in both directions from the equator, the equator is numbered 0° and the poles 90°. We are in effect, in measuring from the equator to a pole, measuring a quarter of the 360° circumference of the earth, or 90°. Thus, 45° north latitude is a circle one-half way between the equator and the North Pole. Except for the equator, the suffix N or S must appear following each latitudinal designation to indicate the hemisphere, since the numbering is the same in each. (Fig. 1–10.)

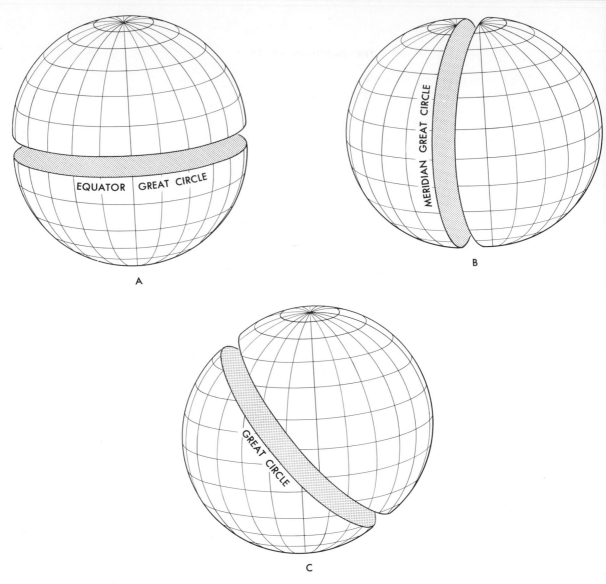

Fig. 1–8. *Great circles. No matter how it is sliced, any cut dividing the earth into two equal halves describes a great circle on its surface.*

It may seem a bit strange to deal here in linear measure using degrees as a unit. We are used to miles, feet, inches, etc., to measure distances. Degrees are legitimate, of course, since the earth is round and we are measuring fractions of a circle, but the concept of latitude being nothing more than the mileage north or south of the equator is equally legitimate. In converting, 69 miles is generally accepted as being the near equivalent of a degree of latitude. It follows then that the latitude circle 10°N is very close to being 690 miles north of the equator.

Since degrees of latitude are 69 miles apart and many locations do not coincide with even degrees of latitude, these degrees may be subdivided into 60ths (minutes) and minutes in turn into 60ths (seconds). Even seconds may be fractionalized into tenths by the use of decimals, so that two places only a few feet north or south of each other will have separate and distinct latitudinal designations. Here is a typical latitude description: 36°22′05.2″S. Do not confuse the 60 minutes of a degree or the 60 seconds of a minute with time. There is not the slightest relationship, and in longitude where time *is* a factor, this nomenclature for degree subdivision can lead to confusion.

How does one determine his latitude if he has no idea where he is relative to the equator? Measurements of heavenly bodies are the standard method, but as it seems at first glance, this process can become a

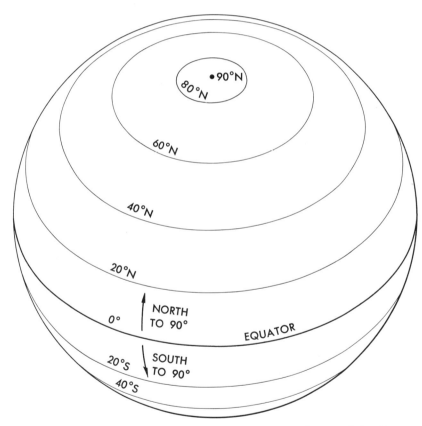

Fig. 1–9. *Latitude. Although they appear to be straight lines on a map, parallels are actually circles, their planes parallel to that of the equator.*

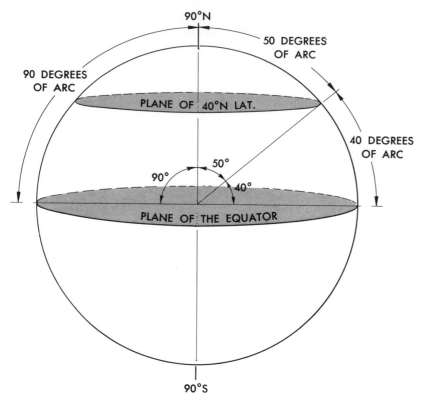

Fig. 1–10. *Measuring latitude. A north latitude of 40° represents 40 degrees of arc measured northward from the equator along the earth's surface, and also a 40° angle at the center of the earth intercepting this arc.*

bit complicated. However, the principle is not complicated, and it can be readily understood if we pick certain specific heavenly bodies at particular times. One of the easiest of these is the sun. Since latitude is measured from the equator, if we can relate the sun to the equator, it immediately becomes a clue. You will recall that at noon on the equinoxes, the sun is directly overhead at the equator. Thus on these two dates each year, we have at noon a brightly shining beacon, observable from everywhere on the earth, marking the position of the equator. The measurement that is made is the altitude of the sun above the horizon, i.e., the number of degrees in the angle between the sun and the horizontal. Let us assume that the observer is standing on the equator. The sun would be directly overhead, and its altitude would be 90° above the horizon. But this 90° is obviously not your latitude. Because of the arbitrary numbering of our latitude with 0° at the equator and 90° at the poles, one more step is required after measuring the sun's altitude to determine latitude—subtract this figure from 90°. Thus, 90 minus 90 equals 0°, which is the latitude of the equator. If the observer steps off the equator, either north or south, the sun is no longer overhead, and its altitude would be something less than 90°. And the farther one goes toward the poles, the lower the sun would appear at noon, until finally at the poles, the sun would appear resting on the horizon with no altitude at all. So it is not difficult to see that the altitude of the sun at noon on the equinoxes leads directly to a determination of distance from the equator, or latitude. Once again, the altitude must be subtracted from 90, or, stated differently, *the latitude of any given location and the altitude of the sun at noon on the equinoxes are complementary (when added, they equal 90°).* For example, if the sun's altitude measures 65°, latitude equals 90° minus 65° or 25° (N or S, depending on whether you are looking north or south to make the observation).

The above, of course, is the simplest possible example. A navigator does not have to wait until noon on an equinox to determine his latitude. Since the apparent movement of the sun and other heavenly bodies follow regular patterns, their positions relative to the equator on any date and at any time can be reckoned and corrections applied to compensate for variation. This principle is a relatively simple one and has been understood and applied for centuries. Old-time mariners could always be sure of reasonably accurate latitudinal measurement even though their longitude was sometimes very questionable.

There is one other simple observation that can lead to rapid determination of latitude, at least in the Northern Hemisphere, and that is Polaris, or the North Star. It is permanently so close to being directly over the North Pole that the slight deviation can be ignored generally. Here the latitudinal numbering works in our favor, for the measured altitude of Polaris requires no processing but *is your latitude.* If you stood at the pole, Polaris would be overhead all night long, and its altitude would measure 90°. Your latitude is 90°N. As an observer moves away from the pole, his latitude decreases and the altitude of Polaris decreases at the same rate. On any date, at any time, as long as you can see the North Star, you can easily find your latitude. (Fig. 1–11.)

Longitude

Longitude is the distance east or west of a base line and is measured by utilizing the aforementioned meridians (great circles passing through both poles and crossing the parallels at right angles). Arriving at a base line from which to begin the numbering was not the

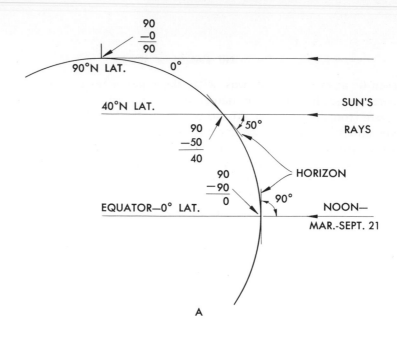

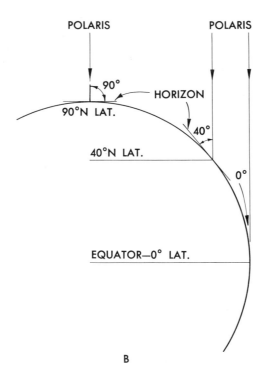

Fig. 1–11. *Determining latitude—Sun and Polaris. In (A), the angle at which the noon sun's rays strike the plane of the horizon is subtracted from 90° to determine latitude. But in (B), the angle at which Polaris' rays strike the plane of the horizon is the latitude.*

simple matter that it was with latitude. There is no natural line corresponding to the equator, and every country thought that the meridian of its capital should merit the honor. However, after many years of international bickering, it became apparent that one meridian would have to receive worldwide approval, and the meridian of the Royal Observatory at Greenwich, England, was officially adopted. This line then, from pole to pole, became the prime meridian or 0° longitude, and all longitude is reckoned either east or west of it. The other half of this great circle running through Greenwich is athwart the central Pacific, and being halfway around the world from the prime meridian is numbered 180°. Only these two meridians, 0° and 180°, require no directional suffix; all others must show a W or E to indicate which side of Greenwich they are. Unlike latitude then, longitude is measured through a half-circle, or 180° (Fig. 1–7). Degrees are subdivided into minutes and minutes into seconds just as in latitude, and every place on the earth has a line of longitude running through it.[4] Thus, it becomes apparent that the latitude and longitude of any place on the earth's surface are peculiar to that spot alone. Any number of other locations may share a given latitude *or* longitude but not both.

The problem of determining longitude when it is not known is no more difficult than latitude; if anything it is easier. And yet all through history, it has been almost impossible to fix accurately because of the lack of reliable instruments. Basically, longitude is a function of time, and the most important requirement in its reckoning has been an accurate clock. These have been produced for years, but they were pendulum clocks whose perfect functioning depended on a stationary mounting, and keeping time at sea was therefore very difficult. It was not until the development of alloy steels for the manufacture of clock springs that an accurate timepiece could be relied upon under all conditions. Today, longitude determination has become a very simple matter.

The basic concept in longitude is the 24-hour day, the sun appearing to make a complete circuit of the earth (360°) in 24 hours. Therefore, its apparent movement in 1 hour is 360° divided by 24 or 15°. This means that by observing the sun, we have a way of relating sun time to longitude. Now we come back to the accurate clock or chronometer. It differs from a standard clock in two ways: first, it has a 24-hour face so that there is never any question as to whether the indicated time is A.M. or P.M.; and second, it always keeps Greenwich time. Now, assume that you do not know your longitude; the first

4 A degree of longitude does not have a fixed distance that can be represented in miles. Only at the equator is a degree of longitude equal to 69 miles, for meridians converge toward the poles, and the closer the poles are approached, the shorter a degree of longitude becomes.

step is to determine your local time. Your wrist watch will not do the job as it is complicated by zone time, daylight saving time, etc., but the sun is accurate. Noon is the easiest time to check. When the sun is at its highest point, it is transiting your personal meridian and will appear due south (Northern Hemisphere). Now it is noon. A glance at the chronometer will give you Greenwich time, and a comparison of the two in terms of hours difference will tell you your longitude. Working with noon and even hours only will simplify the problem and at the same time illustrate the fundamental principle. For example, it is noon where you are and the chronometer reads the equivalent of 5 P.M. What is your longitude? The P.M. has an important meaning—post meridiem. Post stands for "after," and P.M. then means *after* the sun has transited the Greenwich meridian (noon), or afternoon. The sun appears to move from east to west, so if it has already crossed the prime meridian, it is now west of Greenwich. You have just observed it transiting your own meridian (noon), so your longitude must be west of Greenwich. Now it is merely a matter of deciding how far west. At the prime meridian, 5 P.M. means that it was noon there 5 hours ago, so if the sun appears to move 15° each hour, your longitude is 5 × 15 or 75°W. Count it off on a map. If noon is off to the west of Greenwich, then 15°W longitude will be 1 hour closer to noon or 4 P.M., 30°W will be 3 P.M., etc. (Fig. 1–12.)

If after observing local noon, you find that the chronometer reads A.M., then you must be east of Greenwich, for A.M. means ante (before) meridiem, or *before* noon. If the sun has not transited the prime meridian yet, it must be coming in from the east at a rate of 15° per hour, but at the moment, it is just crossing your meridian. How far you are from Greenwich is again simply the number of hours between Greenwich time and noon multiplied by 15.

TIME

Time Zones

The chances are excellent that your watch is not keeping correct time, that is, correct sun time. It is extremely unlikely that even the most expensive timepiece will show 12 o'clock when the sun is due south and at its highest point of the day. Instead, it will indicate local zone time, which for most of us is not the correct time at all and may be as much as a half-hour off.

This has not always been the case. In the not too distant past, everyone attempted to keep his own local time without a great deal of success. For the individual who spent a lifetime on one meridian, this was possible, but anyone who walked east or west, constantly changing

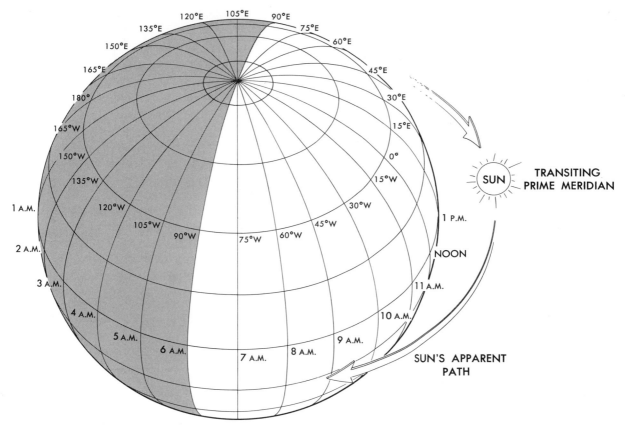

Fig. 1–12. *Longitude and sun time.*

meridians, would continually have to adjust his watch to conform to the time of the immediate meridian. To most, such a situation was inconvenient but scarcely serious, but to the railroads, who pioneered zone time in this country, it became crucial, as several trains, all attempting to keep their own local time, frequently arrived at the same intersection simultaneously. So, with the railroads leading the way, zone time was established, and everyone agreed to keep the *wrong* time but the *same* time for convenience and safety.

The entire world is now divided into twenty-four time zones each 15° wide; the time is based on the correct time of a central meridian. In actual practice, the margins of these zones, except at sea and in unpopulated areas, deviate slightly to conform to state and national boundaries and, as in the United States, are frequently given descriptive names. In the United States, we have four such zones: Eastern Standard Time Zone, all of which keeps the time of the 75°W meridian; Central Standard Time Zone, based on the 90°W meridian; Mountain Standard Time Zone, centering on the 105°W meridian; and Pacific Standard Time Zone, which keeps the time of 120°W longitude. (Fig. 1–13.) So all clocks in the Eastern Time Zone read noon when the sun transits 75°W even though those near the eastern and western boundaries are almost a half-hour off.

This arrangement is, of course, an aid to all business transacted within one time zone but brings about the problem of sudden one-hour changes in time as one leaves one zone and enters another. Suppose you are driving from Ohio to Indiana, the border of which is the changeover point from Eastern to Central Standard Time. You arrive at the Ohio side of the border at noon EST. This means that the sun is transiting the 75°W meridian on which EST is based. You have already spent the hour 11 to 12 on the road and have progressed 50 miles, but as you cross the line into Indiana and CST, the time suddenly becomes 11 A.M. Central Standard Time is based on the 90°W meridian and it will be another hour before the sun gets there. So you have the hour 11 to 12 all over again and can progress another 50 miles. You have gained an hour and you do not have to give it back unless you retrace your steps and the whole process is reversed. Those who travel all the way to the West Coast pick up a bonus of three hours. The general rule then, anywhere on the earth (with the exception of the International Date Line, which will be discussed later), is that *as you go west you gain an hour every 15°, and as you go east you lose one.*

The day is not far off when commercial jets will fly at the same speed as the earth rotates, and this could lead to the seemingly im-

Fig. 1–13. *Standard time zones in the United States.*

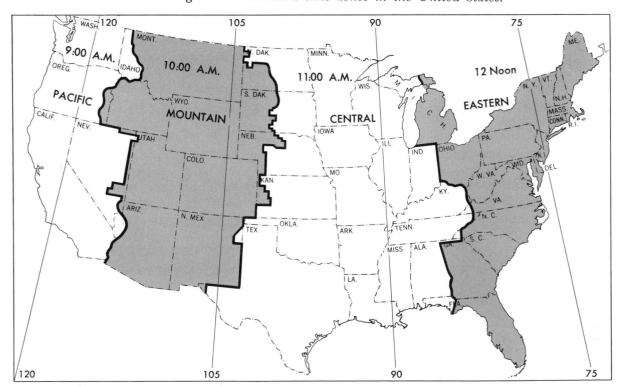

possible situation of taking off from the Eastern Seaboard at noon, flying west with the sun and crossing each meridian as it does, and finally arriving at the West Coast at noon. There would have been three hours' elapsed time in the air, but as far as the clock was concerned, you arrived at the same time you left. Or even more preposterous, if the plane went a little faster than the sun's apparent motion, arriving before you left (sun time).

Daylight Saving Time

Daylight Saving Time has become a widely accepted practice that allows us an extra hour of daylight in the evening during the long summer days. Actually, it is a form of self-deception wherein we get up an hour earlier than usual and go to bed an hour earlier, thereby substituting one of the early morning hours of light, which we normally waste in bed trying to sleep despite the peeping of the birds, for one of the early evening hours of dark when we are still awake but outdoor activity is restricted. This could, of course, be easily accomplished without changing the clock, but therein lies the deception. We like to think that we are getting up at the usual time and still get the bonus of an extra hour of daylight. So we adjust our clocks to read 7 A.M. when it is really 6 A.M. Now whose true local time are we keeping? Normally, we do not keep our own local time anyway but that of the central meridian of our time zone, so if we have changed the clock by an even hour, we must now be reading the time of a meridian 15° away from that central meridian. If we live in the Pacific Time Zone, our usual time is that of the 120°W meridian, and if that is 6 o'clock and we want the clock to read 7 o'clock, we must turn it one hour ahead, and then we will be keeping the time of the 105°W meridian, or Mountain time. Always, in Daylight Saving Time, *the timepieces of any given zone are keeping the time of the next zone to the east.*

THE DATE

In this business of time change as we travel from zone to zone, there is an inherent danger that people traveling west and gaining one hour every 15° of longitude will get carried away and pick up more free time than they are entitled to. A certain amount is legal, such as the time that you gain by going from the East Coast to the West Coast and staying there. You have achieved 3 free hours and they are yours to keep—even 23 hours is considered within bounds. But a complete circuit of the earth would give you a full day's bonus, and here is where the line is drawn—literally—the International Date Line. When this is crossed in a westerly direction, 24 hours is lost.

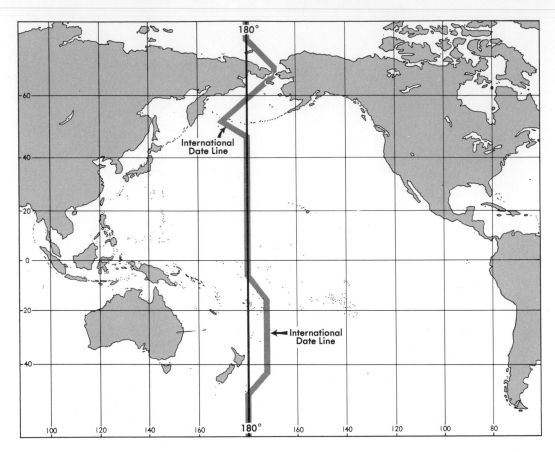

Fig. 1–14. *International Date Line. The Date Line is closely coincident with the 180th meridian.*

There has not always been a Date Line. It is man-made, and until man began to go around the world, there was no need for it. But the first circumnavigation of the globe by Magellan's party demonstrated the need for such a line, for despite keeping careful track of the date, the survivors of that voyage found that upon their arrival in Spain, they were one full day in advance of the calendar. They should have had a day taken away to offset the 1 hour gained for each 15° of longitude in their westward journey. If they had gone around the world to the east, the accumulated 1 hour losses would have been rebated at a date line.

The International Date Line is essentially the 180° meridian running from pole to pole down the middle of the Pacific Ocean. It is exactly halfway around the world from the prime meridian and together with that meridian describes a great circle. In actuality, the Date Line deviates a bit from the 180° meridian so that it can run up Bering Strait to separate Asia from North America, and it detours around islands and island groups to avoid the complication of differing dates on opposite sides of a single political unit. But, for our purposes here, we can consider the two to be essentially identical. (Fig. 1–14.)

In this day of rapid communication, we are constantly being made aware of the existence of two dates on the earth at any given time. News reports from Asia are frequently datelined a day ahead of the time of delivery. There is, however, one instant in every 24 hours when there is only one date on the earth—noon at Greenwich. At any other time, there are always two dates.

Midnight is the time when the date is advanced for reasons of convenience. Therefore, if we can imagine a midnight line sweeping around the earth, as it crosses each location, the date changes. This midnight line would be 180° (12 hours) away from the sun, so that when the sun is transiting the prime meridian, it would be midnight

Fig. 1–15. *International Date Line and midnight date change. The apparent movement of the noon sun around the earth from (A) to (D) illustrates the function of the Date Line. As the midnight line sweeps around the earth opposite the noon sun, it initiates a new day as it passes.*

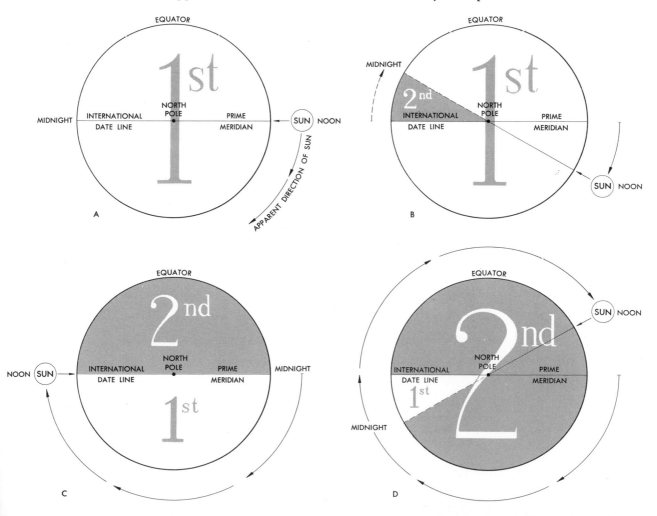

halfway around the world at the 180° meridian. This is the instant
when the entire earth has only one date. But, one hour later when the
sun has moved 15°W, the midnight line has swept a comparable 15°
zone from 180° to 165°E. Each spot within this area has had its date
change, so if the date everywhere one hour ago had been the first, this
one little 15° zone out in the Pacific would be the second. And as the
sun continued to move west, the region of new date would become
larger and larger, until 12 hours later (noon at 180°, midnight at the
prime meridian), one-half of the earth would be the second and one-
half the first. Finally, when the sun had made almost a complete circuit of the earth and was again approaching Greenwich, all but a small
part of the world would have experienced midnight and the date
change, and only this narrow zone short of the prime meridian would
still be the first. (Fig. 1–15.)

Now, if we are crossing the Pacific headed west toward Asia, crossing the Date Line will move us ahead one day (on the calendar). A
full day is lost, and the only way to recover all or most of it is to go
back across the Date Line, or continue west all the way around the
world, picking up 23 hours one at a time for each time zone, and then
stopping before crossing the Date Line again. Remember, the Date
Line operates in opposition to the hour lines bounding our time zones:
*going west across the Date Line a day is lost, and going east a day is
gained.*

2

Maps

A map is merely a symbolized representation of all or part of the earth's surface on a flat piece of paper. As such, it is a highly useful geographical tool, for in attempting any description or analysis of the earth's surface or of the human activity on it, relative location is essential. One of the problems that maps help to solve is that of the man on the ground being able to observe only a very small part of the earth at any one time. With a map, he is enabled to see large segments or even the whole earth, thereby visualizing relationships that are not immediately evident from the restricted local view. And maps are capable of much more than mere location. With the proper selection of data and symbolism, a great variety of concepts may be rendered in visual form.

The urge to map is almost intuitive in all of us. How often have you grabbed a piece of scratch paper to draw a crude map of road directions? How often primitive man must have scratched the same sort of information with a stick in the dirt, long before any means of preserving his artwork for posterity was conceived. The oldest known map is a fragment of clay tablet from Mesopotamia dating back to 2500 B.C., but nobody suggests that this was the first map ever made. Maps are such obviously useful tools that they have surely been in use continuously from the earliest time. (Fig. 2–1.) We have, of course, improved on early mapping practices. The Greeks recognized the sphericity of the earth and introduced a system of coordinates for measuring, and later, with the great voyages of exploration, the distribution of the continents became known. Now *cartography,* the science of mapping, has become of necessity a world encompassing affair and is no longer restricted to the immediate local neighborhood. To-

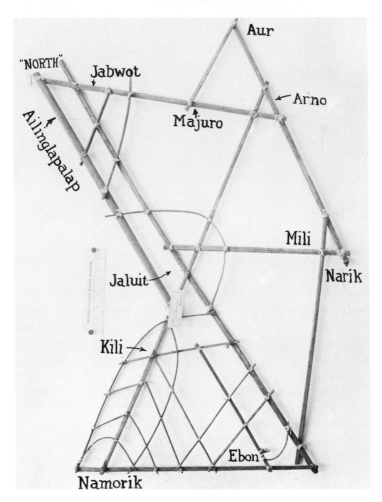

Fig. 2–1. *A Micronesian stick chart dating from prehistory. The southern Marshall Islands are identified, and the sticks indicate the primary interisland currents that are rather constant in this archipelago. These were practical navigational charts. (Courtesy of E. H. Bryan, Jr., Bernice P. Bishop Museum.)*

day, with aerial photography and highly sophisticated techniques of drawing and reproduction, maps are more widely available than at any time in history—cheaper, better, and in greater variety. (Figs. 2–2 and 2–3.) But the average person does not know how to use them except in a perfunctory way. There are a number of basic practices of which any map-user should be aware in order to achieve the maximum understanding of this important geographical tool.

Fig. 2–2. *The improved techniques of aerial photography have speeded up immeasurably the mapping process. Here an Air Force team checks a mosaic of photos against an existing chart as the first step toward the production of new and up-to-date aeronautical charts. (Official USAF photo.)*

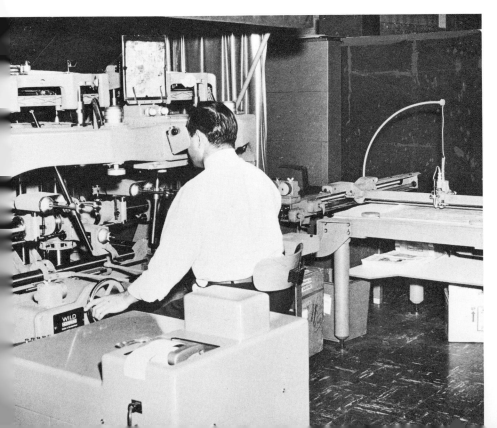

Fig. 2–3. *The operator of the stereoplanograph views a three-dimensional image of a pair of aerial photos. He guides a black dot over the contours of the image to trace the contour lines on a base map. (Official USAF photo.)*

PROJECTIONS

If we once again assume the earth to be a perfect sphere, its only true representative is a globe not a map, for *it is simply a physical impossibility to transfer a curved surface onto a flat one without distortion and error.* (Fig. 2–4.) In other words, *there is no such thing as a perfect map.* Maps of very small areas, where the curvature of the earth is minimal, come close to perfection although not absolutely, but the larger the region the map attempts to show, the greater the error until it reaches its maximum in world maps. So, why not forget maps and use only the globe? Cost is one factor. A good globe is many times more expensive than a map. But of more importance is the fact that the globe just cannot do the job that a map can in certain instances. Imagine the size that a globe would have to be in order to show real detail of the country of Belgium. A map could handle this easily, but the globe would scarcely fit in the room. And a world map is a necessity in many situations, but only half the globe is visible at any one time. Add to this the ease of carrying a map around in your hip pocket and its simple storage in a flat case and it becomes apparent that despite their distortions of the areas they purport to show, maps have many advantages over the globe. This does not mean that you should throw away your globe, for it is useful too in other ways. Only on the globe can great circles be properly understood, and true direction or earth-sun relationships. Maps and globes are complementary then, and not competitive, although they both attempt to represent the earth at a reduced scale.

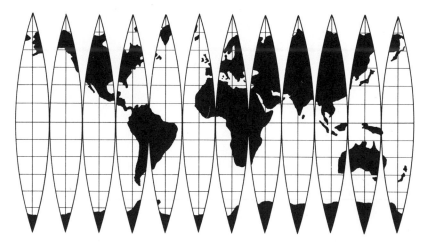

Fig. 2–4. *Globe gores. Stripped off the globe where they form a perfect picture of the earth, globe gores leave a great deal to be desired as a flat map.*

So if maps are necessary and we must accept their inherent defects, then the problem of control arises. How can we keep general distortion to a minimum and limit specific error to that part of the map where it will do the least harm? This is the function of *projection,* the process of transferring the latitude-longitude grid from the earth's or globe's surface to a flat piece of paper.

The earth and globe have a number of important properties which a cartographer would hope to retain on his map. The most vital of these are: (1) true direction, (2) true distance (scale), (3) true shape (conformality), and (4) equivalence of area. Unhappily, no map can successfully emulate the globe and have all of these properties, but depending on the method of projection, certain critical ones can be retained at the expense of others. So this matter of which projection to select relates very closely to the purpose of the map. A navigational chart must be conformal above all else, but this means that it cannot be equal area too, for no map can be both. (Fig. 2–5.) If true direc-

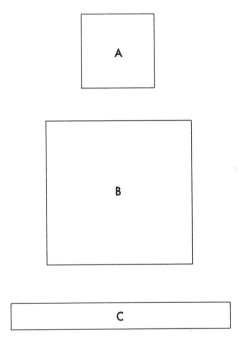

Fig. 2–5. Conformality and equivalence of area. (A) and (B) are the same shape (conformal) but obviously different in size. (A) and (C) are equal in area but far from conformal. These are the choices that the map-maker must face, for no map can be both conformal and equal area.

tion and distance can be maintained, and they frequently can be, at least along certain lines, so much the better, as these are useful properties in navigation. On the other hand, if the map is to be for classroom use to show distribution of terrain or population and the like, equivalence of area is more important than true shape, and again one must be sacrificed to gain the other. Some maps are compromises, achieving none of these qualities but coming close enough in all so as not to destroy an effective visual image. But, in every case, the map-user must select the projection that will give him the properties that he needs. Free military maps, for instance, often distributed by the government, will not always work well in the classroom any more than atlas maps can be used for navigation.

Literally thousands of map projections are in existence today, and no student can be expected to know the properties of them all, but most can be categorized into four broad groupings and their general characteristics easily understood. These four types are: (1) *azimuthal* (zenithal)—projection onto a plane, (2) *conic*—projection onto a cone, (3) *cylindrical*—projection onto a cylinder, and (4) *mathematical* or all others. The first three of these might be termed "true projections" in that although they can be arrived at mathematically, they also can be constructed by the use of a model of the globe or graphically. That is, these surfaces (plane, cone, and cylinder) may be placed tangent to a model globe and the grid of latitude and longitude actually *projected* out onto them.

Azimuthal Projections

Imagine a globe made up entirely of selected latitude and longitude lines represented by wires—an open hollow wire cage. In the center of this put a light. Now place a flat piece of paper tangent anywhere on the globe and turn on the light. (Fig. 2–6.) The shadow pattern of the wire grid will be *projected* onto the paper and can be traced, thus giving us a latitudinal-longitudinal base on which to draw in the details of continental outline. Now we have a map on our paper actually projected from the globe. Since it was done onto a plane, it is an azimuthal projection; the name is derived from the fact that all projections constructed in this manner have the property of true direction (azimuth) from their center or point of tangency.

If we turn the globe so that the point of tangency is the North Pole, this true direction becomes apparent. The grid pattern now appears as a series of concentric circles (parallels) about the pole at their center and radiating straight lines (meridians) from the pole. (Fig. 2–7.) These meridians are azimuths or true compass headings, and if we follow any one of them out from the center, we are going south. But notice the spacing of the concentric parallels. Although they were evenly spaced on the globe, on the projection they are increasingly farther apart with distance away from the pole, evidence that the projection is not a true picture of the globe. Land areas drawn on this projection will exhibit increasing distortion in size and shape toward the margin at the same rate.

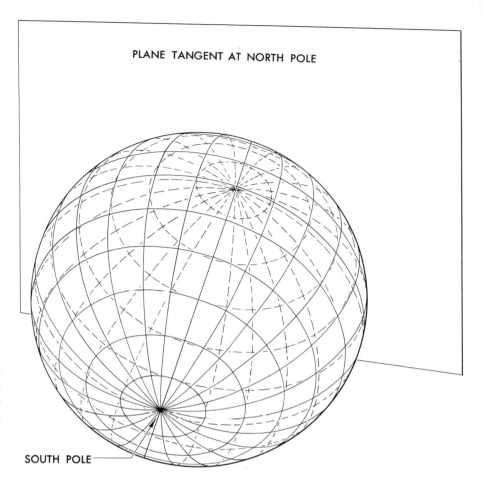

PLANE TANGENT AT NORTH POLE

SOUTH POLE

Fig. 2–6. *Tangent plane. A globe grid projected onto a tangent plane (in this case at the North Pole) is called an* azimuthal *projection.*

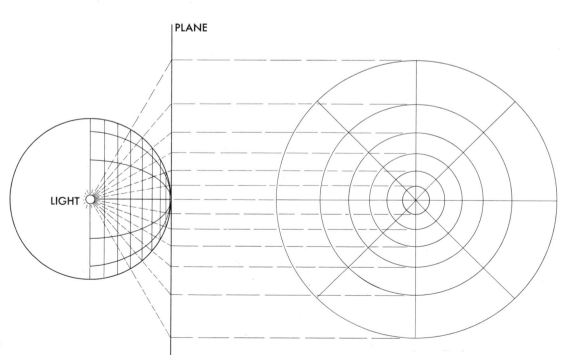

PLANE

LIGHT

Fig. 2–7. *Gnomonic azimuthal projection. Any straight line on this projection is a great circle route.*

When the light is at the center of the wire cage, the resulting projection is termed "gnomonic"; in the above case, "gnomonic azimuthal polar phase" in recognition of a projection onto a plane tangent at the pole. As it happens, this particular projection has, in addition to true direction from the center, the singular quality of any straight line being a great circle route and therefore a very valuable projection for certain types of work.

Now, if we leave the plane tangent at the North Pole but move the light (or eyepoint as it is called) to the South Pole, it becomes a "stereographic" projection (i.e., *"stereographic azimuthal polar phase"*), and a slightly different grid pattern results, one that, although superficially similar to the gnomonic, has the property of conformality. (Fig. 2–8.) Area is badly distorted, especially around the margins, but shape is true, and this is the most frequently used navigational chart for the world's polar regions.

Finally, if we move the light out to infinity and its rays of light come in parallel to each other, the projection is called "orthographic" (i.e., *"orthographic azimuthal polar phase"*). Now the concentric latitude circles get closer together with distance from the pole exactly as they would appear if we were to look down at the North Pole of a globe, with its increasing curvature foreshortening the distance between the outermost parallels. (Fig. 2–9.) Such a projection has none of the desirable properties of the globe (except, of course, as always in an azimuthal projection, true direction from the center), but does give

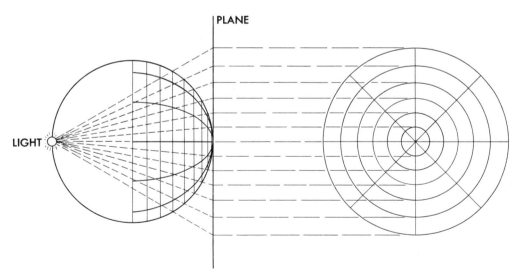

Fig. 2–8. *Stereographic azimuthal projection. This conformal projection is widely used for polar navigation.*

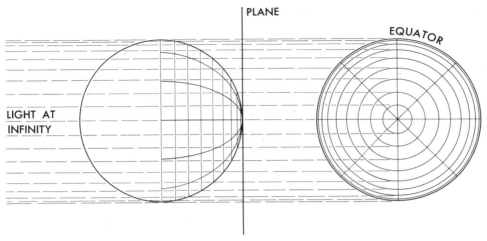

Fig. 2–9. *Orthographic azimuthal projection. Neither conformal nor equal area, this projection displays a globular appearance.*

us the familiar image that we actually see, making the projection appear globular. (Fig. 2–10.) It is useful for pictorial maps and for advertising purposes.

The point here is to illustrate some of the diversity obtainable by merely moving the eyepoint. There are many other possibilities; for instance, adjusting the spacing of the parallels according to careful mathematical formulas to achieve equality of area, or to achieve true distance from the center, etc. And remember, the plane may be tangent anywhere on the globe, not just at the North Pole.

Fig. 2–10. *Oblique phase, orthographic azimuthal projection. The three-dimensional quality is most obvious in the oblique phase.*

Conic Projections

If we take our wire cage, representing the earth, and place a cone over the top of it with its peak over the North Pole, the cone will be tangent at a particular line of latitude; which latitude depends on the angle of the cone. If we construct a very low-angle cone, like a Chinese coolie hat, it will be tangent at a latitude not far from the pole, whereas a high-angle cone, like a dunce cap, will be tangent near the equator. Obviously, no cone could be so flattened as to be tangent at the pole or it would have become a plane, and in order for a cone to be tangent at the equator, it would have to be transformed into a cylinder. Therefore, conic projections are especially suited to regions in the middle latitudes. (Fig. 2–11.)

Let us construct a conic projection on which to map the United States. We would select a cone that would be tangent at a latitude running through the middle of the country, say 40°N. Now turn on the light at the center and trace the shadow outline on the cone. Slit the cone up the back and lay it flat and we have a base on which to draw our map. The lines of latitude will be curved but unequally spaced parallel lines crossed at right angles by equally spaced straight line meridians converging toward the tip of the original cone. At the critical central 40° parallel, scale, shape, and area are all true, but since

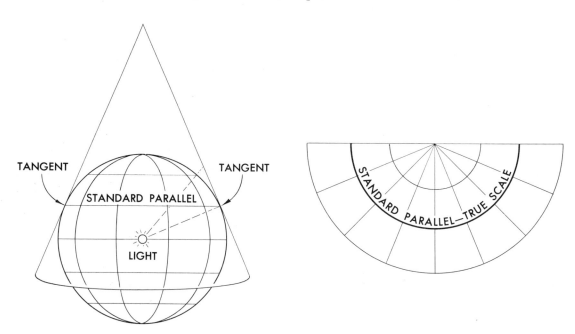

Fig. 2–11. Conic projection. The size of the cone can be adjusted so as to be tangent at any selected standard parallel.

the other parallels, although representing equally spaced lines of latitude on the globe, become increasingly farther apart with distance from the 40° parallel, those portions of the map will exhibit greater and greater distortion.

Since the latitude line of cone tangency is an error-free line on the map, it would be highly desirable to have the cone tangent at more than one parallel. Such a seemingly impossible situation can actually be accomplished. One way is by the use of a secant cone, i.e., a cone that cuts through the globe. (Fig. 2–12.) At the two points where it actually intersects the surface, we get the equivalence of tangency. Now if we construct such a cone cutting the globe at 30°N and 45°N, those two lines on the projection will be true, and the relatively small area in between will display only minimal error. Two of our most widely used projections for mapping the United States utilize this principle—*Alber's equal area conic* and *Lambert's conformal conic*. (Fig. 2–13.)

It should be emphasized that the simple secant conic projection is neither equal area nor conformal, but with minor adjustments can be made to achieve one or the other of these important qualities. In all conic projection, the meridians do not converge as rapidly as they do on the globe, for they are converging toward the tip of the cone that is high above the pole. This means that in any given area, the meridians are spaced more widely than on the globe, and the map representation of that area is "stretched" a bit in an east-west direction. If we

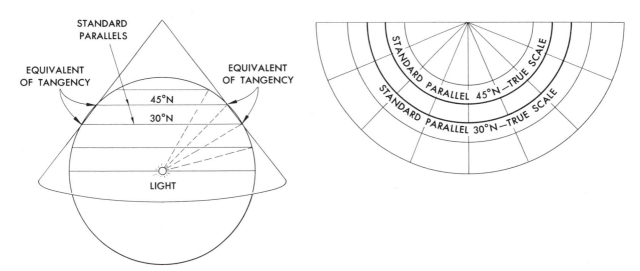

Fig. 2–12. *Secant cone. In cutting through the bulge of the globe, the cone achieves the equivalent of tangency at two standard parallels.*

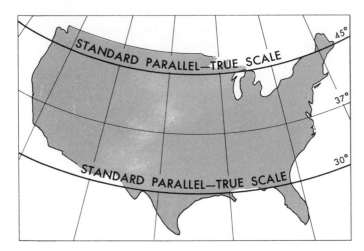

Fig. 2–13. *Two standard error-free parallels.*

wish conformality, then the parallels must be pushed farther apart exactly the same amount. This, of course, makes the area larger than it should be but has corrected its shape. However, if equality of area is to be achieved, then the parallels are pushed together just enough to offset the east-west stretching, and true area is gained at the expense of shape. This adjusting of the parallels to compensate for meridional error is the means employed in the Alber's and Lambert's projections to make them equal area and conformal, respectively. The Lambert's conformal conic projection is probably the most commonly employed of the middle latitude navigational projections.

Another means of making cones tangent at more than one parallel is to utilize a multiplicity of cones. The *polyconic* projection ("poly" means many) does this. In essence, it is a series of strip maps of differing curvatures each based on the tangent parallel of a different cone. (Fig. 2–14.) For a relatively small region, such an arrangement is not unreasonable, but the varying curvatures cause difficulties in fitting the various elements of the map together if it encompasses too large an area. Furthermore, aside from true scale on the standard latitude lines of each cone, this projection is a compromise between conformality and equivalence of area—achieving neither. Nonetheless, it is in wide use for official United States government maps.

One of the difficulties in the use of maps drawn on conic projections is the tendency to read a map as though it had horizontal parallels and vertical meridians, even though we know better. The old quiz question, "Where is the northernmost point in the United States (exclud-

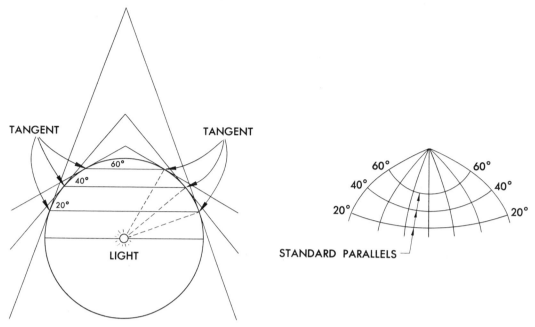

Fig. 2–14. *Polyconic projection. Many cones, each tangent at a different standard parallel. This is a compromise projection, coming close to but achieving neither conformality nor equality of area.*

ing Alaska and Hawaii)?" will almost always draw an answer of Washington or Maine. We have never seen a map of the United States on anything but a conic projection, and the upcurved parallels at the margins of the map make it appear that way. Actually, the Lake of the Woods, Minnesota, is farther north, but it is at a point where the parallel curves down and thus farther from the top border of the map. But that border is not an east-west line—lines of latitude are, whether they appear curved or straight. And this means that the southern tip of Florida is much farther south than the southern tip of Texas, even though it does not look that way. Also those angled meridians at the fringes of the map are by definition due north-south lines, not the right- and left-hand map borders; so to make these areas "look right," you have to tilt your head. There is no law that says north must be at the top of the map, but old habits are hard to break, and maps that deviate from this norm invite difficulty in reading.

Cylindrical Projections

Here we fit a cylinder over a globe. If the globe is upright with the North Pole at the top, the cylinder will be tangent at the equator. Then, having turned on the light at the center and traced the grid, the cylinder is cut down one side and laid out flat. Once again we have constructed a projection, this time of virtually the whole world. (Fig. 2–15.) One of the weaknesses of both the azimuthal and the conic projections was their inability to reproduce a great deal more than a hemisphere, but here we have a grid that, except for the poles themselves, represents the entire earth. Offhand it looks pretty good. The parallels are nice straight lines (although spaced unequally again) instead of those disconcerting curves, and the meridians are straight too at right angles to the parallels. But once we draw the continental outlines onto the grid, it becomes obvious that there are inherent problems. Only at the equator do things look right; elsewhere shapes and sizes get stretched in all directions. The meridians are primarily at fault; they are parallel to each other and do not converge at all. This means that at the higher latitudes where the meridians should be closer together, they are as far apart as at the equator and tremendous east-west distortion results. Because the parallels are spaced increasingly farther apart, some of this meridional stretching is compensated for, but not enough. If only the parallel spacing exactly equaled the error in meridian spacing, we would have a conformal projection. This is exactly what an early map-maker by the name of Mercator did; he

Fig. 2–15. Cylindrical projection. If the cylinder is large enough, a reproduction of virtually the whole earth is possible.

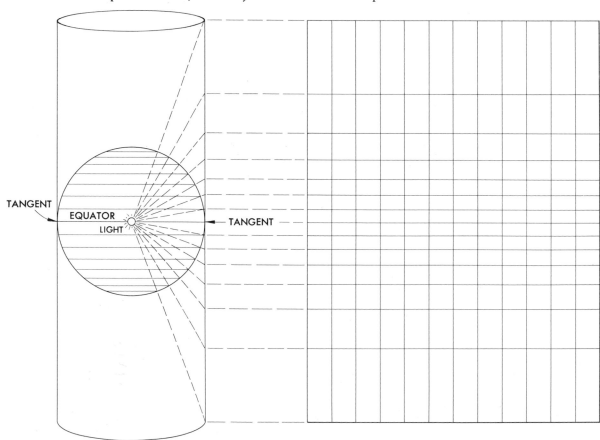

adjusted one to precisely compensate for the other. So the famous *Mercator* map is a world map on a cylindrical projection, slightly doctored to achieve conformality. As it happens, any straight line on a Mercator projection is a true compass heading (*rhumb line*), and this quality plus conformality have made this the most widely used of all navigational charts. But somehow the Mercator map found its way into the classroom and the atlas, and here it was out of its element. Proportions were all wrong. (Fig. 2–16.) Greenland near the pole was true shape but was so badly distorted in size that it appeared to be larger than South America, which, being astride the equator, came much closer to its true size. Obviously, a map explicitly constructed for navigational use could not be used for other purposes.

There are many other kinds of cylindrical projections possible; the Mercator is simply a well-known representative. The eyepoint can be moved from the center of the earth, the cylinder may be made tangent at some other place than the equator, or a secant cylinder may be in-

Fig. 2–16. Mercator projection. This famous conformal projection of the world is still a basic navigational chart, but it contains the obvious flaw of gross distortion of size in the high latitudes, which limits its use.

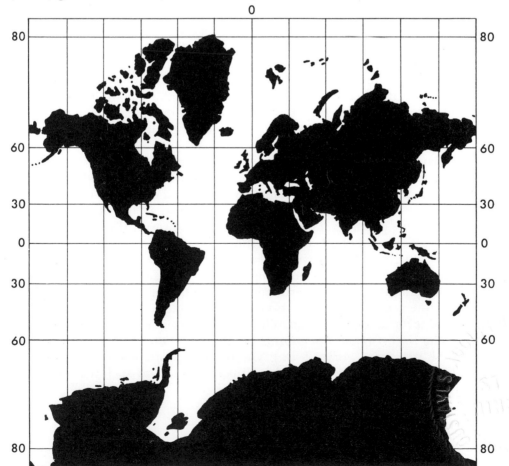

troduced. Any arrangement is legitimate as long as it produces a usable end product.

Mathematical Projections

Now that we have exhausted the many applications of the wire cage globe and the light, there remain endless possibilities. Some of the resulting mathematical projections look like butterflies, some feature involved curving grid systems—but all are aiming at capturing at least a few of the qualities of the globe and earth in order to meet a specific need. The variations are infinite; the only test is utility.

An example of one type of mathematical projection is the series of world maps based on a grid whose equatorial dimension is twice that of its polar dimension—the sort of thing that we would get if the paper covering the globe were slit down the back and then carefully peeled off and spread out flat. The whole world would be visible now rather than merely one side, and the distance from pole to pole would be just one-half of that along the equator. If we draw a straight line equator and, crossing it at right angles at its midpoint, a straight line meridian, we have the bare bones of a world projection. Mollweide drew an ellipse connecting the ends of these two lines, while Sanson and Flamsteed tied them together with sine curves. The resulting projections with varying curvature of meridians (except the central one) and straight parallels are very similar. Both achieved equality of area by adjusting the spacing of the parallels slightly to compensate for the curving meridians, and both are absolutely true only along the equator and central meridian. Mollweide's (called the *homolographic* projection) exhibits slightly less distortion in the polar regions, while Sanson-Flamsteed's (called the *sinusoidal* projection) is somewhat more accurate in the tropics. (Fig. 2–17.) Recognizing their basic similarity and at the same time certain regional advantages of one over the other, the American map-maker Goode cut the sinusoidal at 40°N and S and spliced on the homolographic in the high latitudes. The resulting hybrid, given the name *homolosine,* is less distorted than either of its parents. There still remained, however, the curved meridians which, although by definition are north-south lines, appear sharply angled, especially near the outer margins of the map. In order to make land areas that seem to be lying on their sides stand up straight, Goode simply took the meridians running through them and straightened them out. This operation essentially "tore" the map apart, but if the tears or gaps are controlled so as to occur in the oceans, the resulting *interrupted homolosine* is probably the best of our world equal area maps. (Fig. 2–18.) Of course, ocean currents or intercontinental trade routes cannot be properly shown on such a projection,

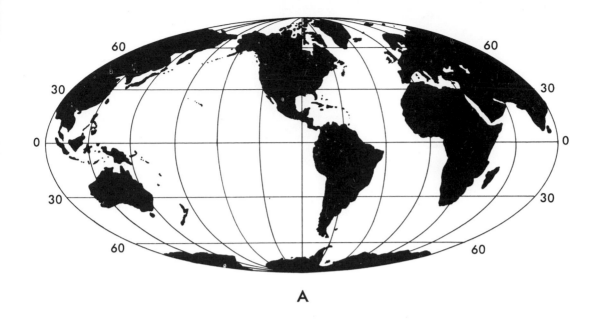

A

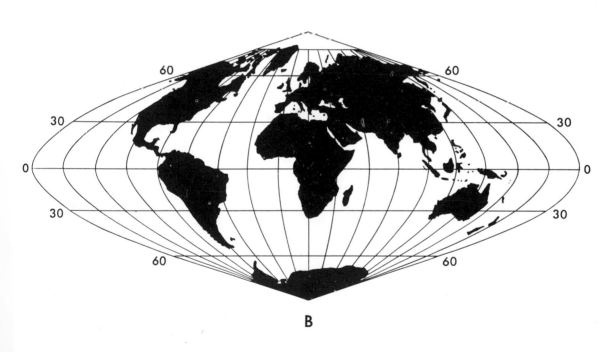

B

Fig. 2–17. *(A) Mollweide's homolographic projection. (B) Sanson-Flamsteed's sinusoidal projection. The polar distance is exactly one-half the equatorial distance on both of these projections, and both achieve equality of area.*

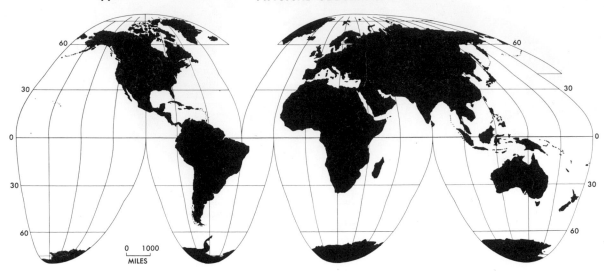

Fig. 2–18. *Goode's interrupted homolosine projection. A combination of the homolographic and sinusoidal, interrupted to make the continents appear properly oriented. (By permission from* Goode Base Map Series, *Dept. of Geography, Univ. of Chicago. Copyright, Univ. of Chicago.)*

unless it is reversed and the interruptions are introduced in the continental areas. But, like all maps, we must accept some defects, and for certain purposes, this type of map is unexcelled.

SCALE

All maps are reductions of the region they are depicting; there are no enlargements. This means that once a portion of the earth's surface has been rendered onto a flat projection, there must be some indication of how much reduction has occurred in the process so that the map-reader can measure distance and properly interpret relative size. *Scale, then, is simply the index of reduction* and is written at the bottom of each map in one of three ways: (1) *graphic scale,* (2) *stated scale,* and (3) *representative fraction.* The simplest and easiest to use, especially for the general map-reader, is the graphic scale. It is the common bar scale marked off in tens or hundred of miles so that we can simply measure with a straightedge the distance between any two places.

Graphic Scale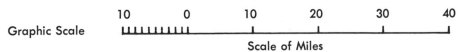

It may also be in kilometers or feet—whatever is most convenient. Subdivisions for more finite measurements are frequently introduced at the left end of the bar. But this scale, like all others, cannot be applied with impunity all over a map, for no map is perfect, especially if it is of a large area. The general rule is: *trust your scale only at the center of the map and regard it as a mere generalization near the margins.* There is one advantage that the graphic scale has over all others and that is, if the map is to be enlarged or reduced, its scale changes, but the length of the bar changes at the same rate and so remains true. Any other scale must be reworked to conform to the varied size of the map.

The stated scale is a prose sentence that merely states the number of miles that is the equivalent of 1 inch, so that again with a ruler, distances can be readily determined.

Stated Scale **1 inch equals 8 miles**

The representative fraction is in many ways the most versatile of the lot and is in very common use, but since it is merely a number, it does not appear very useful to the uninitiated. It is shown as a fraction, or more frequently a ratio, and by carefully avoiding any reference to inches, miles, or feet is applicable in many situations where other scales are not.

Representative Fraction (R.F.) **1:316,800**

The ratio, alone, simply states that *1 unit on the map is equal to 316,800 of the same units on the earth.* This means that such a scale is just as applicable in a country using the metric system, or any other, as it is where we use inches and miles, and it does tell us how much reduction has occurred. The large number, 316,800, is the number of times the map has been reduced. Obviously, if a map of the world were reduced sufficiently to fit on a piece of paper of manageable size, the R.F. would be even larger, on the order of 1:10,000,000. (Fig. 2–19.)

It is all well and good to know that a map has undergone reduction several million times, but our minds sometimes do not grasp exactly what this means. A snapshot of a person is a considerable reduction from the original too, but we have seen him and know how big he is, and our minds take care of the reduction problem automatically. But we have never seen the United States at one glance or probably even our county, so a simple notation of how many times it has been reduced does not help much. Somehow we have got to make better sense out of that number. Let us come back to our original scale of 1:316,800 and use inches as our unit; so now this reads, 1 inch on the map equals 316,800 inches on the earth. Still not much help; 316,800

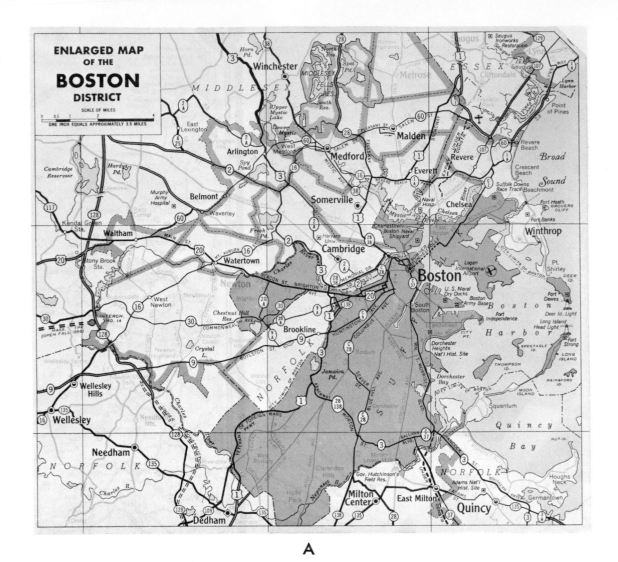

A

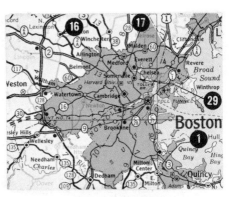

B

Fig. 2–19. *Scale. The large-scale map of Boston (A) at RF 1:199,584 has been reduced many less times and therefore shows more detail than the small-scale map of eastern Massachusetts (B) at RF 1:583,012. (By permission from The H. M. Gousha Co., San Jose, Calif. Copyright, 1956.)*

inches is hard to visualize. Let us change the inches to miles and then we will have something useful. If 1 inch on the map is equal to so many miles, measurement has suddenly become easy. The critical key to all this is 63,360, *the number of inches in a mile*. This number will make sense out of any R.F. scale when it is applied to the large number. In this case, $316,800 \div 63,360 = 5$, or 1 inch on the map is equal to 5 miles.

Maps are not much more than pictures without a scale, and no intelligent interpretation can be made without referring to it. Therefore, the first point of business upon attempting to read any map is to check its scale.

DIRECTION

On any map with latitude and longitude lines, the determination of direction is a simple matter, for they are by definition east-west and north-south lines. But on the occasional large-scale map without these lines and on any map that might be taken out into the field, there will appear an arrow pointing to true north and often a second arrow pointing to magnetic north. (Fig. 2–20.) Their direction may differ by a significant amount (termed "declination" or "variation"), for the North Magnetic Pole is over a thousand miles from the North Pole at Prince of Wales Island, Canada.

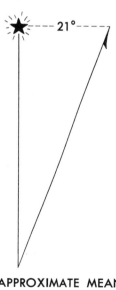

Fig. 2–20. Compass variation. The star represents the North Star or true north; the arrow the direction of the magnetic compass needle. A symbol such as this frequently appears at the margin of a map to indicate the proper correction to be made when the map is used with a compass in the field.

21°

APPROXIMATE MEAN
DECLINATION
1966

If you were to stand near the southern tip of Lake Michigan and observe a magnetic compass, it would point to true north because this particular point is on a great circle passing through both the true and magnetic poles. This is called an *agonic line,* and anywhere on it the two poles are in line and a magnetic compass will point true north— anywhere else there will be variation of some degree. Oddly, the earth's lines of magnetic force change from time to time in an unpredictable manner so that the agonic line wanders a bit and at any given moment will display waves and therefore is never quite a true great circle. Consequently, the map arrows showing the amount of compass variation are usually dated to call attention to the fact that they may be in slight error if the date is not recent.

SYMBOLISM

A map in its entirety is merely an assemblage of symbols. Even that line representing a coastline is a symbol, for it attempts to demark mean sea level, a line that does not exist in nature. Or, if it shows the broken Norwegian coast on a small-scale map, only the major fiords are at all accurate, and the rest is merely generalized to indicate a ragged character. Roads, if they are to show clearly, may be actually represented as 5 miles wide, and railroads display a single rail 3 miles wide with 10-mile-long ties 50 miles apart. These are all deliberate exaggerations to call attention to features of importance; other major features that are not deemed useful in what that particular map is attempting to show are left out. A map can show political boundaries, latitude and longitude, etc., all of which are symbols representing features invisible in nature.

It has been said that an aerial photo is essentially a map. It is not. For one thing, it shows too much. Forest foliage may hide a road, and the tremendous amount of minutiae detract from the important things. A map is selective; a map is intelligently generalized; a map is often exaggerated to illustrate a particular synthesis—and it does this through the use of selected symbols.

Through long use, most basic symbols have become standardized so that even foreign maps can be read rather easily, although the printed words may be unintelligible. To a considerable degree, symbols are pictorial, especially on large-scale maps, that is, those depicting a small area in great detail. Schools, churches, mines, and the like are denoted by symbols that even the novice can recognize immediately. (Fig. 2–21.) With the increasing use of color on maps, symbolism becomes even simpler, for here too international standardization of basic colors aids in recognition. Blue, of course, is always used for hydro-

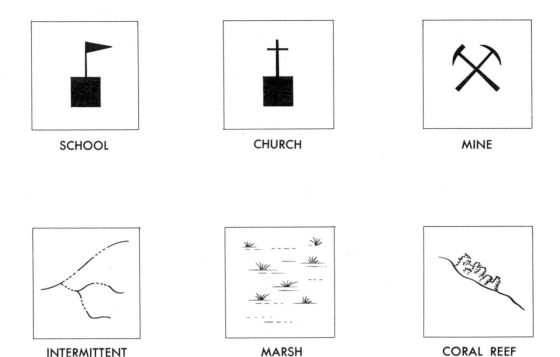

SCHOOL   CHURCH   MINE

INTERMITTENT
STREAM   MARSH   CORAL REEF

Fig. 2–21. *Examples of internationally standardized symbols for use on medium- to large-scale maps.*

graphic symbols, rivers, lakes, springs, and swamps; black and red are used for cultural features such as roads, buildings, and political borders. Any symbol illustrating terrain or topography is shown in brown, while green refers to vegetation, both natural and cultivated.

But symbolism must be adjusted to conform to scale. A perfectly legitimate symbol on a world map simply will not do on one of a county. Cities, as an example, are merely a dot on a small-scale map, and even that dot may have to be exaggerated in size in order to show up readily. But on a large-scale map, the entire street pattern of the city may be called for with major buildings, parks, and airports indicated in their exact location. The important requirement for map symbols is that, within the limitations of scale, they should be readily recognizable if at all possible. Obviously, the occasion arises now and again for the use of unusual symbols, and a legend explaining their meaning is appended to the map. This is perfectly all right, and most people have no difficulty in understanding legends if their notations are clear and succinct. But the less explanation required, the better the map.

Thus far, we have been dealing with symbols which are indicative of location alone, and there is no question that this is the prime function of map symbolism. But if a symbol can do double duty and show

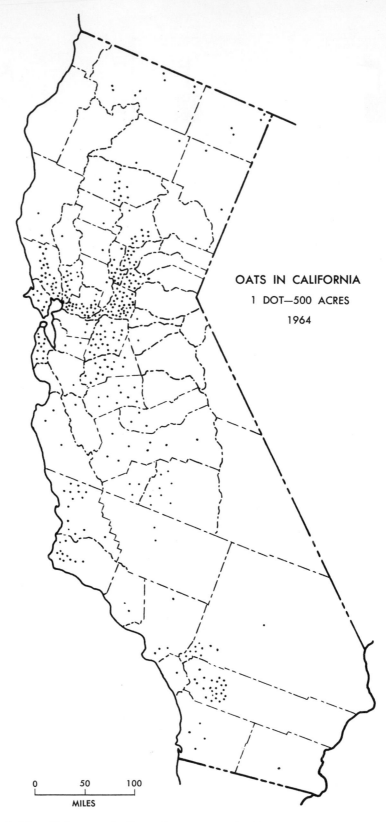

OATS IN CALIFORNIA

1 DOT—500 ACRES

1964

0   50   100

MILES

Fig. 2–22. *Value symbolism—dot map. The size and value of the dots can be varied to attain maximum clarity.*

something else in addition to location, so much the better. We have such symbols and they are highly useful; as a general term, let us call them *value symbols.*

Value Symbols

The common dot map is an example of a value symbol. The location of the dots immediately tell us *where,* for instance, oats are grown in California; but also, if we consult the legend, we find that each dot is given a value of so many acres, and such a map then tells us *how many* oats are grown in a certain locale. (Fig. 2–22.) Perhaps you have seen a map locating cities with circles for those with over 1,000,000 population, and triangles, squares, or smaller circles to indicate a population of 500,000 to 1,000,000, etc. These are value symbols. So are bales of cotton, stacks of dollars, or rows of little men—the variations are endless, but all show location plus. (Fig. 2–23.)

One particular kind of value symbol that is applicable to many situations is the *isopleth* or *isarithm, a line connecting all points of equal value.* Within this group are many applications, some of which are

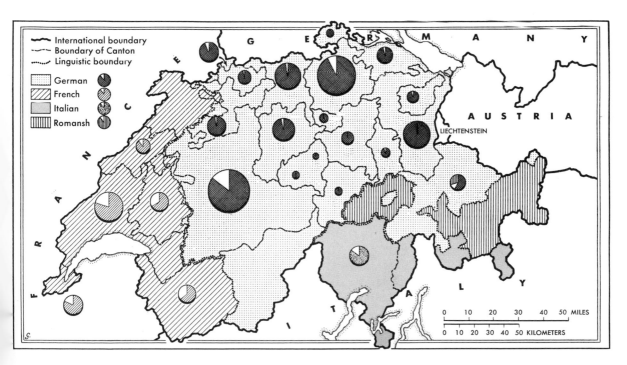

Fig. 2–23. Value symbolism—divided circles. The linguistic pattern of Switzerland. (By permission from A Geography of Europe, *2d ed., edited by George W. Hoffman, p. 445. Copyright © 1961, The Ronald Press Co., New York.)*

undoubtedly already familiar to even the most casual map-reader. Examples include:

Isotherm—a line connecting all points of equal temperature.
Isobar—a line connecting all points of equal barometric pressure.
Isohyet—a line connecting all points of equal precipitation.
Isagon—a line connecting all points of equal compass variation.
Contour—a line connecting all points of equal elevation.

And there are many more, often without specific names. Corn production in a given county may be plotted by the use of these lines. All areas with over 80 per cent of each farm planted to corn will be enclosed by one line, over 50 per cent by another, and so on. The use of color or shading supplement, with the darkest shade representing the heaviest production, will make the picture very effective. Maybe it is political affiliation, soup consumption, or the percentage of men wearing derby hats that is to be mapped—the isopleth can do the job. (Fig. 2–24.)

The third dimension. One of the most difficult problems faced by map-makers is how to show nature's third dimension on a flat map. All sorts of methods have been tried, from little crude pen strokes to indicate a mountain range, but which appear to be a caterpillar crawling across the map, to highly artistic sketches of mountains and valleys. (Fig. 2–25.) Recently, a process called plastic shading has become widespread, wherein, assuming a low sun, usually in the northwest, the artist shades deeply those sides of the ridges that would be in deep shadow and highlights the sunny side. (Fig. 2–26.) Actual construction of a plastic model followed by the placement of a low-angle light and then photographed gives much the same effect. This is very striking and the third dimension is strongly suggested; however, the weakness in most of these methods, not including exorbitant cost and a high degree of artistic ability required on the part of the cartographer, is that the symbolism merely represents terrain character without allowing the map-reader to pick off specific elevations anywhere on the map except perhaps certain prominent peaks that may be labeled.

Contours. All things considered, the map using contour lines is the most accurate from the point of view of depicting actual elevations throughout. These maps have their drawbacks too in that they are costly to construct, are most applicable only as relatively large-scale maps, and are not easy to read without some practice and training. But the general map-reader is likely to come across them, especially via the widely distributed U.S. Geologic Survey sheets that cover a large part of the United States, and he should know a few basic rules so that such maps can be meaningful.

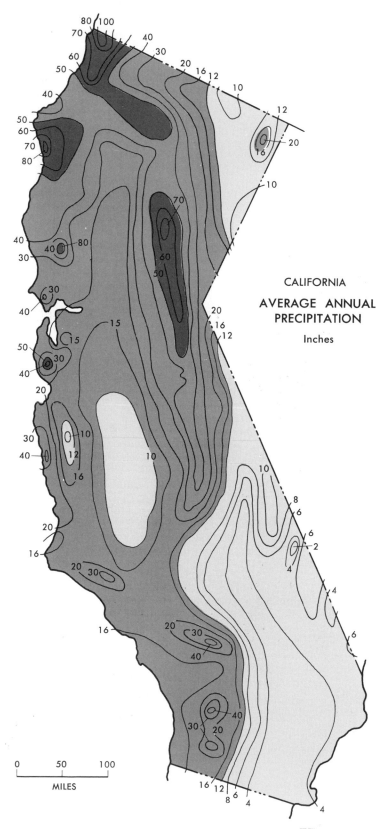

Fig. 2–24. *Isohyets. These isopleths, supplemented by shading, bring out sharply the wet vs. the dry regions of California.*

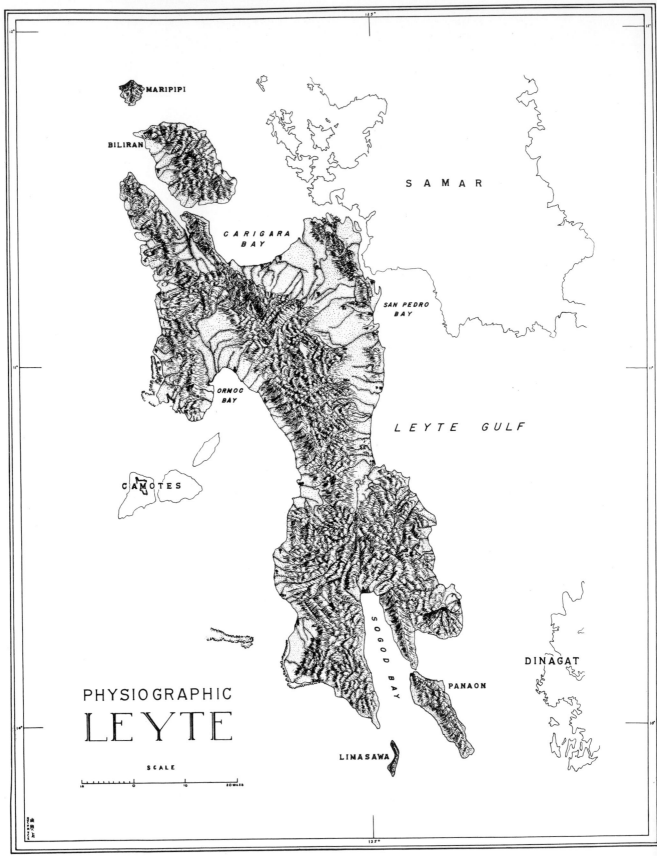

Fig. 2–25. *This realistic pen-line treatment to show terrain is called physiographic diagramming. (Courtesy of Phillip H. Schmuck.)*

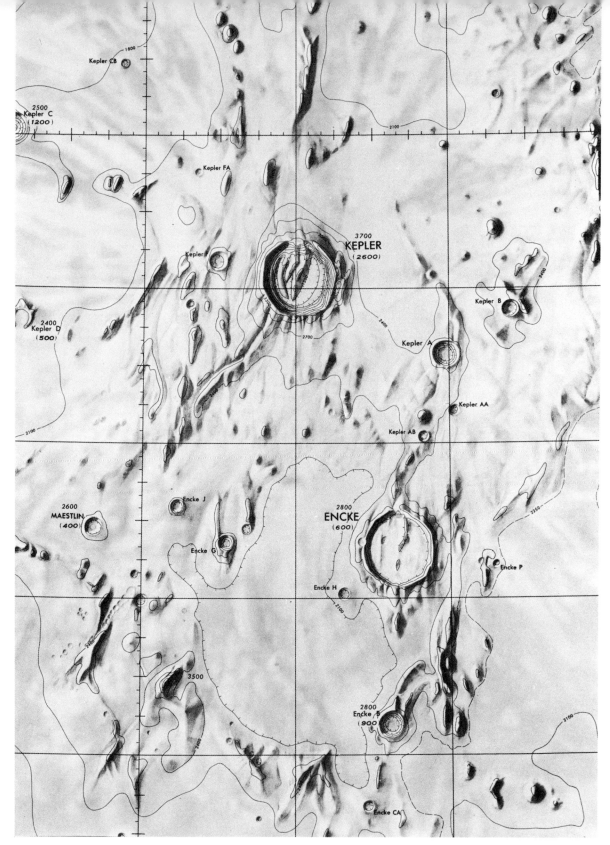

Fig. 2–26. *The contoured surface of this map of a portion of the moon has been made to appear three dimensional by shading the right side of the slopes. The steeper the slope, the darker the shading. This effective technique is widely used on all sorts of maps and is called* plastic shading. *(Official USAF photo.)*

Atlases and wall maps of continents very frequently represent topographic variation by the use of graduated colors—greens grading through yellows and browns indicating lowland vs. highland. These are contour maps, albeit highly generalized. The legend tells that everything colored green is under 500 feet. The outer margin of green then is a 500-foot contour line connecting all points 500 feet above sea level. (The green color does not mean flat, merely under 500 feet.) Similarly, the limit of each of the other colors is a contour line. But the usual contour map is of a much smaller area than a continent, and much more detail is shown.

The secret to reading contours (usually drawn in brown) is to recognize that each line represents a certain vertical distance; and, therefore, the closer they are together, the steeper the slope. Always at the bottom of the map there will be indicated a *contour interval* in feet, the amount of elevation between any two contour lines. As an illustration, let us examine a round but asymmetrical hill rising from sea level with a contour interval of 100 feet. Since elevations are virtually always reckoned from mean sea level, we measure a series of points all the way around the hill 100 feet above the sea. When these are connected by a line, we will have drawn a contour line completely encircling the hill 100 feet above sea level. Now, since the contour interval specifies that contour lines must represent 100-foot differences of elevation, our second line will be constructed above the first in the same manner at 200 feet above sea level—a smaller circle since the hill tapers to a peak, but parallel to the sea and the contour line below it. Similarly, the 300- and 400-foot contours are drawn on the hill. Since the top of the hill is above 400 feet but under 500 feet, its exact elevation is often written in at, say, 450 feet.

If we were to fly over this hill and look down on it from the top, we would see these contour lines as a series of concentric circles, but they would not be evenly spaced. On the steep side of the hill, the foreshortening of the overhead view would make them appear close together, while the gentle slope would be represented by wider spacing. (Fig. 2–27.) We know that all these contours have been accurately measured and are at the proper distance above sea level, yet the plan or map view from above gives us a direct relationship between slope and line spacing.

Let us assume that a road on a map is 1 inch long, that 1 inch equals 1 mile, and during the course of that mile, the road crosses five 100-foot contours. This means a change of elevation of 500 feet in 1 mile or quite a steep slope. But elsewhere on the same map, another 1-mile road might cross only two contours and thus climb only 200 feet—a much more gentle slope. A quick glance at the average contour map can tell us the essence of the terrain immediately. In the areas that

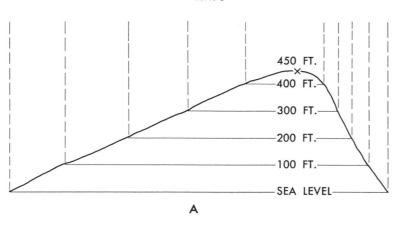

A

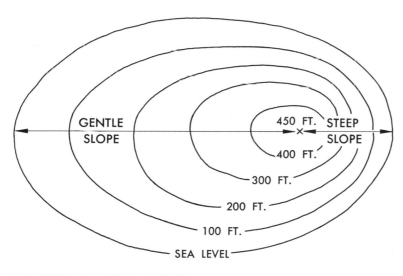

CONTOUR INTERVAL, 100 FT.

B

Fig. 2–27. Contours. All contour lines represent 100 feet of vertical distance, but on the map, they appear closer together on the steep slopes than on the gentle ones.

appear brown because of great crowding of many contour lines close together, the country must be very rough (or steep), while in the white regions where only a few contours show up, the topography is subdued. Just how rugged the mountains are and what the exact elevations might be will, of course, require somewhat closer scrutiny.

The contours themselves are labeled—often every fifth line, which is drawn slightly darker—and any place falling directly on a line can be assigned an accurate elevation. Also, prominent peaks, road junctions, lakes, etc., will usually be marked with their exact height. Locations between contour lines must have their elevations interpolated within the limits of the contour interval. The selection of the contour interval is determined by the scale of the map and particularly by the character of the terrain. If a section of the Rocky Mountains is to be mapped, a large contour interval, 100 feet or more, must be used, since there are huge changes of elevation within very short distances. If in such country a 10-foot contour interval were used, there would be so many brown lines on the map attempting to show every 10-foot change of altitude that they would merge and be indecipherable. On the other hand, a map of almost flat terrain must utilize a very small contour interval in order to bring out the minor undulations. A 100-foot interval on such a map would result in no contour lines at all if nowhere on the plain was there a 100-foot change in elevation.

Theoretically, every contour line must close, i.e., eventually come together to form a circle, for all land masses in the world are islands, and since we are measuring from sea level, closure becomes mandatory. In actual practice, however, only limited areas are represented on a single map, and a single closed line or a series of concentric circles means a hill. This is a good general rule to keep in mind as one at-

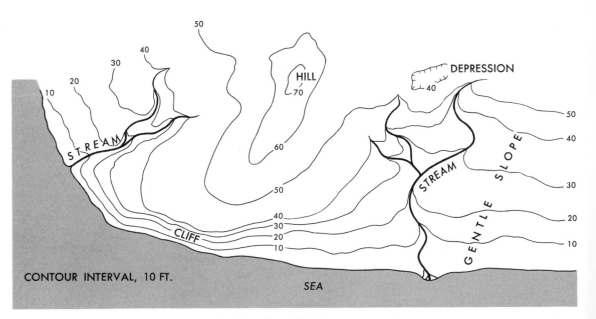

Fig. 2–28. Simplified contour map.

tempts to interpret contour maps, but there is one exception. A hole in the ground must also be represented by closed contours. In order to distinguish one from the other so that the map can be read intelligently, the depression contours have little hachures on the downslope side. For instance, we might encounter a volcano with a substantial crater at the top. The mountain would be represented by a series of closed contours, but the crater, if its depth were more than the contour interval, would also be closed, and the only way that we could tell that it was a depression rather than a simple extension of the cone would be by the hachures. (Fig. 2–28.)

One of the best guides to interpreting terrain slope is an assessment of the stream pattern, for streams flow in valleys and therefore slope will inevitably be up as we move away from the stream. But streams must flow down hill and therefore must cross contours which represent slope. At first glance, it often appears that contour lines parallel stream valleys, indicating the steepness of the valley sides, but if the map-reader carefully follows a given line, he will find that it eventually crosses the stream. Normally, however, each contour line will run far upstream before it crosses, for the elevation of the stream bottom some distance upstream is equal to the height of the bank below. Remember then, *contours must cross streams but they will point upstream.* This concept is useful in determining the direction of stream flow on the frequent maps where a stream enters on one side and flows off the other with no other indication of which way it is going.

3

The Lower Atmosphere

COMPOSITION OF THE ATMOSPHERE

As the earth wheels through space, meticulously following its pre-scribed orbits about sun and axis, it is accompanied by a gaseous at-mosphere held closely to it by gravity. This mechanical mixture of a large number of gases extends outward for well over 600 miles and, in sheer abundance, is dominated by nitrogen, 76 per cent, and oxy-gen, 21 per cent.[1] In relation to these, all others are mere trace gases —argon, hydrogen, carbon dioxide, krypton, ozone, neon, etc. Some of these are diffused rather widely throughout the entire atmosphere, but others display great concentrations at various levels and are almost totally lacking elsewhere. Nearly all the ozone, for instance, is en-countered in a narrow band at about 65,000 feet above the surface of the earth, while most of the carbon dioxide, deriving from the earth initially, is found in the lower atmosphere. It is thought that carbon dioxide is probably increasing gradually as we burn our fossil fuels and produce combustion gases more rapidly than the oceans and plants can absorb them. But in terms of weather and climate, abundance is not the measure of significance. By far the most important gas in this respect is water vapor. Constantly changing its form from gas to liquid to solid, water vapor is highly variable relative to the measur-able stability of most of the other gases. And since it is of earthly origin, its amount at a few feet above the surface may be as little as 0–2 per cent over deserts or as much as 10 per cent over tropical seas.

---

[1] Gases may be measured by either weight or volume, thus giving minor variations in percentage.

Also variable, and a significant part of the atmosphere, although not gaseous, are particles of solid matter that are maintained in suspension by moving air. The general wastebasket term "dust" is applied here to any and all solids, soot, soil, plant spores, salt, or the like. Although much more strongly represented in the lowest portion of the atmosphere, tiny dust particles may be carried to extreme heights, and meteor dust emanating from outer space has been demonstrated as existing far out at the ephemeral margin of the atmosphere. The blue sky and colored sunsets, which are particularly evident after volcanic explosions or forest fires, are manifestations of this dust in the air. Less spectacular than red sunsets, but considerably more important, is the function of dust as nuclei for the formation of raindrops. Theoretically, moist air cooled below the point of condensation will not actually condense unless such nuclei are present. Thus, atmospheric dust and water vapor operating in conjunction are major factors in the formation of our weather.

Although the atmosphere is held to the earth by gravity, like all gases, it is highly mobile. Vertical turbulence and horizontal winds set in motion by terrestrial variations in relief and temperature are constant features of the atmosphere, for the air near the earth is never still. This motion causes it to keep in suspension the water droplets of clouds and the aforementioned dust and allows the transfer of air of differing character from place to place. The atmosphere is also compressible; its own weight compresses the greater part of it into the lower few miles. It is this dense air near the earth with the largest amount of water vapor, dust, and general turbulence that we will deal with in our consideration of weather. This zone is called the *troposphere* and averages some 40,000 feet thick (somewhat less than this in the winter and near the poles, and a bit more than 40,000 feet in the summer and in the tropics). (Fig. 3–1.) Its upper limit, which separates the troposphere from the stratosphere, is called the *tropopause*. Beyond this are many other layers of lesser importance in the day-to-day weather picture, but in our discussion we will ignore them.

ELEMENTS AND CONTROLS

There are four basic elements that make up the weather as we know it: temperature, pressure, moisture, and storms. The amount, intensity, and general character of these elements at any given place are determined by a great number of factors that may be called controls. Latitude, for instance, is a major control of temperature as is altitude, while a mountain range may be an important control of moisture, as it blocks the passage of moist air to its leeward side. A list of possible controls could be a long one. However, we are concerned in this chap-

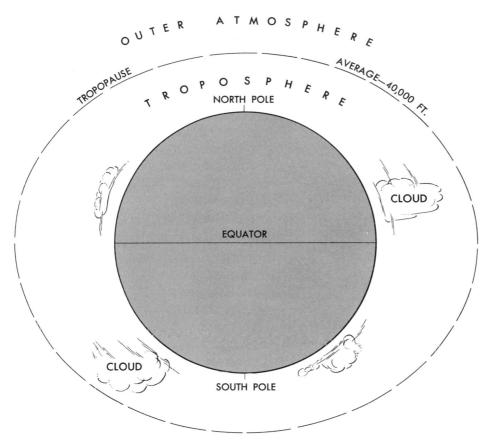

Fig. 3–1. *The troposphere. The largest portion of atmospheric tur-bulence, dust, water vapor, and clouds occur in the relatively shallow layer of the troposphere.*

ter largely with an examination of the elements, once these are under-stood, a subsequent chapter on climate will emphasize the influences of the various controls as they operate to give character to the many world climatic regions.

Temperature

The thing we call temperature is the measurement of the heat of the earth's atmosphere, not just anywhere, but a few feet off the ground where a thermometer is normally exposed at about eye level. The official temperature of any particular station in the world is taken from such a thermometer. So our problem is simple—how is this particular part of the atmosphere heated?

The sun is the exclusive basic source of all atmospheric heat, but the sun's energy that is intercepted by the earth (*insolation*) has a particular characteristic that must be recognized—it is short-wave radiation. All bodies are radiators of energy, but the hotter the body, the shorter the wave length of that radiation. So the sun, being very hot, emanates short-wave energy. However, do not equate sunshine with insolation, for the visible portion of the sun's spectrum, although short wave like most of the rest, is only a small part of the total radiation.

But this energy from the sun does not reach the surface of the earth unimpeded. Presumably, it gets through outer space with very little trouble, but it must also pass through the atmosphere before it reaches the earth, and here some selective processes begin. Far out in the atmosphere, tiny dust particles are encountered that, curiously, pick out the normally invisible blue waves in the spectrum and refract them so that they become visible and give the sky its blue coloring. This is called *selective scattering,* and although an interesting phenomenon, it does not contribute to the heating of the atmosphere. *There is no heating without absorption,* and these dust particles absorb so little energy as to be negligible. Also much of the ultraviolet portion of the spectrum combines with oxygen 12–30 miles up to form ozone, but again little heat results.

As the sun's rays penetrate the lower atmosphere, they encounter clouds that act largely to reflect. The brilliant white upper surface, often observed from an airplane, is reflecting back into space most of the visible light rays and many of the invisible waves as well. They are bounced off back into space without being absorbed and thus without adding heat.[2] However, the water droplets making up the cloud are capable of absorbing some of the longer waves so that some heat is added to the atmosphere here in small quantity. Much of the short-wave energy arriving at the cloud top however, penetrates on through to the earth, including some of the visible light rays, keeping it from being totally dark under the cloud. Also encountered near the earth in addition to the clouds, are carbon dioxide, water vapor, and large dust particles which have the ability to absorb and transfer into heat some of the longer waves. So by the time the sun's waves that entered the outer atmosphere reach the ground as insolation, their passage through the atmosphere has resulted in some little heating and in the loss via reflection of a part of their original energy. But the remarkable part of this process is that *so little* happens to the rays of the sun in this passage, especially as regards their contribution to the ultimate heat of the lower atmosphere. At most, only about 15 per cent of the

[2] Approximately 32 per cent of the total energy reaching the outer atmosphere is reflected or scattered back into space.

total atmospheric heat is achieved from the sun's waves as they pass through, and normally not that much.

The short waves from the sun, having traversed the atmosphere so successfully, now encounter the earth. This is a different situation, as the earth on the whole is an excellent absorber and its surface becomes heated rapidly. Now the earth becomes a radiator of energy, but since it is much less warm than the sun, radiates long waves (or heat waves). The gases of the lower atmosphere, especially water vapor, which totally rejected or absorbed only small amounts of the short waves from the sun are able to absorb virtually all these long heat waves and the air warms rapidly. This concept of the bulk of the lower atmosphere being heated indirectly from the sun with the earth as an intermediary has been called imaginatively *the greenhouse effect,* for this is almost identical to the greenhouse mechanism. The sun's short-wave energy passes through the glass virtually unimpeded, is absorbed by the earth inside, and changed to long waves. The glass now acts as a block to their escape and heat is trapped. Substitute the atmosphere for the greenhouse glass and the simile becomes apparent. (Fig. 3–2.)

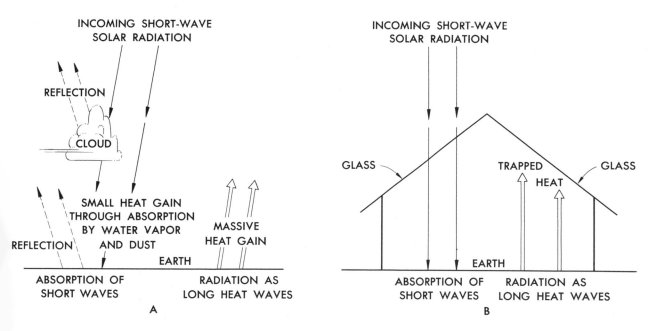

Fig. 3–2. *(A) Heating of the lower atmosphere. (B) The Greenhouse effect. The glass in the greenhouse (B) is the equivalent of the atmosphere (A) in allowing short-wave energy to reach the earth, but trapping the long heat waves as they are reradiated.*

But the earth's surface is not a homogeneous mass. It is made up of a great many various elements, each with a differing absorption and reflective capacity. Snow cover, for instance, will reflect most of the short waves received from the sun back into space much the same way as the tops of clouds do, while dark-colored plowed fields or macadamized surfaces will be very efficient absorbers and radiators. Also, the angle at which the sun's rays strike the earth, as controlled by latitude and time of day, has an effect on their heating capacity. The more direct these rays are, the more energy is concentrated in a smaller area. But although of considerable importance locally, we can, for the moment, rule out these minor variations and emphasize two major surfaces that evidence great differences in their abilities to absorb and reradiate the sun's energy—land vs. water.

Land, on the whole, is a good absorber and in the summer heats up rapidly, while water is a relatively poor absorber and over the period of a three-month hot season changes temperature only slightly. Why should this great variance occur between the continents and the oceans? The reasons are several. First, land is opaque and the energy arriving on 1 square foot is strongly concentrated at the surface. A similar square foot of transparent water allows the penetration of energy to a considerable depth, thus dispersing the heat through two dimensions, and the surface warms only a fraction of that of land. Also, water is moving, both vertically and horizontally, so that no given square foot of surface remains exposed to the continuing receipt of the same amount of energy as does a comparable land surface. And, of course, the cooling effect of evaporation over the water is more continuous and effective than over land. Add to these the fact that water has a higher *specific heat* than land; that is, it is simply a physical law that other things being equal, it requires almost five times as much energy to raise a gram of water 1 degree as it does a gram of dry earth. So we see a continent heating intensely during the summer relative to the oceans. Experiment on a small scale sometime by walking barefoot on the sidewalk at midday and then stepping into a puddle. The puddle may be warm—it is no ocean—but it will be a great deal cooler than the cement.

A good absorber is a good radiator. This means that during the winter and at night when the receipt of sun's energy is reduced or lacking, the earth will rapidly lose its heat, while the water will tend to maintain that which it has managed to pick up, releasing it very slowly. The temperature of the earth's surface in the middle latitudes will vary from summer days to winter nights as much as 150 degrees, while that of the oceans may exhibit a change of only 3–5 degrees. Since the lower atmosphere takes its temperature characteristics from the earth's surface, it is easy to see how oceanic air masses may differ radically from those that are normally resident over land areas. The oceans and their attendant air masses tend to maintain very much the same temperature the year round, while the land and the air above it will frequently show seasonal extremes.

There are two related mechanisms involved in the transfer of heat from the earth to the air above it—*conduction* and *radiation*. Conduction involves the transfer of heat from a warm body to a cold one in *contact*. Heat will flow from the warmer to the colder until they are of equal temperature. Place a sterling silver spoon in a cup of hot coffee and note how the handle heats to the temperature of the coffee. This principle applies to the earth and the atmosphere at their point of contact. Here, the warm earth will heat the adjacent cooler air through conduction. At first, this heated layer will be shallow, only a few feet deep, but as the day wears on, it will become both warmer and deeper. At the same time, there will be occurring a transfer of heat through space or radiation. This is much like conduction except that contact is not necessary; therefore, a wide zone of the lower atmosphere is heated in this manner. But conduction is the more efficient of the two, and the air at the surface will be heated much more intensely. Try placing your hand on the room radiator. It will be heated intensely by conduction. Now, hold your hand a foot above the radiator and heat will still be received, but with considerably less intensity. This is radiation. (Fig. 3–3.)

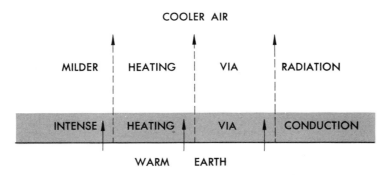

Fig. 3–3. *Heat transfer. Because conduction is much more efficient than radiation, the most intense heating occurs immediately above the surface.*

In addition to conduction and radiation, there are two other commonly occurring means by which the atmosphere may be heated— *compression* and *condensation*. Compression involves the loss of altitude of an air mass. As it descends, the greater pressure of air from

Fig. 3–4. *These delicate snow crystals, no two alike, result from the sudden change of gas to ice as the temperature is lowered. They have not gone through the intermediate water stage or they would appear as frozen raindrops. (Courtesy of U.S. Weather Bureau.)*

above causes it to compress into a smaller volume and this produces heat. This is not an unlikely situation, as sizable masses of air are constantly shifting their altitude for reasons that we will delve into later. Condensation, the change of water vapor into liquid, also releases heat into the atmosphere. Where did the heat come from? Well, it has been there all the time, latent in the water vapor, for in the process of becoming a gas, heat was expended. Let us suppose that you are perspiring. As that perspiration evaporates from your skin, you feel cooler—heat has been subtracted. Where did it go? It is in the water vapor waiting to be released when the process is reversed and the gas becomes a liquid. This is condensation. It may not seem like a significant amount of heat to be considered, but when literally millions of raindrops are formed instantaneously in a storm, a great deal of heat is released into the atmosphere. We can carry this a step further. Heat is required to change ice into water, so each drop of water has an increment of latent energy. Then heat is used up in changing water to gas, and water vapor now has two increments of latent energy. If water vapor is suddenly changed directly to ice, as in the formation of snow (sublimation), two increments of energy are released and the air is heated rapidly. (Fig. 3–4.) Actually, this latent heat of condensation is credited with being an important element in the formation and perpetuation of most of our storms. (Fig. 3–5.)

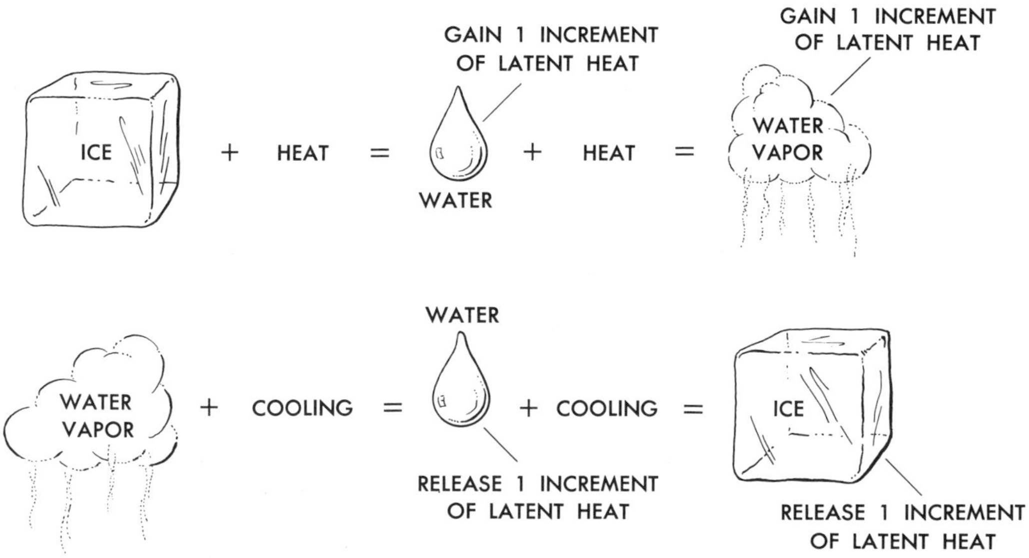

GAIN 1 INCREMENT OF LATENT HEAT

GAIN 1 INCREMENT OF LATENT HEAT

ICE + HEAT = WATER + HEAT = WATER VAPOR

WATER VAPOR + COOLING = WATER + COOLING = ICE

RELEASE 1 INCREMENT OF LATENT HEAT

RELEASE 1 INCREMENT OF LATENT HEAT

Fig. 3–5. Latent heat.

So there are four basic means of heating the atmosphere: conduction, radiation, compression, and condensation. Two of these, conduction and radiation, may also function to cool the atmosphere, and *expansion* (the reverse of compression) and *evaporation* (the reverse of condensation) are cooling mechanisms also.

Heating	*Cooling*
Conduction	Conduction
Radiation	Radiation
Compression	Expansion
Condensation	Evaporation

We have found that where the warm earth is in contact with cooler air, there is a transfer of heat from warm to cold and the air is heated through conduction. Now, if we turn this about as on a long winter night with the ground snow covered and the air still, it is entirely possible for the earth to be colder than the air above it. When this condition occurs, heat moves via conduction in the opposite direction and the lowest strata of air is cooled. The air at a higher level can also lose heat through radiation to the colder earth as well as out into space. So conduction and radiation may function at any given time to either warm or cool the lower atmosphere.

Compression warms by causing a mass of air to decrease its volume as it loses altitude. If that same air mass were to go aloft, its volume would increase as expansion took place and its temperature would decrease. And finally, if condensation releases heat, then when evaporation is occurring, the air is being cooled.

Since the air is seldom still, once it has achieved its temperature characteristics in one place, it is likely to be transported elsewhere. Horizontal air movement of this type resulting from simple winds is common. We have all experienced invasions of cold air from farther north that become exposed to the warming influences of more southerly regions. But vertical mixing or turbulence is also frequent; the most usual cause being *convection*. To understand and visualize convectional circulation, a laboratory demonstration may be set up utilizing a tank of water with a Bunsen burner heating a point at the bottom. The heated water will rise visibly above this spot, and the colder water from the top and sides will be seen to be moving in to take its place. This rising central column and sinking side columns is convection, triggered by heating at the bottom. The principle works equally well in gas as in liquid, so if the narrow band of atmosphere directly in contact with the warm earth is heated by conduction, it will rise and colder air from above will sink to replace it. (Fig. 3–6.) Convection is often explosive, as the trapped warm air breaks through the colder air above it suddenly during the hottest time of the day. This mechanism transports intensely heated air to great heights and allows cool

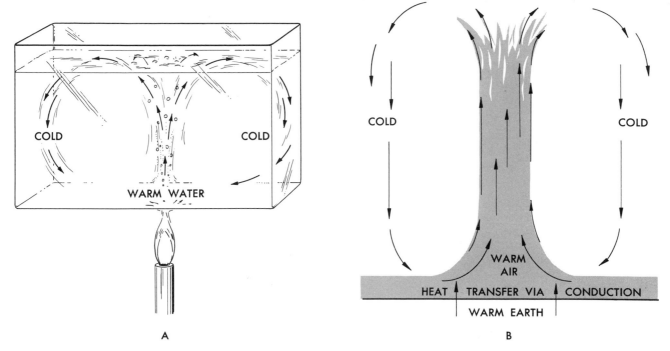

Fig. 3–6. *Convection. Heat applied at the bottom of either a liquid (A) or a gas (B) causes a rising central column and sinking (cold) side columns.*

air from aloft to be exposed to the heating effects of the earth. However, neither horizontal winds nor the vertical transfer of air in convection add or subtract any heat to or from the atmosphere that was not there already. They are turbulence or mixing factors that help to distribute heat throughout the lower atmosphere and cannot be properly called heating or cooling mechanisms by themselves.

Lapse rates. Under normal circumstances, a thermometer attached to a balloon will indicate a constantly lowering temperature as it rises —the tops of mountains will support snow while the lower levels do not. That is, the closer the sun is approached, the colder it gets—seemingly paradoxical until it is remembered that the lower atmosphere receives its heat from the earth, and the farther one gets from the radiator or source of heat, the colder it gets. This loss of temperature with increase of altitude (or gain with decrease) is called the *lapse rate,* and if we assume the air to be reasonably still and the observer or instrument to rise through it, the rate of temperature loss approximates 3.3 degrees per thousand feet. This loss is fairly predictable, at least to the tropopause, and is called the *normal lapse rate.*

There is another type of lapse rate, however, that should be differentiated from the normal lapse rate; this is the *adiabatic lapse rate*. Where the normal lapse rate assumed still air, the adiabatic lapse rate involves the lifting of a sizable mass of air. As it rises, its receipt of heat from the earth will become less and less, but since we are dealing with a large mass of air, the temperature loss from simply being farther from the source of heat will be slow and scarcely noticeable for some time. But there is a cause of instantaneous heat loss that will show up immediately; this is expansion and it results in a decrease of about 5.5 degrees per thousand feet. This is called the *Dry adiabatic lapse rate* and applies to any rising expanding air mass *if no condensation is occurring within it*. If condensation occurs in any of its forms during the ascent of an air mass, then the *Wet adiabatic lapse rate* becomes applicable. This lapse rate will vary with situation, but is *always less than 5.5 degrees per thousand feet.*

Let us consider a Chinook (United States) or Foehn (Europe) wind as an example of the practical application of the Wet and Dry adiabatic lapse rates. These winds are warm dry air currents blowing down from the mountains. The Chinook, experienced along the eastern slope of the Rockies and Cascades in winter and early spring, melts the snow, thus opening up the range for grazing, but also frequently causing serious floods. If we set up a simplified and somewhat exaggerated example, the mechanics will become apparent. We will place a 10,000-foot mountain range in the path of prevailing winds, thereby forcing the air mass on the windward side up the slope. If the temperature of this air mass is 60° at the foot of the mountain, as it rises it will lose 5.5 degrees per thousand feet because of expansion. At the 2,000-foot level, it will have lost 11 degrees and the original 60° air mass will now have a temperature of 49°. If we establish this 2,000-foot level as the dew point, that is, the point where any further cooling will cause condensation, then from the dew point to the top of the mountain, the Wet adiabatic lapse rate must apply. Since this rate is always less than 5.5 degrees, let us, for the purposes of this example, place it at 3 degrees per thousand feet. Now, as the air mass continues to rise from 2,000 feet to the 10,000-foot crest, it loses 3 degrees per thousand feet, or 24 degrees for the total 8,000-foot uplift. Thus, the air mass arrives at the top of the mountain at a temperature of 25°. Now, if it descends the lee slope, it will be compressed and warmed as it goes. Condensation requires cooling, so it will cease at the crest; and as the air mass comes down, it will be warmed at the Dry rate of 5.5 degrees per thousand feet. In bringing the air mass back down 10,000 feet, it will gain 55 degrees, and this added to the 25 degrees at the crest gives it a temperature of 80° at the foot of the mountain. (Fig. 3–7.) By simply taking a 60° air mass over the top of a mountain and down the other side, we have added 20 degrees to its temperature. Where did that heat come from? The only difference in ascent and descent is the zone of precipitation between the 2,000- and 10,000-foot levels on the windward side, so the heat must have been that released by condensation. There was still a net loss of heat as the air went up through this zone, but only at the rate of 3 degrees per thousand feet. In other words, the air continued to expand and lose heat at the normal rate on the way up, but condensation replaced a part of that loss, and the 80° air mass at the foot of the lee slope is not only warmer but drier than when it started out.

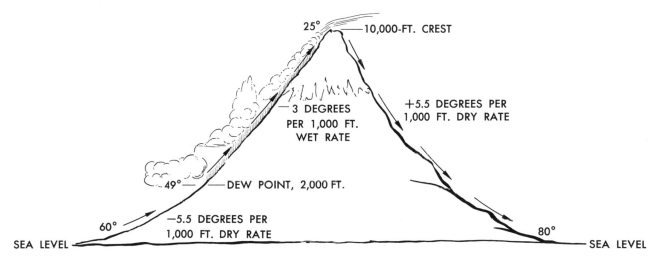

Fig. 3–7. *Chinook. The heat gained through condensation on the windward slope is reflected in the higher temperature at the base of the mountain in the lee (highly exaggerated).*

Lapse rates then are simply the rate at which there is a loss or gain of temperature with a loss or gain of altitude. The *normal lapse rate* assumes a still atmosphere with the observer moving through it, while the *adiabatic lapse rates* apply when an air mass changes altitude and expansion or compression are in operation.

Inversions. On occasion, the normal lapse rate may be reversed; that is, a gain in altitude will result in a gain in temperature. This situation is called an *inversion,* or simply an inverted normal lapse rate. They are usually of short duration but quite common nonetheless. A long winter night with a clear sky and still air is an ideal situation for the development of the most common type of inversion.

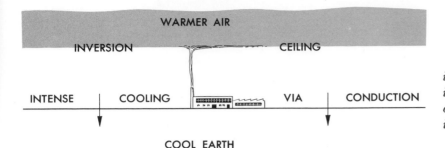

INVERSION   CEILING

INTENSE | COOLING   VIA | CONDUCTION

COOL EARTH

Fig. 3–8. Temperature inversion. Depicted here is the abnormal situation of temperature gain with increased altitude.

The heat of the day is radiated off the earth during the night, and by the early morning hours the surface of the earth is cooler than the air above it. Heat moves via conduction from the lower atmosphere to the earth and there forms a cool stratum beneath warmer air above. This means then that if a thermometer were taken aloft, as it passed upward and out of this cool zone, it would indicate warming—just the reverse of the normal situation.

Everyone has seen smoke rising from a chimney on a cool morning suddenly flatten out and move laterally. This makes visible the top of the cool layer and the beginning of the warmer air. (Fig. 3–8.) Such inversion ceilings can act as traps to hold in a wide variety of contaminants and often are responsible for smog concentrations at low levels. (Fig. 3–9.) Luckily in this connection, this type of inversion is usually short lived, for as soon as the sun has been out a few hours, the earth becomes heated and in turn heats the air adjacent to it and normal conditions are restored. Subsidence inversions, on the other hand, sinking compressing air, may introduce a heated stratum aloft, and these inversions often persist for days.

Fig. 3–9. Downtown San Francisco viewed from Twin Peaks. A shallow inversion has trapped the many contaminants that make up smog beneath it, and rendered the ceiling visible from above. Notice that the taller buildings and hills are above the· ceiling. (Courtesy of Bay Area Air Pollution Control District.)

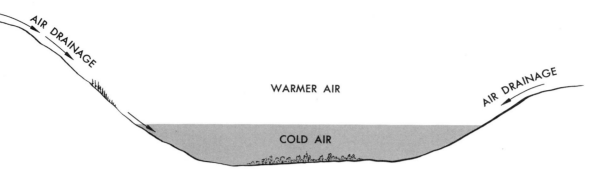

Fig. 3–10. *Air drainage. Cold air flows downslope like water, filling up terrain depressions to a considerable depth.*

Air drainage. Cold air at the surface, as during an inversion, flows under the influence of gravity and the local topography. Being heavy and dense, cold air acts almost like water and moves down the slope to pile up deeply in pockets and valley bottoms. This is called *air drainage.* (Fig. 3–10.) If any significant altitude is lost, there is adiabatic warming due to compression, but on the relatively small-scale local scene, there may be a good many degrees difference in temperature between valley floors and sloping foothills. It is common practice to plant frost-touchy citrus or peach orchards on slopes so that as cold air develops at the surface, it will flow away. The moving cold air remains shallow on the slopes, affecting directly only the trunks of the trees, but it will often accumulate to a considerable depth in the valley, causing frost damage to the delicate fruit and foliage. (Fig. 3–11.)

Fig. 3–11. *Young lemon trees on the valley floor are susceptible to occasional frost damage through air drainage. The orchard heaters are effective in raising temperatures a degree or two, but have been replaced in California because of air pollution legislation by wind machines which break up the stratification of cold air. (Courtesy of U.S. Weather Bureau.)*

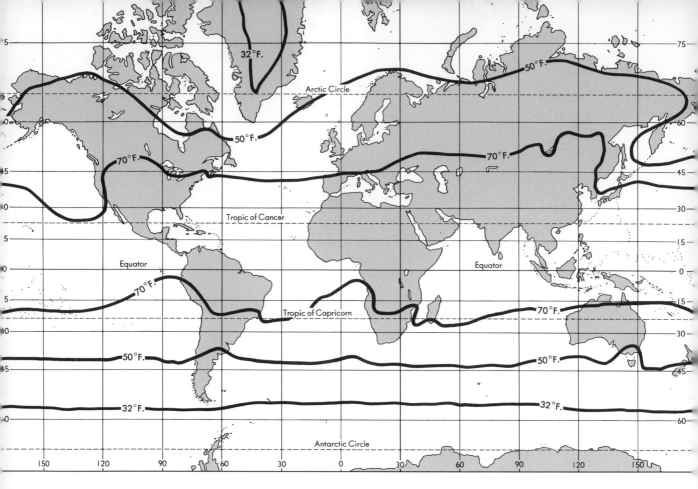

Fig. 3–12. *World mean July isotherms (reduced to sea level).*

Isotherms. Frequently, it becomes necessary and useful to plot accumulated temperature data in map form to make visual to the map-reader the distribution of particular temperatures at a given time. One method would be to simply write the temperature at the locations of the various reporting stations. But imagine the welter of figures on a map of the world or the United States if all reporting stations were represented. It would require long and careful study for any sort of meaningful pattern to emerge from this method. This is a good start, but the reading of such a map can be greatly simplified by the use of *isotherms;* these are lines that connect all points of equal temperature.

Normally, the isotherms are drawn on a map on which have been plotted monthly temperature averages, and in connecting certain selected temperatures, they divulge a pattern of occurrence that is not at all readily apparent from the written figures alone. We see immediately that isotherms exhibit a general east-west trend expressing the influence of latitude as the major control of world temperature.

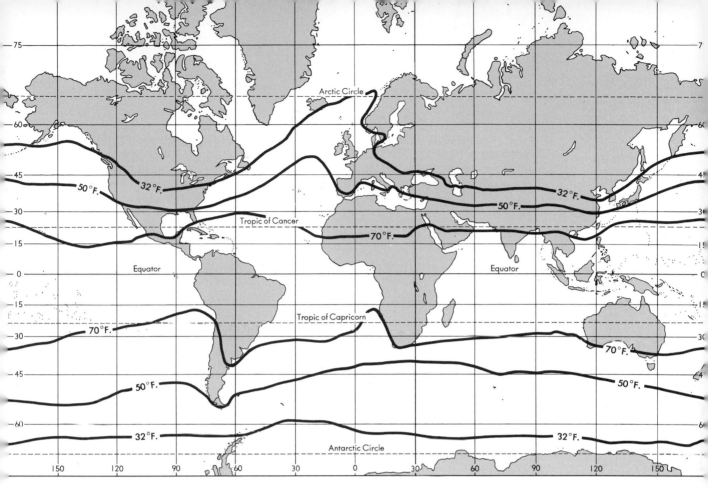

Fig. 3–13. *World mean January isotherms (reduced to sea level).*

But over the middle latitude continents, they tend to deviate sharply from this trend, especially along west coasts. For instance, the January 32° isotherm in the north Pacific is a fairly straight east-west line just south of the Aleutians, striking the West Coast of North America at about Juneau, Alaska. Obviously, it cannot continue directly eastward into the continent, for we know that the winter temperature averages in northern Canada are well below 32°. In order to find as mild a January in the interior of the continent as that of Juneau, we may have to drop as far south as central Kansas. So the isotherm in connecting these similar temperatures will show a sharp break at the West Coast and trend almost north-south. In Europe, this deviation in direction is even more apparent. So by drawing a single isotherm, it becomes obvious immediately that in this particular part of the world, latitude as a temperature control is of considerably less importance than coastal vs. inland location. Isotherms are simply man-made value symbols to help us make useful interpretations from temperature data plotted on a map. (Figs. 3–12 and 3–13.)

Pressure

Pressure is nothing more than the total weight of the atmosphere pressing down on the surface of the earth. At any given spot, the column of atmosphere immediately above it exerts an average pressure of about 15 pounds per square inch called *one atmosphere* (this varies with altitude and latitude). If something occurs to increase this weight, i.e., to cause the air to push down a little harder, the pressure is increased at the surface, and this particular spot becomes a high-pressure center (*anticyclone*). On the other hand, there may be a lifting of the column, thus relieving some of the pressure and causing a low-pressure center (*cyclone*). Temperature, for example, is a common cause of pressure differentiation (although by no means the only one). Air that is cooled at the bottom will sink and increase pressure, whereas warming will cause the air to rise and thus lower the pressure.

Unlike the other weather elements, pressure is something of an intangible. We cannot hear it, smell it, or feel it; in other words, the human body is a terrible barometer. It is not the best thermometer in the world for that matter, but one can tell general temperature changes, even if humidity variations and the like prevent us from being very accurate. But only those occasional individuals whose rheumatism and war wounds ache or whose noses bleed are able to sense changes in pressure.

Therefore, we are strongly dependent on instruments to keep us informed of changing pressure conditions. The critical instrument is the mercury barometer, which is not very different from the simple original invented by Torricelli. This first barometer was merely a glass tube with a vacuum in it, closed at one end. The open end was placed in a dish of mercury. As normal air pressure was exerted on the mercury surface, a column was forced up the tube to a height of roughly 30 inches (sea level and middle latitude). Variations in pressure caused variations in this height.[3] It seems a little strange at first to measure pressure, a force, in linear units, but the height of the mercury column measured in inches is a direct indication of the pressure of the air. Today's modern barometers have only a few modifications on this original. Inches are subdivided into tenths or more for added accuracy, and a minor correction is made for the effect of temperature on the mercury. Such barometers, because of their awkward dimensions, are usually firmly fixed in a permanent wall mounting. (Fig. 3–14.) A more convenient but somewhat less accurate barometer is the *aneroid*. It is a small metal diaphragm with a partial vacuum

---

[3] Water might be used; it is cheaper than mecury; but it is also lighter, and normal air pressure would push it up a tube approximately 33 feet.

Fig. 3–15. *The compact aneroid barometer is easy to transport. Notice that the dial face is calibrated in inches and millibars to conform with comparable readings from the mercurial barometer. (Courtesy of U.S. Weather Bureau.)*

Fig. 3–14. *Mercurial barometers. (Courtesy of U.S. Weather Bureau.)*

inside. As the outside air pressure becomes less, the sides bulge outward. This movement is shown on a dial that indicates the pressure change. (Fig. 3–15.)

Coming into much more common use today, and officially adopted by the U.S. Weather Bureau in 1940, is another unit of air pressure measurement called the *millibar*. It is a more logical unit than the inch since a millibar is a direct measure of force. A millibar is equal to a force of 1,000 dynes per square centimeter, and a dyne is the force that will accelerate 1 gram of mass 1 centimeter in 1 second (1 dyne is approximately the weight of 1 milligram). Since both the inch and the millibar are widely used, the important thing to remember is their relationship. An inch of mercury is equal to 33.9 millibars; i.e., *one standard atmosphere is normally said to equal 30 (29.9) inches or 1,000 (1,013.2) millibars.*

Once again the use of isarithms, in this case *isobars,* allows us to transfer data from an instrument to a map so that the actual pattern of pressure differences may be made visible. These isobars, drawn at 0.1-inch pressure variations, take the form of roughly concentric circles indicating centers of high or low pressure. Remember, pressure is relative—no specific number of inches is always low or high. If, for instance, we have a place with a barometric reading of 29.7 inches, and the pressure rises in all directions from that spot, then it is a low-pressure center. However, this same 29.7 inches might very well be a high-pressure center if the pressures on all sides of it were lower.

Wind. Nature, abhoring inequalities, attempts to compensate for pressure differences by the transfer of air. High pressure represents a surplus of air and low pressure a deficit, and the general lateral movement of air, or wind, is from high pressure to low. Thus, wind is the resultant of pressure differences, and both its direction and velocity are determined by the relative location and intensity of highs and lows. If we can envision a low center as a lifting of the air above a given place, then "a vacuum of sorts" is formed at the surface that pulls air to it from all directions. The greater the lifting, the more effective the vacuum and the pulling effect of the low. A high, on the other hand, is at the bottom of a column of air being forced down, and the air at the surface is being forced out away from the high. (Fig. 3–16.)

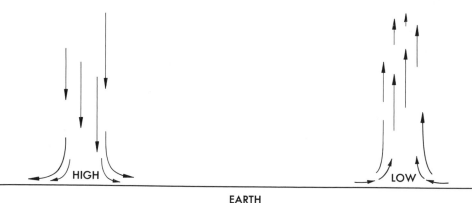

Fig. 3–16. Pressure. At the surface, air flows into lows and out of highs.

Intensity of high and low, and thus velocity of winds, is represented on the map by the spacing of the isobars. If each isobar represents 0.1-inch pressure difference and they are close together, then there is a rapid change of pressure within a short distance, and wind will move across these isobars at a high velocity. This change of pressure as represented by the isobaric spacing is called the *pressure gradient,* and wind will always flow *down* the pressure gradient *from high to low.* (Fig. 3–17.)

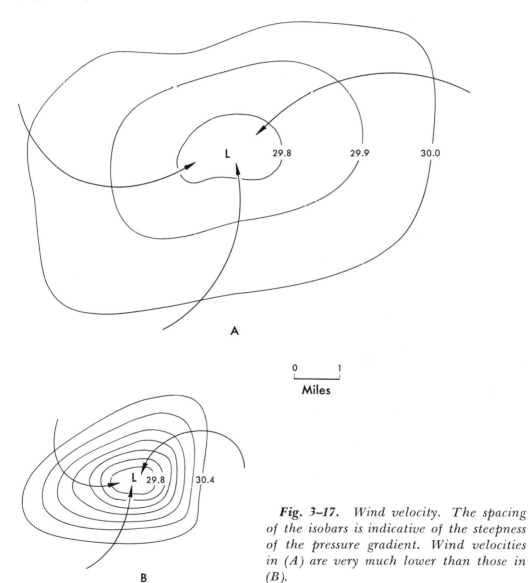

Fig. 3–17. *Wind velocity. The spacing of the isobars is indicative of the steepness of the pressure gradient. Wind velocities in (A) are very much lower than those in (B).*

But once the wind is set in motion by pressure differentiation, it does not flow directly from high to low as might be expected; instead, it appears to us, observing it from the moving earth, to follow a somewhat devious course in arriving at its destination. This comes about through the effects of *Coriolis force.* Ferrel's Law states the effect of this force: *Any horizontally moving object in the Northern Hemisphere will exhibit an apparent right-hand deflection and in the Southern Hemisphere an apparent left-hand deflection.* At the equator no such force exists, but its effect increases with latitude and reaches a maximum at the poles. This applies to ocean currents, rivers, rifle bullets, baseballs, and, of course, air currents. Pull the plug in the bathtub and watch the water flow down the drain in a right-hand spiral. Once a wind begins to move, two forces affect its flow: the pressure gradient causing it to move from high to low, and Coriolis force causing it to veer off course. Let us consider a Northern Hemi-

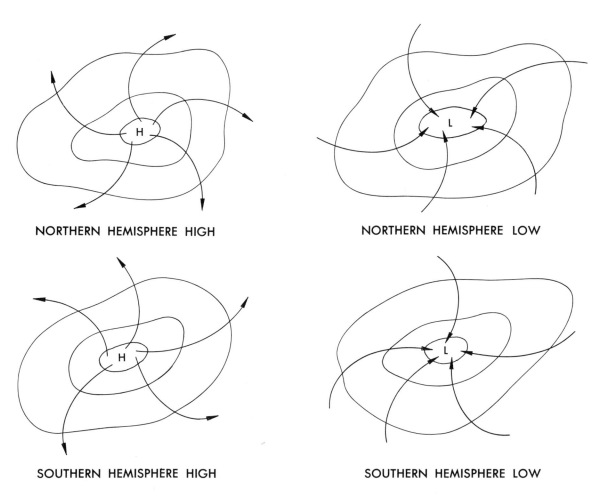

NORTHERN HEMISPHERE HIGH

NORTHERN HEMISPHERE LOW

SOUTHERN HEMISPHERE HIGH

SOUTHERN HEMISPHERE LOW

Fig. 3–18. Wind direction. The pulling and repelling influences of lows and highs, respectively, set the air in motion, but its ultimate course is determined by Coriolis *force.*

sphere high-pressure center with air moving away from it in all directions. *We must face with the wind* to determine which direction is right and then add a right-hand deflection to the general air flow. The end result is air not moving directly out of the high but *spiraling out in a clockwise spiral*. In the low, the winds attempt to move directly into the vacuum of the low-pressure center but are diverted to the right as they move. They arrive at their destination eventually but follow an indirect course, a counterclockwise spiral. In the Southern Hemisphere, these spirals are reversed. (Figs. 3–18 and 3–19.)

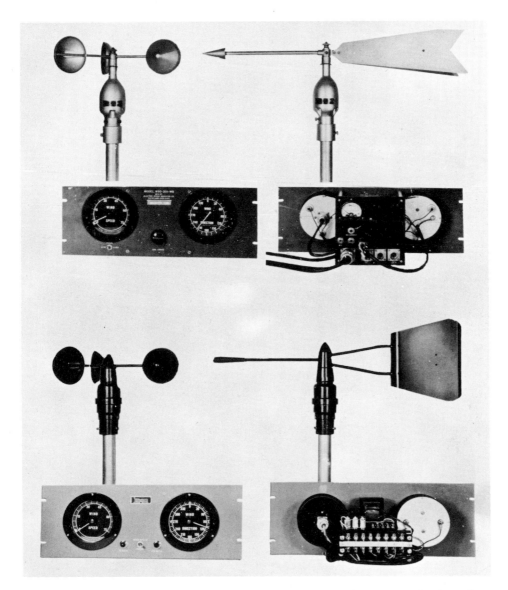

Fig. 3–19. *Wind vanes, on the right, indicate wind direction. The broad tail flies with the wind and the arrow points upwind. At the left are cup anemometers that spin at varying rates in the wind, measuring its velocity. (Courtesy of U.S. Weather Bureau.)*

The world pressure pattern. Over the oceanic areas of the world, a general and fairly predictable pattern of surface wind and pressure systems can be traced, largely because extensive water bodies do not effect appreciable temperature changes from season to season as do middle latitude land masses. Temperature changes in turn induce pressure variation so that if we could for the moment erase the major continents off the globe and visualize a *rotating but all-water globe,* it would be possible to establish an idealized wind and pressure pattern comprising a number of belts parallel to the equator. (Fig. 3–20.)

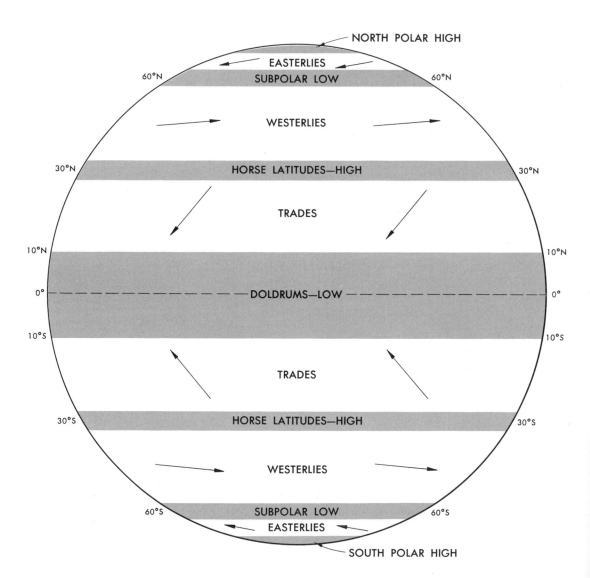

Fig. 3–20. *Idealized world wind and pressure pattern.*

The belt immediately astride the equator and extending for roughly 10° on either side is called the *Doldrums* or *Equatorial Low*. Its outer margins are not constant at 10°N and 10°S because the entire zone, along with all the others on the earth, shifts north as the overhead sun moves to the Tropic of Cancer and somewhat south when the sun moves to the Tropic of Capricorn. Nonetheless, the Doldrums is generally coincidental with the equatorial region and is the result of the constant high temperatures of this part of the world. The overall movement of this constantly heated air is *up*, and thus the pressure is low. And since the air movement is vertical, there are no winds, or at most only variable breezes, so that this zone is characterized by calm. The old sailormen who first recognized and named these belts dreaded the Doldrums and were often becalmed for long periods of time in these latitudes. The expression "in the doldrums" meaning to feel blue has come down to us from these times, for there was nobody as unhappy as a sailor caught in the tropical calms.

Some little distance out from the equator both north and south, at about 30°, is a second zone of calms. This is a narrow belt called the *Horse Latitudes* or *Subtropical High*. Again, vertical air movement is dominant—in this case sinking rather than rising air. Obviously, temperature is not a factor here in causing the air to descend, as we are at the edge of the tropics and temperatures are high. The usual explanation is that the *antitrades,* upper air winds flowing away from the equator, are deflected increasingly (Coriolis force) as they move, and since there is no retarding of this deflection due to friction with the earth, by the time the antitrades have reached about 30°N and S latitude, they are flowing parallel to the equator. Air piles up here and sinks of its own weight, and the result is high pressure at the surface.

Now, between this permanent high and the permanent low of the Doldrums is a broad zone in which air flows horizontally along the surface toward the equator (i.e., from high to low). This belt in both hemispheres is called the *Trades*. In the Northern Hemisphere as the air moves from the Horse Latitudes, it is canted to the right and takes a southwesterly course (or from the northeast). Remember two things: first, winds are named by the direction *from which they come;* second, always face *with* the wind when determining right- or left-hand deflection. Applying left-hand deflection to the Southern Hemisphere Trades, we find that they flow from the southeast toward the equator. Characteristic of the trade winds is constancy of flow always from the same direction, and moderate velocities—in a word, perfect winds for sailing. Every westward bound mariner took advantage of them if at all possible, and the appellation *trade* winds became a truly descriptive term.

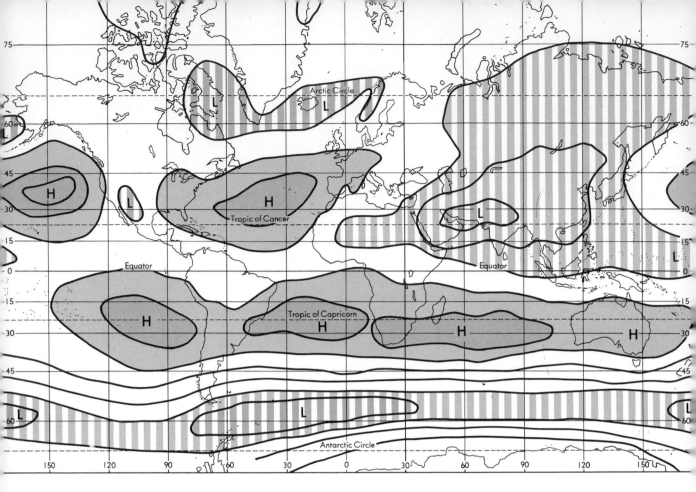

Fig. 3–21. *World July isobars.*

Have you ever wondered why if Columbus sailed due west from Spain he did not discover the Carolina coast? The fact is that he did not sail due west from Spain at all, but being a practical sailor went south from Spain to the Canaries and then west via the Trades, thus winding up in the West Indies.

Considerably farther away from the equator at about 60°N and S latitude is a narrow belt of low pressure called the *Subpolar Low.* Like the Horse Latitude, the pressure here has little relationship to surface temperature. One explanation is that poleward flowing upper air currents spiral, causing a vortex or low that should occur at the pole. However, the intense cold of the polar region creates a high that pushes the low out to its outer margins or about 60°. In any case, long observation has definitely established a permanent low belt in these latitudes.

Between this Subpolar Low and the high of the Horse Latitudes, surface winds flow poleward across an extensive zone. But as they move from high to low, they are deflected right or left, depending on the hemisphere, much more strongly than the Trades, as deflective

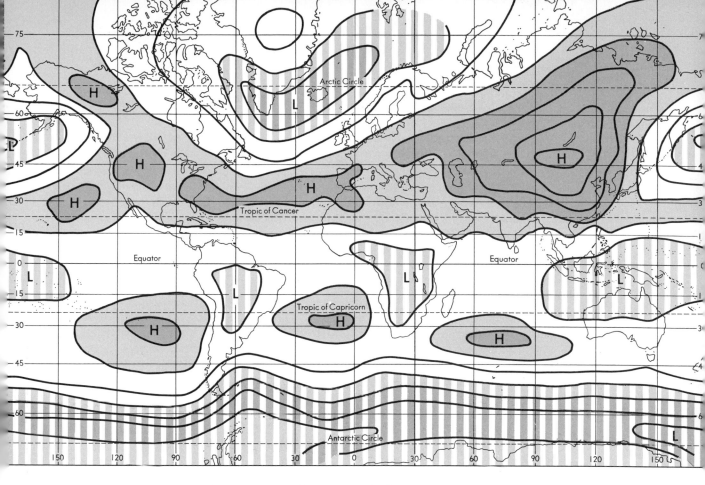

Fig. 3-22. World January isobars.

force increases with latitude. Thus, they blow from almost due west (slightly southwest in the Northern Hemisphere and northwest in the Southern Hemisphere) and are called *Westerlies*. These are somewhat higher velocity winds than the Trades and less constant, complications being introduced by storms that will be discussed in detail in a later section.

Finally, the cold polar regions induce descending air and *Polar High* zones. And flowing from the Polar Highs toward the Subpolar Lows are strongly deflected surface winds. These are called *Easterlies* or *Polar Easterlies* and flow almost from due east (slightly northeast in the Northern Hemisphere and southeast in the Southern Hemisphere).

So this is the series of wind and pressure systems that would develop over the earth *if* it were all water. In actuality, such a pattern occurs only over the oceans at all seasons of the year, important variations existing in the continental regions as they alternately cool and heat seasonally. So, now let us see what the true picture might be on a normal rotating earth where both oceans and land masses are represented. (Figs. 3-21 and 3-22.)

The Doldrum belt of our idealized all-water earth is very little disrupted by the insertion of continents in that, irrespective of land and water, temperatures remain high and pressure low. But in the high-pressure belt of the Horse Latitudes, the heating of the land areas in summer causes a continental low to develop, thus breaking up the earth encircling high belt into fragments that maintain their high pressure only at sea. In the summer, the Horse Latitudes become a series of isolated cells at sea. In the Northern Hemisphere, there are two: one in the Pacific called the *Hawaiian High;* and one in the Atlantic, the *Bermuda* or *Azores High.* In the Southern Hemisphere, there are three oceans, the Pacific, Atlantic, and Indian, each with its high-pressure cell. In the winter as the continents cool and their lows subside, these oceanic highs are connected across the land and the idealized belt reasserts itself. But in the Northern Hemisphere where the continents increase their bulk in the higher latitudes, the winter cold is most severe in Canada and Siberia, causing intense high pressure; so here the high-pressure belt linking Atlantic with Pacific becomes badly deformed with great northerly bulges. Winds which are, of course, the resultants of pressure differences will exhibit seasonal variations then in the vicinity of the continents.

The Sub-Polar Low Zone is a simple matter in the Southern Hemisphere in that these latitudes completely lack sizable continents, and we have virtually an all-water earth again. But in the Northern Hemisphere, the land masses are huge and the ocean basins severely restricted so that, once again, isolated cells at sea become the pattern. They are called the *Icelandic Low* and the *Aleutian Low* and are permanent in these areas. When the intense winter high asserts itself over adjacent Canada and Siberia, these lows, despite their small size, are very deep and well developed; but in the summer when the continents are warmer (although not really hot at these latitudes), they are quite weak. The polar regions, which continue cold at all seasons, remain as permanent highs.

Local winds. It is not surprising that except at sea all sorts of complications to the orderly pattern established earlier will become apparent. An excellent example of the kind of local winds that result are the relatively large-scale monsoon winds of Asia. Basically, their cause is differential heating of land vs. water, a theory that was espoused as early as 1686 by Halley (of comet fame). The general features of this concept are as follows. In the summer, the land mass of Asia heats up much more rapidly than the surrounding oceans, especially in its tropical portion. Local pressures, then, exhibit a seasonal high over the cool sea contrasting sharply with the heat-induced continental low that reaches its maximum development in the desert of northwest

India-Pakistan. Reacting to this pressure difference, air flows onshore (from high to low), displaying as it moves a characteristic counter-clockwise spiral. The entire procedure is reversed in winter. A cold continent develops high pressure, especially in north-central Siberia, and the warmer sea, which has changed temperature very little from the summer, becomes a relative low. Now the air flows offshore, spiraling in a clockwise direction. (Fig. 3–23.)

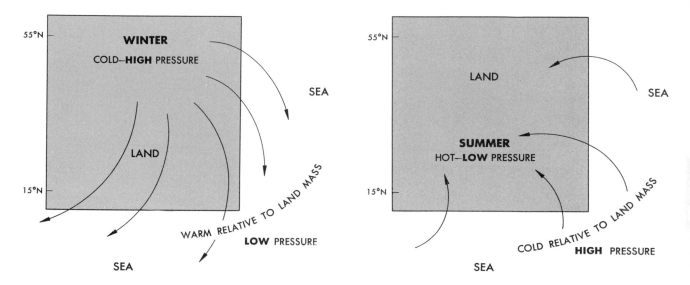

Fig. 3–23. *Idealized Northern Hemisphere monsoonal circulation.*

However, this simple explanation of monsoon circulation, while correct as far as it goes, fails to take into account many of the intricacies of the local scene. For instance, the summer monsoon "breaks" with great suddenness in India, an unlikely situation if it were tied to the gradual progression of the seasons. But then, India is almost hermetically sealed off from the continent by the great Himalayan barrier, and the easy flow of seasonal winds is disrupted, channeled, or even blocked completely. It is entirely possible that India, home of the classic monsoon, has a circulation system virtually independent of the rest of monsoon Asia.

Entering into all of this is the role of a well-defined jet stream, an eastward trending, high velocity, upper troposphere air current that flows south of the Himalayas in summer and north in winter. More will be said of jet streams in general and their relationship to storms and precipitation, but each year as our knowledge of their behavior is augmented, an increasingly important part has been assigned to the jet in explaining monsoon phenomena.

There are also the generally southwest summer winds, which have been explained as deflected Southern Hemisphere Trades rather than merely spiraling onshore breezes. The contention is that as the heat equator (as opposed to the geographic equator) follows the summer overhead sun into the Northern Hemisphere, it pulls with it the southern southeast Trades. As they cross the equator, Coriolis force causes them to swerve right, thus becoming the southwest summer monsoon.

So, without question, the monsoon is involved and much is yet to be learned regarding its variations and their causes. Yet the underlying genesis remains, simplified perhaps, but basic—the differential heating of land vs. water. By placing a huge land mass in the middle of the ocean, we have developed local winds. Out at sea, the Trades, Westerlies, etc., continue to blow in their predictable paths, but the continental influences dictate the distinctive winds that are so characteristic of Asia.

If the requisites of monsoon development are a land mass of continental size, and one with sufficient latitudinal spread to encompass both high latitudes and tropical to subtropical latitudes, then North America appears to be a possibility. Interior North America can get almost as cold as Asia in the winter, and although the true tropics are almost lacking, southern United States does become quite warm in summer. As a result, we have a monsoon. Not as well developed as that of Asia, which is larger, but a monsoon nonetheless. Canadian cold air forces itself clear down to the Gulf on occasion and sticky tropical air invades the Middle West. We do not have a name for this phenomenon as the Asians do and sometimes its effect is overpowered by other more dominating weather factors, but the general tendency is there and we can see it operate close to home every year.

The rest of the world's continents are large enough, but their mass is concentrated in the tropics. They get hot and pull air onshore in summer, but except for Antarctica there are no cold air masses represented. And yet oddly, Australia, the smallest of the lot, displays a typical monsoonal circulation along its north coast. This is explained by its proximity to the huge Asian continent. During the Australian winter, there is no really cold air over the continent and only a mild high develops—scarcely sufficient to cause significant offshore air currents. But when it is winter in Australia, it is summer in Asia, and the pulling power of the Asian continental low pulls the air off the Australian north coast. In summer, the desert heart of Australia develops the deep low required to complete the annual wind reversal. If Australia were located far from Asia, it would have no monsoon.

Similarly, the east coast of Africa, from whence the traditional Arab voyages to Asia and back took advantage of the seasonal wind reversal, is like northern Australia. Without propinquity to Asia, there would be no monsoon.

On a much smaller scale, this same sort of air circulation occurs along coastlines on a day and night basis rather than a seasonal one. This is called *land and sea breeze* and is characteristic of the tropics during the entire year and the summer season in many other parts of the world. (Fig. 3–24.) As the land heats up during the day, low

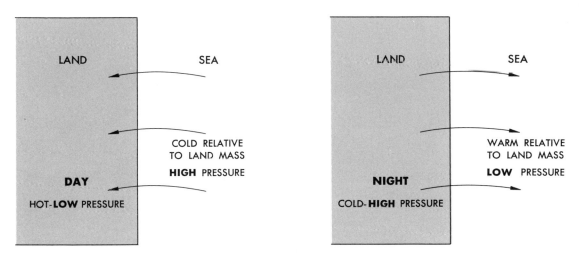

Fig. 3–24. Idealized land and sea breeze.

pressure gradually develops in contrast to the high over the cooler sea. The mild pressure difference causes gentle cooling breezes to move onshore. At night, the reverse occurs and the breezes blow in the opposite direction. The entire phenomenon is extremely shallow and normally affects only a coastal strip a few miles wide, but often it is the difference between reasonable comfort and oppressive heat.

The monsoon and land and sea breeze are examples of local winds that defy the standard concept of worldwide belts of pressure and winds. Occasionally, they are strong enough to completely obliterate the effects of these belts for a time; more often, they merely modify them.

Moisture

In terms of weather, water vapor is undoubtedly the most important of the atmospheric gases. It is the measure of the precipitation and

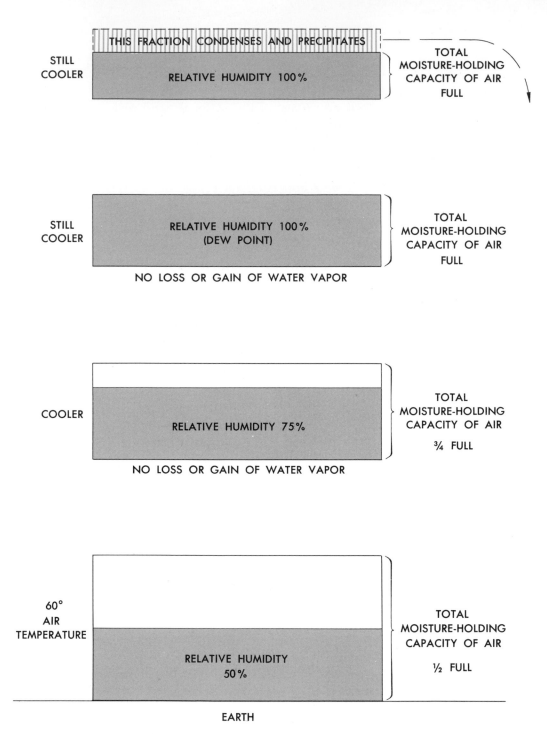

Fig. 3–25. Relative humidity. (Read from bottom to top.) An air mass lifted progressively from the surface to a higher elevation becomes cooler, thereby gradually reducing its moisture-holding capacity. (The size of each quadrilateral represents moisture-holding capacity, not volume.)

cloud potential of any given air mass. It contains within it latent heat to be released on condensation. And it is an effective absorber of radiated heat. We call this water vapor humidity, and its measurement at a particular time and place may be expressed in any of several ways. The most common, and by all odds the most useful type of humidity measurement for the non-professional, is a percentage or ratio expression called *relative humidity*. Briefly stated, this is *the amount of water vapor in the air relative to that which it is capable of holding at a given temperature. At a given temperature* is the critical part of the definition, as the air's capacity to hold water vapor varies with temperature. Cold air can hold much less water vapor than warm. Thus, air at 50 per cent relative humidity is holding half the amount of water vapor that it is equipped to hold. (Fig. 3–25.) If we had such a mass of air at sea level and caused it to ascend, the air would cool through expansion. Its volume would increase but its moisture holding capacity would decrease, and without any gain of moisture, the relative humidity would become greater than 50 per cent. We would be, in essence, decreasing the size of the container, and the same amount of water that filled the larger container half-full now fills the smaller one almost to the top. When further cooling continues to decrease the moisture holding ability of the air, it will eventually become filled to capacity. This is saturation; the air is holding all the water vapor that it is capable of holding, and the relative humidity is 100 per cent. This is also the *dew point* because any further cooling will make the container too small to hold all the water and the surplus will spill out as condensation. The dew point is where condensation begins as cooling continues. If this point is above freezing, condensation will be in the form of rain; if below freezing, snow. Continued cooling will result in continued condensation, and the relative humidity will be maintained endlessly at 100 per cent.[4] Now if we were to bring this same air mass back to its original temperature, the relative humidity would no longer be 50 per cent but something less, for a portion of the original water vapor has been lost through condensation.

---

[4] Condensation does not necessarily mean precipitation. Rain or snow must be of sufficient size and weight to precipitate. Normally, raindrops form through collision, attraction of smaller to larger or to ice crystals, or through electrical discharge between droplets.

Supercooled vapor may be present also, under certain conditions, refusing to condense, although its temperature is below the dew point; and supercooled water droplets may refuse to become ice. Under these circumstances, the application of dry ice and silver iodide has proved useful in forcing precipitation. But the exact mechanics of precipitation and those changes leading to it are still nebulous. For instance, the ice crystal theory utilizing dry ice and various chemicals to cause sublimation of supercooled water and thereby bring about precipitation is being questioned in its application to certain tropical situations where temperatures remain constantly above freezing.

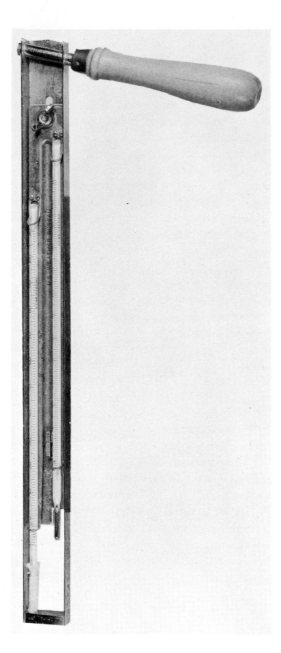

Fig. 3–26. *These are merely two thermometers, but when one bulb is covered by a moist cloth and they are mounted together, it is called a* psychrometer *and utilized to measure humidity. The handle is to allow swinging of the instrument through the air to insure maximum evaporation of the wet bulb. (Courtesy of U.S. Weather Bureau.)*

To determine relative humidity, an instrument called a *wet and dry bulb psychrometer* is employed. (Fig. 3–26.) It is a simple affair, made up of two standard thermometers mounted on a frame, but one has a moistened piece of muslin wrapped about the bulb. If the air is saturated, there can be no evaporation of the moisture in the cloth and so no cooling. Under these circumstances, the two thermometers will register the same temperature. However, the drier the air becomes, the greater the evaporation and the greater the cooling of the wet bulb, and a significant difference in the temperature readings of the two thermometers will become apparent. This difference of temperature, then, is directly related to the amount of water vapor in the air, and when applied to a table that is published by the Smithsonian Institution, it will give us an accurate relative humidity measure.

Dew and fog. If cooling will cause condensation, then moist air brought into contact with a cold surface will condense on that surface as the air is suddenly brought to the dew point. This is *dew*. Any surface that is an especially good radiator, such as the metal top of an automobile or broad leaves of plants, will rapidly lose the accumulated heat of the day after the sun goes down and through conduction will then cool the air immediately adjacent until dew is formed. (Fig. 3–27.) The outside of a glass with a cold liquid in it will "sweat."

Fig. 3–27. Dew is not precipitation, for it forms on a cold surface when that surface is touched by warm, moist air. (Courtesy of U.S. Weather Bureau.)

The glass is not leaking but is removing moisture from the atmosphere by cooling. Similarly, the inside of windows in the kitchen and bathroom are likely to "fog" as they transfer the outside cold and bring it into contact with the high humidity of these rooms. If the surface is below freezing, sublimation will occur and delicate ice crystals form on that surface as frost. (Fig. 3–28.)

Fig. 3–28. *Visible hoar frost is very much like dew, except that the surface contacted by moist air must be below 32° F. These intricate patterns were formed on windowpanes and indicate a direct change from water vapor to ice. (Courtesy of U.S. Weather Bureau.)*

Fig. 3–29. *Normal* radiation *or* ground fog *first develops in a shallow layer near the surface, but as cooling continues, it may build up to considerable depth. (Courtesy of U.S. Weather Bureau.)*

On calm, clear nights when loss of the earth's heat through radiation is particularly efficient, dew will form rapidly, and then gradually as the night wears on, a deeper stratum of air will be cooled below the dew point, and tiny droplets of moisture will be released throughout this zone. These will be kept in suspension by normal minor air turbulence. This is *fog*. (Fig. 3–29.) It may vary in thickness from a few inches to several hundred feet, depending on the degree of cooling and the moisture content of the air. Most fog is formed in this manner and is properly called *radiation* (or ground) *fog* because the lower atmosphere loses its heat via conduction and radiation to the cooler earth. However, if a normal radiation fog is wafted by gentle breezes away from its place of origin and is experienced then in a region where conditions are not suitable for the development of fog, it is called *advection* (or transported) *fog*. The California coast experiences this type of fog habitually. The cold current offshore provides the cooling for saturated oceanic air masses moving onshore at night, and these fog banks forming over the cold current are then brought onto the coast. (Fig. 3–30.)

Fog is usually a transitory phenomenon, for as soon as the sun comes out, it begins to evaporate. The longer waves in the sun's spectrum are intercepted and absorbed by the top of the fog stratum, while the short waves go through it and heat the earth. So the fog is "burned off" by being heated from both the top and the bottom and is usually dissipated by noon. The last remaining wisps of fog are not at the ground but at some intermediate level.

Fig. 3–30. *The high towers supporting the Golden Gate suspension span are obscured here by the daily* advection fog *that sweeps in off the cold current paralleling the coast outside of San Francisco Bay. (Courtesy of San Francisco Chamber of Commerce.)*

Precipitation. The formation of dew and fog is all very interesting but somewhat academic from the standpoint of significant amounts of usable moisture. Nowhere in the world is any sizable agricultural venture carried on that is dependent for its moisture on dew or fog. So somehow large masses of air must be forced to give up their moisture in sufficient quantities to cause "real" rainfall (or snowfall). The principle remains the same whether we are dealing with dew, fog, or heavy rain—the air must be cooled below the dew point; but to cause rain, this must be accomplished rapidly and on a large scale. The obvious way is to force a large mass of moist air to go aloft and cool adiabatically. There are three common ways that this may be accomplished, and all of the world's significant precipitation occurs from one or a combination of these methods. They are: *orographic, convection,* and *cyclonic* or *frontal.* (Fig. 3–31.)

The word "orographic" means mountains, so in order to have this type of precipitation, there must be a topographic barrier in the path of prevailing winds. Such situations occur widely, as along the west coast of North and South America, and this is a common cause of precipitation. As we have discussed previously relative to adiabatic lapse rates, moist air forced against a mountain front ascends, resulting in expansion, cooling, and precipitation. The type and amount of pre-

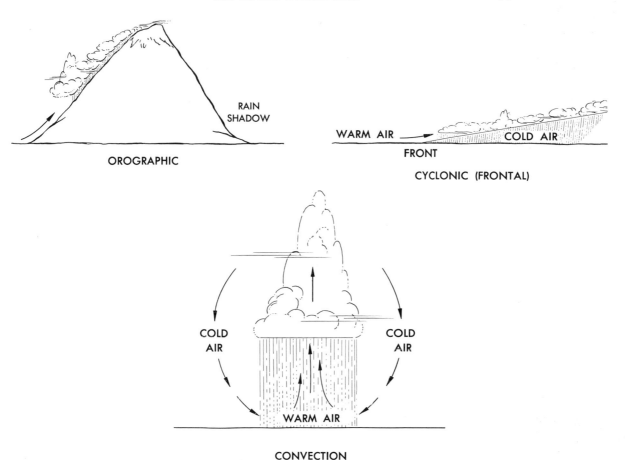

OROGRAPHIC

WARM AIR → FRONT COLD AIR

CYCLONIC (FRONTAL)

COLD AIR   COLD AIR

WARM AIR

CONVECTION

Fig. 3–31. Causes of precipitation.

cipitation is controlled by the height of the mountain and the temperature and moisture content of the air mass. In the lee of such a topographic feature, there is a relatively dry zone called the *rain shadow*. Orographic precipitation may occur at any season of the year or in any part of the world where the above conditions prevail. The windward slope of the mountain will be the wet side and the leeward side will be dry.

"Convection" is not a new term but was dealt with previously in conjunction with transfer of heat to high altitudes. It also operates as a major cause of precipitation. You will remember that heat is the requirement to set convective currents in motion—buoyant heated air

Fig. 3–32. *Lightning often results from convection—if the air is very moist and the updraft is violent. (Courtesy of U.S. Weather Bureau.)*

at the surface trapped below cooler air aloft, is a very unstable condition. As the hot earth on a summer day transfers its heat to the air above it via conduction, the increasingly warm air bursts explosively through the cooler air above it. In this violent updraft, the warm air cools rapidly through expansion as it rises several thousand feet in a matter of minutes, and condensation of a tremendous amount of moisture is virtually instantaneous. The resulting rainfall, often accompanied by thunder, lightning, and hail,[5] is violent and of short duration. (Figs. 3–32 and 3–33.) Such rainfall (never snow), because it requires heat as a trigger, is a tropical or summer phenomena and is typical of many parts of the world.

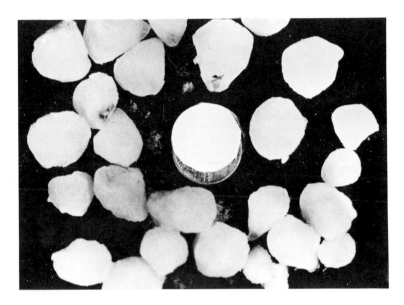

Fig. 3–33. *The silver dollar serves as a size reference to these hailstones from Oklahoma. Thunder, lightning, and hail usually occur in conjunction when the upper part of a rising convectional column pushes above the freezing point. Moisture carried to these heights turns to ice, then often falls below the freezing line and collects water on its surface, only to be caught in the updraft again and a new strata of ice added. The size of hailstones depends upon the number of times this occurs. If a hailstone is cut in half, it will be found to be layered like an onion, each layer representing a trip beyond the freezing point. (Courtesy of U.S. Weather Bureau.)*

[5] Hail is unknown in the tropics, for although it may form near the top of a convective current, it melts before it reaches the ground.

"Cyclonic" or "frontal" precipitation results when two differing air masses are side by side and one is forced against the other (the details of air masses will be explained later). The lighter air will ride up over the heavier air and thus be forced to cool adiabatically, producing condensation and precipitation. For instance, in the middle latitudes, we frequently have warm and cold air in close conjunction. The warm air being lighter than dense cold air will run over the top. This is not unlike the warm air being forced up a mountain slope in that it cannot invade the cold air and must move up over its sloping front. Frequently, this slope is low angle and thus the rate of expansion is slow, with gentle drizzle or snow flurries resulting. This type of precipitation occurs most often in the belt of the Westerlies or near the equator where differing air masses commonly meet.

Clouds. Like fog, clouds are tiny drops of liquid water held in suspension by air turbulence; and like fog, clouds are a result of moist air being cooled below the dew point. But there is a major difference and that is in the method of their formation. To be sure, clouds are usually encountered at moderately high elevations, while fog is normally at the surface of the earth, but high fogs and low clouds may also be distinguished and properly labeled. If the cooling and subsequent condensation results from moist air in *contact* with a cold surface, i.e., cooling through conduction and radiation as described previously, then it is called fog. But if the condensation results from *adiabatic cooling,* the resulting suspended water droplets make up a cloud.

Our chief concern here is the classification of clouds on the basis of their appearance. These are the well-known three standard types of clouds.

(1) *Cumulus* (Fig. 3–34)—The cumulus clouds have as their chief characteristic a certain depth. The general appearance is fleecy, fluffy, or cottony, and they vary from the towering convectional thunderhead with its flat bottom marking the dew point and its top thousands of feet above to the tiny fair weather puffball. The cumulus cloud never covers the entire sky and its bottom at least, is seldom at a very high level.

(2) *Stratus* (Fig. 3–35)—The stratus clouds cover the entire sky, are usually gray in appearance because they have cut out a large part of the light, and show little of the vertical development of the cumulus cloud. Usually low to medium in elevation, the stratus cloud is commonly formed along fronts and often emits light drizzle or snow flurries.

Fig. 3–34. *Cumulus clouds. The flat bottom marks the dew point. (Courtesy of U.S. Weather Bureau.)*

Fig. 3–35. *Stratus clouds. These clouds are typically low hanging and cover the entire sky. (Courtesy of U.S. Weather Bureau.)*

Fig. 3–36. *Cirrus clouds. These clouds are made up of ice crystals and are insubstantial in appearance. (Courtesy of U.S. Weather Bureau.)*

(3) *Cirrus* (Fig. 3–36)—The cirrus clouds are high-level clouds made up of ice crystals and exhibit a characteristic fragile feathery appearance. They are invariably fair weather clouds, and even when covering the entire sky are so insubstantial that they are usually described as a cirrus haze.

These three are the basic cloud types, but in order to refine the classification, they may be used in combination to properly identify intermediate variations. On the whole, this is merely common sense; for instance, a thunderhead whose top is so high that it is above the freezing point will exhibit wispy feather-like cirrus clouds streaming downwind from the top. Such a cloud is properly described as *cumulo-cirrus* since it has the characteristics of both. Or if the entire sky is gray and cloud-covered at a low level, but the cloud is a series of coalesced cumulus puffs, it obviously is both stratus and cumulus, and its proper classification is *strato-cumulus*. (Fig. 3–37.) Many other combinations are possible.

We also may use such prefixes as *fracto, alto,* or *nimbo (nimbus)* to further classify our descriptions. If a typical stratus cover is rent here and there by high winds, showing glimpses of blue sky, it might be called *fracto-stratus.* Or if a normal low cloud cover is higher than usual, alto should be applied. Nimbus means rain and is used in conjunction with the name of the cloud if it is black and dirty and precipitation is obviously imminent or actually occurring.

Fig. 3–37. *Strato-cumulus clouds. These clouds are obviously cumulus, yet cover the entire sky like a stratus layer. (Courtesy of U.S. Weather Bureau.)*

Air Masses, Fronts, and Storms

Following World War I, a major revolution in meteorology and weather forecasting took place with the introduction of the radical Bergen school of air mass analysis by eminent Norwegian researchers. It was hailed as an important step forward, and by the 1930's adopted almost universally. Today, with relatively minor modifications, it remains the most widely accepted basic concept in middle latitude meteorology, although it is being critically tested, especially in connection with new developments such as the jet stream. And there is some question as to its worth as a research vehicle in the tropics.

The key to this system of forecasting and analysis is the recognition of (and labeling with standardized symbols) air masses with certain typical moisture and temperature characteristics. These characteristics are derived from the surface over which these air masses are normally resident, and if along their margins they occasionally surge out of their region of normal residence, they affect the invaded region with these typical characteristics. The line marking the contact of two of these differing air masses is called a *front* which has a strong tendency to maintain itself as a sharp line—not necessarily a straight line because it exhibits frequent advances and retreats in lobes or waves, but always sharply separating one air mass from the other. If, for instance, warm and cold air are adjacent at a front, there is little mixing and establishment of a zone of tepid air. Instead, like oil and water, each air mass keeps its own character and the front is a line of sharp contrast.

In both hemispheres, there are two major air masses, and in the equatorial region a third. *Polar air masses* dominate the high latitudes; the *equatorial air masses,* the region of the Doldrums; and *tropical air masses* in between. At their points of contact are fronts. Where the polar and tropical air masses meet, somewhere in the middle latitudes depending on season, is the *Polar Front.* It should be noted that there is no middle latitude temperate air mass, and those of us who live in these areas are in a zone of conflict between warm and cold air. In the general area of the Doldrums is the *Intertropical Front.*[6] (Fig. 3–38.)

Subdivisions of these basic air masses are generally made, of which those below are by no means all but will be indicative.

   A. Polar air (P)—generally cold and dry
   1. Polar continental (Pc)—very cold and dry
   2. Polar maritime (Pm)—not quite as cold and a bit more moist

---

[6] Supposedly, there are arctic and antarctic air masses at the poles and presumably an Arctic Front and an Antarctic Front. However, these masses and fronts have not been studied carefully as yet and little is known of them or their attendant cyclonic disturbances.

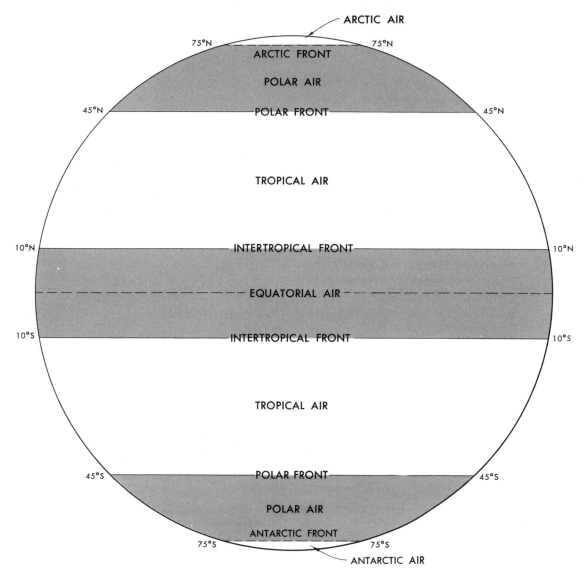

Fig. 3–38. *World air masses and fronts (highly diagramatic).*

Polar Front

B. Tropical (T)—generally warm
  1. Tropical continental (Tc)—warm and dry
  2. Tropical maritime (Tm)—warm and fairly moist

Intertropical Front

C. Equatorial (E)—warm and very moist

Notice that the Polar Front between polar and tropical air exhibits temperature differences as its most striking contrast. There is also frequently a moisture difference in that warm tropical air has a large moisture holding capacity and may, if it is Tm air, be quite moist relative to cold polar air. Because of this strong differentiation, especially in temperature, the Polar Front is normally sharp and well defined.

The term "Intertropical Front" was introduced into tropical meteorology following the successful application of air mass analysis and frontal theory in the middle latitudes. It was postulated that as the heat equator shifted north and south of the geographic equator with the seasonal migration of the overhead sun, the Trades from the winter hemisphere would be pulled across the equator. Not only would they then have a longer trajectory than the summer hemisphere Trades and thus exhibit greater surface modification of moisture and temperature, but they would also react to the opposite hemisphere's Coriolis force and shift their direction of flow by some 90 degrees. The end product, the Intertropical Front, would appear where the two trade-wind currents met head-on and the lighter was forced up over the denser. Temperature differences are not great, and the Intertropical Front is certainly less well defined than the Polar Front, disappearing entirely over the continents and blurring periodically at sea. And although we are using here the term "Intertropical Front" since it has become fairly well established, there are those who argue persuasively for the substitution of "Intertropical" or "Equatorial Convergence Zone" in its place. But whatever the name, all agree on the existence of a tropical trough (low pressure) at the point of theoretical meeting of the opposing Trades; and further, it is agreed that it marks a line of precipitation, cloudiness, and apparent storm genesis.

Associated with, and to some extent products of, these two fronts in each hemisphere are a series of storms, cyclones, or low-pressure centers (these three terms are used synonymously here). On or near the Polar Front are found what we can call (1) *standard* (everyday, garden variety) *middle latitude cyclones*. These are large (up to 1,000 miles in diameter) slow moving, relatively mild (as far as wind velocities and general destruction are concerned), and quite common throughout the year. In opposition to these storms in the general area of the Polar Front, there appears a second type of cyclonic disturbance, (2) *tornadoes*. These are different in every way from the standard middle latitude cyclones in that they are the most violent and destructive storms known to man; they occur in only limited regions at only certain times of the year, are extremely small in size, and move very rapidly. The Intertropical Front also is related to two types of unlike storms: (1) *weak tropical cyclones,* which are large, mild, and common, vs. (2) *hurricanes or typhoons* (the appellation differing for the same type of storm in various parts of the world), which are small, seasonal, and occur in only certain limited locations.

The jet stream. Involved in the generation of these various storms to some degree is the so-called jet stream. First discovered less than 25 years ago by high-flying aircraft whose pilots were greatly chagrined to find that they were making almost no progress despite full power ahead, the jet stream is a high-velocity upper air current flowing from west to east roughly above the Polar Front. It is erroneous to speak of a single jet stream, for there are many that are known, but only the original Northern Hemisphere jet has been studied with some care. And even here, much remains to be learned, for obviously, voluminous data on a writhing subject near the top of the troposphere are hard to come by. Nonetheless, enough reliable work has been done to more than hint at a considerable relationship between the various jet streams and moisture and temperature characteristics of surface climates, and particularly of storm genesis. So recent has been the discovery of jets and so promising their potential application to old problems that many long accepted verities are being re-examined, and it has become popular to assign jets as the tentative answer to any sticky question that seems to defy immediate solution. They are being introduced here because of the almost certain influence of the upper Westerly jet stream on the storms of the Polar Front and vicinity, and a very probable relationship between the lesser known tropical jets and the cyclonic disturbances on and near the Intertropical Front.

The Northern Hemisphere upper Westerly jet stream varies in both height and velocity with season, being lowest (4–5 miles up) and strongest (150–400 mph) in winter, and highest (7 miles up) and weakest (50 to 75 mph) in summer. It is a narrow twisting band of air meandering wildly at times and often breaking down into several parallel elements rather than a single current. And its main course is much farther south in summer than winter, suggesting an affinity with the similar advance and retreat of the Polar Front below it or the seasonal surface temperature variations that control that front. A similar jet exists in the Southern Hemisphere middle latitudes, presumably acting much as its Northern Hemisphere counterpart, although the lack of large continents and resultant differing air masses undoubtedly causes variations. Also, there are milder and less-continuous jets in the tropics and polar regions. One of these, a trade-wind jet stream, appears to be generally coincident with the Intertropical Front much of the time, and there has even been identified recently a westward flowing jet in the equatorial region.

Standard middle latitude cyclones. Of the four storms previously mentioned, very much the best understood is the standard middle latitude cyclone. Because it has been the major weather-maker in the

United States and Western Europe where the bulk of the world's scientists are concentrated, and because of its frequent occurrence and mild slow-moving character, it has been carefully studied and analyzed for many years.

According to the Norwegian frontal wave theory, standard middle latitude cyclones may form anywhere along the Polar Front that a wave or protuberance of one air mass advances against the other. If cold air advances against warm or vice versa, the warm air is forced aloft and a low-pressure center comes into being. Around it, the air begins to circulate in a typical Northern Hemisphere counterclockwise spiral and a storm is born. However, it has been rather conclusively shown that when the jet stream coincides exactly with the Polar Front, strong cyclonic activity almost invariably results, an indication that upper-air influences are of perhaps equal significance with the surface waves. Certain locations along the front appear to be particularly active in cyclogenesis: the Texas Panhandle, Gulf of Lions, and the upper Yangtze Valley to name but a few. But outstanding in this regard, producing more and bigger storms than all other Northern Hemisphere sources combined, are the two permanent Subpolar Low cells, the Aleutian and Icelandic centers. These spew out a steady stream of cyclones, especially in the winter. In the Southern Hemisphere where the Subpolar Low is a belt in the uninterrupted sea, storms typically form almost at random anywhere astride the Polar Front.

Once the cyclone is formed on the Polar Front, its general slow movement is to the east as it is pushed by the Westerlies and it faithfully follows the front. As long as the center of the storm "rides" the front, it can maintain itself, for it depends on the interaction of both cold and warm air to sustain its vigor. If it were to "jump the track," i.e. move to either the warm or cold air side of the front, the interaction of warm and cold air would cease and the storm would die. (Fig. 3–39.)

Imagine a cyclone astride the Polar Front in the Northern Hemisphere. The air would spiral about the low-pressure center in a counterclockwise circulation. On the western side of the storm, this would cause cold air to move against warm at the front, forcing the warm air aloft, and very likely precipitation would result. This segment of the Polar Front within the storm where cold air is advancing against warm is called the *Cold Front*. On the eastern side of the storm, warm air would attack cold at the front. Again, the warm air would flow over the cold, expand, and cool as it rose, causing precipitation. This portion of the Polar Front where warm air is forced against cold is called the *Warm Front*. Thus, the Cold Front, the Warm Front, and the center of the storm where air is rising vertically

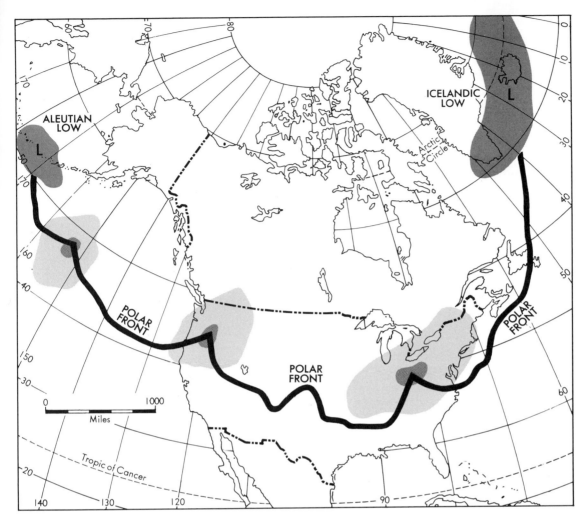

Fig. 3–39. *The Polar Front and standard middle latitude cyclones. The great bulk of North American cyclones emanate from the Aleutian Low and are carried eastward by the Westerlies along the Polar Front.*

are the precipitation zones within a cyclone. However, the pattern and character of precipitation differ slightly between the two fronts.

At the Warm Front, the advancing light and buoyant warm air experiences a great deal of difficulty in pushing cold air back, but in flowing up and over it, modifies the cold air into a thin, low-angle wedge. Warm air moving up this gentle slope is cooled slowly. Stratus clouds form along the line of contact, and a broad zone of drizzle or snow flurries develops on the cold air side of the front.

On the western side of the storm where cold air is advancing against warm at the Cold Front, a somewhat different situation prevails. Since cold air can move against warm easily, the depth of the cold air may be considerable, and its leading edge will be close to vertical as opposed to the thin wedge slope at the Warm Front. This means that as the warm air is forced aloft, it follows up this steep leading edge, cooling rapidly and producing high cumulus clouds and heavy precipitation. Frequently, the cold air above the surface moves forward more rapidly than that which is in contact with the ground and is slowed a bit by friction, and warm air is trapped below this overhanging bulge. When this trapped warm air bursts aloft suddenly, thunder, lightning, and torrential precipitation results. Because of this, the Cold Front is sometimes referred to as the *Squall Line*. Note that this precipitation zone is rather narrow and in advance of the Cold Front. There may also be precipitation of a much less vigorous character behind the front (or in the cold air sector) as the warm air swings up over the cold air. (Fig. 3–40.)

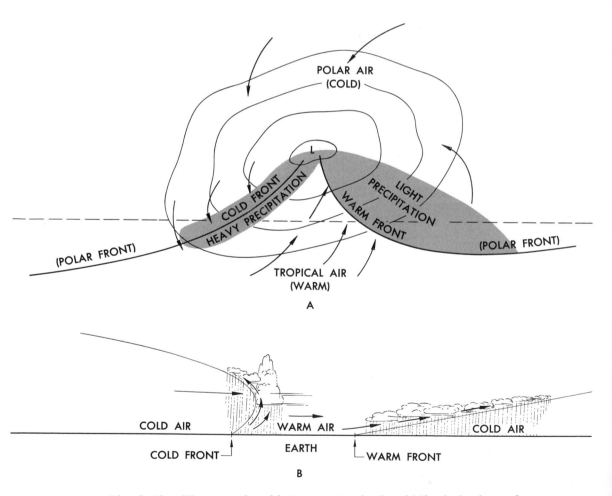

Fig. 3–40. *Warm and cold fronts—standard middle latitude cyclone. The fronts as they would appear in a typical Northern Hemisphere storm are shown in (A). A cross-section across the same storm along the dashed line is shown in (B).*

The chief differences between Warm and Cold Front precipitation are these: (1) Warm Front precipitation is of the light-drizzle variety, while that of the Cold Front is likely to be much heavier. (2) Warm Front clouds are usually stratus, while Cold Front clouds are cumulus, often thunderheads. (3) The Warm Front precipitation zone is broad and wholly on the cold air side, while the Cold Front precipitation zone is quite narrow and is astride the front with the greater part of the precipitation occurring in the warm air sector.

Occlusion. Since the Cold Front advances more rapidly than the Warm Front, it is possible for it to catch up with the Warm Front after a storm has been in existence for several days. When this occurs, it is called an *occlusion* (or Occluded Front). As the Cold Front gradually moves in on the Warm Front, the warm air sector becomes progressively smaller until finally when the fronts come together, warm air is forced aloft. At the surface, only cold air remains; however, the new front is represented by cold air of slightly differing degrees of coldness. The rising warm air above the front gives off precipitation, and the vortex at the storm's center maintains itself weakly, but in essence the storm has "jumped the track"—it is no longer astride the Polar Front. (Fig. 3–41.) The important interaction of warm and cold air is no longer represented, and the storm usually dies out gradually. Every cyclone does not develop to the occluded stage, but the possibility is always present.

Be careful to recognize that there are two basic air circulations involved in these standard middle latitude cyclones: (1) the primary Westerlies forcing the general movement of all storms in the middle latitudes from west to east, (2) and the local spiral winds about each individual low center. It is this steady parade of slow-moving storms migrating through the middle latitudes of both hemispheres that gives the basic character to our day-to-day weather.

Tornadoes. The second of the storms associated with the Polar Front, the tornado, is quite different from the standard middle latitude cyclone, and certainly less well understood. Its sudden appearance without much advance warning, violent character, small size, and rapid movement make it extremely difficult to study. What we know of tornadoes is pretty much a matter of merely cataloging the number, frequency, time of occurrence, and location of all known tornadoes over a period of many years. Why they occur and when and where they do is speculative at best.

Tornadoes are largely all-American storms, the greatest frequency occurring in the central plains states from the Gulf to Canada. They also occur somewhat less commonly east of the plains in the South,

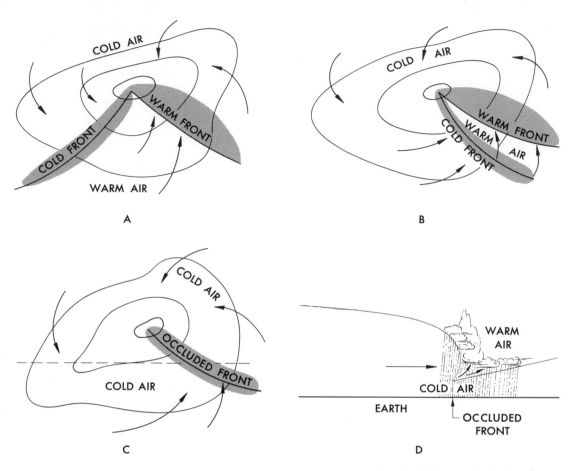

Fig. 3–41. *Occluded front. In (A) and (B), the Cold Front is depicted as advancing more rapidly than the Warm, culminating in an occlusion (C); (D) is a cross-section of the occlusion along the dashed line in (C).*

Middle West, and even now and then along the Eastern Seaboard into New England. West of the Rockies, tornadoes are virtually unknown. The rest of the world is not immune, Australia reporting the largest number, but by far the greatest tornado frequency is in the United States.

Summer is the season when most of these storms manifest themselves, although the entire warm half of the year is subject to at least occasional tornadoes. The region of maximum frequency appears to exhibit something of a northerly seasonal migration; i.e., the greatest number appear in the south in the spring and gradually move north with the onset of summer. By late summer, the number of storms has decreased, but these may be experienced as far north as the Dakotas or Canadian prairie provinces.

Like the standard middle latitude cyclones, tornadoes move in a general easterly direction, but they are a great deal smaller and advance with greater speed. The dimensions of a typical tornado may be only a few hundred yards across, and they have been known to completely wipe out all the houses on one side of the street while scarcely affecting those on the other side. Furthermore, they commonly exercise a curious pattern of skipping as they go. Although the funnel remains active and visible and torrential rains accompany it, the bottom of the funnel lifts off the ground for a while before coming back down to carve out a path of destruction. Luckily, the storm is normally of short duration, and although in its short life it may run a great distance, it generally disappears abruptly after only a brief period of activity. (Fig. 3–42.)

The accumulated observations of thousands of tornadoes show a definite pattern relative to their genesis. Almost all (90 per cent of

Fig. 3–42. *A tornado funnel approaches an apprehensive photographer in Texas. (Courtesy of U.S. Weather Bureau.)*

the average 400 per year in the United States) appear to originate somewhat in advance of a Cold Front. Temperature differences on opposite sides of the front seem to be of less importance than the moisture difference. If the warm air temperature is high enough to enable it to hold a large amount of water vapor and if its humidity is near saturation, then the advancing cool dry air, with the upper air moving more rapidly than that at the surface, will cause a violent updraft accompanied by extremely heavy and rapid condensation. Given these conditions in Kansas in June or July, a tornado or whole cluster of tornadoes is likely. This is the best that the weatherman can do— forecast tornado likelihood. Just how many will develop, if any, or exactly where is beyond his knowledge. Once a tornado has shown itself, then he knows that it will quickly outrun the front heading east, and developments from then on are in the lap of the gods. Thunderstorms too are formed in this same zone ahead of the Cold Front, and some tornadoes appear to spring from them as they do occasionally from isolated thunderstorms elsewhere. And, once again, we must credit the jet stream with an assist in storm formation, although general agreement has not been reached as to its exact role relative to tornadoes.

The destructive power of a tornado is enormous and it is without doubt the most violent storm in nature. Wind velocities certainly are in excess of 200–300 mph, but nobody knows how much because they have never been measured. The results of such velocities can scarcely be exaggerated, and weird stories are legion—straws driven through trees, babies snatched from mothers' arms, and on ad nauseam. But in conjunction with the wind are other equally powerful forces. The lifting capacity of a tornado as the violent winds spiral upward can, for example, pick up houses off their foundations. The dark appearance of the storm funnel may be at least partially attributed to great volumes of soil, fences, and assorted livestock sucked up into the vortex. Also, since a tornado center is probably the deepest low-pressure center experienced anywhere on earth, as it suddenly envelops a building, the normal air pressure trapped inside is many times that outside and the building explodes. Only a steel reinforced construction with a high percentage of windows is relatively safe from this type of destruction because the glass blows out to relieve the pressure. (Fig. 3–43.)

Weak tropical cyclones. The dramatic hurricane has largely overshadowed any other type of tropical storm, both in the popular mind and in organized research. But there is a much more common type that is receiving belated recognition as not only a significant element

Fig. 3–43. *After a tornado at Westboro, Mass. Note the narrow path and the completeness of destruction. (Courtesy of U.S. Weather Bureau.)*

in day-to-day tropical weather, but as the seed, so to speak, from which hurricanes flower. The simple name "weak tropical cyclone" lacks real character, but so does the storm that it designates. Scarcely visible on the weather map, a weak tropical cyclone is an amorphous entity, displaying no outstanding wind or temperature features. It appears to be a product of the Intertropical Front and Doldrums, and distinguishes itself chiefly by exhibiting a continuous cloud cover and heavy rain. The mild temperature and moisture differential between the impinging trade-wind currents at the Intertropical Front are seldom sufficient to account for any major updraft of air, but saturated tropical and equatorial air masses require very little lifting to produce rain and clouds. These large but mild storms are common features the year round, and once formed, display a general tendency to drift to the west. Their progress, however, is slow and halting, and they often stagnate, drip heavily, and after a few days or weeks of existence, unobtrusively fade away.

Hurricanes or typhoons. As unspectacular as the weak tropical cyclones appear to be, some of them, at certain places and particular times of year, develop for unknown reasons into very spectacular and dangerous hurricanes or typhoons. These storms are limited to the summer and fall seasons and occur almost exclusively in the western part of major ocean basins in both hemispheres. Specifically, these regions include: the southwest corner of the North Atlantic (Caribbean and southeast U.S. coast), the southwest corner of the North Pacific (Philippines to Japan and southeast Asiatic coast), the northwest corner of the South Pacific (northeast Australian coast and adjacent islands), and the northwest corner of the South Indian Ocean (Madagascar and the east coast of South Africa). The South Atlantic is excepted here, probably because the Intertropical Front does not move south of the equator as it does in the other oceans. Also, less frequent storms may be encountered in the Bay of Bengal, Arabian Sea, off the west coast of Baja California, and the northwest coast of Australia.

Despite the difference in names, both hurricanes and typhoons are the same type of storm, typhoon being the Far Eastern name and hurricane applying in the Caribbean. Other local names also refer to the identical phenomenon, such as cyclone (India), baguio (Philippines), and willy willie (Australia). But whatever it is called, it shows up in the general region of the Intertropical Front and seems to develop from what first appears to be another simple weak tropical cyclone. The low center becomes deeper and deeper, the winds spiral about it with higher and higher velocity, and the general dimension of the storm becomes more compact (100–200 miles across). The U.S. Weather Bureau's Hurricane Warning Center in Florida has decided, rather arbitrarily, that when the winds reach 75 mph, such a storm will be classified as a hurricane, although as it continues to grow, winds commonly exceed 100 or even 150 mph. In spite of these high winds, the storm itself advances quite slowly, on the order of 5–10 mph.

At one time, violent tropical storm formation was explained quite simply as the result of the interaction of contrasting air masses at the Intertropical Front. In the summer, this front migrates a good many degrees beyond the equator in all western ocean basins except the South Atlantic, and nearly all hurricanes–typhoons were observed to originate in this general vicinity during the warm season. However, it has become increasingly obvious with the discovery of tropical jet streams and high-level fronts and cyclonic disturbances that storm development is quite complex, although the details have not been wholly worked out. Like the tornado, the hurricane–typhoon is a bit too robust to study easily, but hurricane-hunter planes have been flying into the centers of these storms for several years in an effort to unravel their mysteries; and the pioneer TIROS and much more sophisticated Nimbus weather satellites will undoubtedly supply us with a great deal more data than have been available in the past.

We do know that the initial appearance of these storms 8–10 degrees off the equator is related to the requirement of sufficient Coriolis force to allow the violent spiraling of the winds about a low-pressure center. The equatorial regions are thus immune from these destructive phenomena because of lack of Coriolis force. Heavy concentrations of hurricanes–typhoons on the western sides of oceans may be partially a result of the generally exaggerated poleward shift of the Intertropical Front here, but also because of somewhat higher air and water temperatures. Since the vigor and driving force of this type of storm undoubtedly derive from the latent energy that is released as warm saturated oceanic air is sucked up the vortex to be condensed into torrential showers, the warmer the air and the higher its moisture content, the greater the energy potential.

One of the curious features of the hurricane–typhoon that has long been observed but never explained in adequate fashion is the eye—a warm, calm, cloudless region at the very center that has no counterpart in any other cyclone. Any number of first-hand accounts are available describing the sudden cessation of the wild wind, warmer temperatures, and the clearing of the sky, with only a heaving sea to hint of storm conditions. This is the eye and its passage is of short duration, with the wind picking up abruptly and this time blowing 180 degrees from its previous flow. Only a column of sinking air could account for all these characteristics of the eye; yet it is unusual, to say the least, to encounter sinking air in the midst of a brisk vortex that is obviously accomplishing mass uplift of huge volumes of moist air.

Once the storm is fully formed, it begins to follow a typical path —a path that is reasonably predictable in its general outline, but wholly unpredictable as to detail. Impelled by the easterly Trades, hurricanes–typhoons, irrespective of hemisphere, begin a slow movement westward. At this stage, they may very well gain in strength and intensity, for they are still over tropical seas and tap a constant supply of warm moist air. But sooner or later, a high percentage of these storms begin to curve away from the equator, generally following an approximation of the western end of the permanent oceanic Subtropical High cell. No two are exactly alike and herein lies the difficulty in forecasting. On rare occasions, one may not curve at all; others will curve at varying rates; and some may even stop or form a

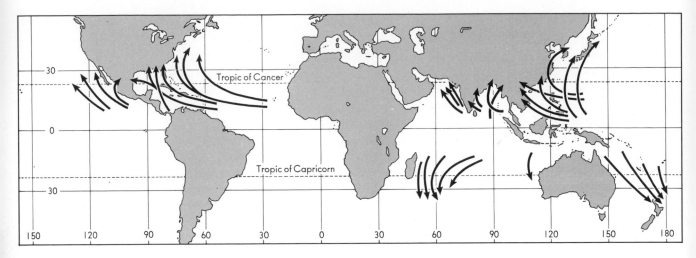

Fig. 3–44. *Average hurricane–typhoon tracks.*

ιoop in their course. The disastrous Cuban hurricane of 1963 crossed the southern end of that island and then turned and recrossed it before resuming its northward curve. (Fig. 3–44.)

There are two ways to stop a hurricane; both involve the removal of the moist air that is its fuel. If it invades a large land mass, there is an abrupt decrease in the moisture content of the air sucked in at its base, and the storm will fade out, often very rapidly. Or, if it survives to complete its poleward curve, it will finally recurve at higher latitudes and move to the east. Here, the ocean is colder and the air above it less capable of holding moisture, so that a tropical storm at these latitudes will gradually become a mere Westerly squall.

The high winds accompanying violent tropical storms are the obvious destructive force that accounts for the awe in which they are held, especially in those regions of the world where such insubstantial construction materials as nipa and bamboo are the rule. The wind is not all that is to be feared. Heavy seas kicked up by the wind and torrential rains are widespread for many miles, far from the center of the storm. (Fig. 3–45.) The combination of overtaxed surface drainage channels attempting to carry off the rainfall and excessively high tides and storm waves running up the river mouths from the sea can result in disastrous floods. One of the great natural calamities of all time occurred in this manner on the Ganges Delta in 1737 when over 300,-000 persons were killed outright and uncounted others starved later because of flooded fields and subsequent crop loss. And in May of 1965, an almost exact duplicate struck East Pakistan, killing many

Fig. 3–45. *Storm waves lash a seawall as a hurricane builds to its full fury. (Courtesy of U.S. Weather Bureau.)*

thousands. Still another type of destruction was displayed when, on October 3, 1964, hurricane Hilda plowed into the Gulf Coast of the United States. A dancing vanguard of tornado clusters preceded it, causing great damage well in advance of the storm proper.

In the United States, our hurricane warning system has become increasingly effective through the years in allowing the populace adequate advance time for evacuation and "battening down." Luckily, hurricanes move slowly, and although they cannot be deterred, a careful check on their movements does make a warning system practical. But even in the United States where hurricane warnings are best developed, over 500 people lost their lives in the Cameron, Louisiana, storm of 1957 when they refused to heed the warning and stayed in their homes. (Fig. 3–46.)

Fig. 3–46. *Hurricane—the aftermath. High winds and pounding seas have roughed up Atlantic City, N.J. (Courtesy of U.S. Weather Bureau.)*

4

The World Climate Pattern

In Chapter 3, we dealt with the weather elements: temperature, pressure, moisture, and storms—their functions and simple mechanics. The orientation of our approach was not toward any particular region of the world, but toward each particular element taken one at a time. Now we come to where the frame of reference changes to the region, and we will be concerned primarily with climatic controls. How much insolation arrives at a particular place? How much precipitation? When does it occur through the year and in what manner? And, of course, always the question, "Why?" It is an amalgam of all these things and more that endows a region with a certain climatic personality that is distinct from any neighboring area. This is the climatic region that we attempt to isolate.

There is another factor involved in dealing with climate in addition to regionalization—that is, *time*. Climate is essentially a mean or average of daily weather conditions. The longer the records have been kept, the more reliable our conception of a given climate, for a long-term mean tends to iron out the freak year and short-term oscillation. Such places as Antarctica, for instance, have had weather recorded for such a short period that only the gross outline of climate is clear at the moment. There are weaknesses inherent in the simple average, of course. A climate that regularly features great extremes as one of its outstanding characteristics will not be properly served by an artificial mean "somewhere in the middle." So, as we attempt to sort out, describe, explain, and locate the climate of the world, we must keep in mind that a climate is a complex of many things, not the least of which is a little perspicacious interpretation and analysis.

CLASSIFICATION OF CLIMATES

It must be recognized at the outset in any attempt at classifying the world's climates that *no two places in the world have identical climates*. Even within a very tiny area, climates differ. The south side of a building with its reflected sunlight has quite a different set of factors at work than the shady north side; the top of a cornstalk exists in a different climate than the base; and the windward side of a fence post, building, or hill will inevitably exhibit variations from the lee side. Certainly then, if differences exist at this microscale, no two sizable regions can be expected to have identical climates. Yet the effort to establish some rational classification of climate on a worldwide basis is well worth making because a cognizance of the world distribution of climate is essential to an understanding of world geography.

With a bit of intelligent generalization wherein we set some relatively broad limits beyond which a given climate cannot trespass, we can establish a classification in which groups of similar (if not identical) climates can be recognized, and thereby make a fairly orderly arrangement of what at first appears to be a worldwide chaos of slightly differing climates.

The ancient Greeks were the first to attempt large-scale climatic classification with the familiar Torrid Zone, Temperate Zone, and Frigid Zone. Such a breakdown based on the simple relationship of latitude to temperature is obviously very primitive, yet with the paucity of accurate climatic data, it was about all that was possible at the time. Today, we find it repeated in school texts notwithstanding the present knowledge of the world. There are a number of climatic elements besides temperature that give a climate distinctive personality, and even temperature responds to other controls besides latitude alone. Any cogent classification must consider, among other things:

I. Moisture
  A. Precipitation
    1. Amount
    2. Distribution (seasonal)
    3. Type
    4. Causes
    5. Reliability
    6. Extremes

  B. Humidity
  C. Clouds
  D. Fog

II. Temperature
  A. Average
  B. Range
    1. Annual
    2. Daily
  C. Extremes
  D. Causes

III. Storms

IV. Prevailing winds

A good many classifications based more or less on these criteria have been established through the years, some better than others. But the generally accepted standard in the twentieth century has been a classification set up by the Austrian Köppen.[1] Working with botanical data on the highly tenable theory that natural vegetation closely reflects the climate of a given region, he established his now famous classification in the early 1900's (subsequently revised several times). Because of the rather involved and detailed nature of the Köppen system, most introductory treatments of climate such as this use a much simpler version, but virtually all commonly employed classifications today are simplifications or modifications of the Köppen system.[2] We will use a descriptive title for each climate, such as Tropical Rain Forest in place of Köppen's symbolic Afi designation; we will generalize rather broadly, whereas Köppen is specific; and we will set the limits of most climates somewhat wider than Köppen has, thereby incorporating into one a number of his minor subdivisions. The end result will be a series of eleven separate climates, each having its own peculiar characteristics and each repeating itself a number of places throughout the world.

The classification of climates may appear at first glance to be nothing more than a tedious memory exercise akin to the old routine of the states and their capitals. But there is logic here, an application of cause and effect, and a large element of predictability. The factors and controls that explain the character of your own climate operate in a similar manner if that same situation is duplicated anywhere else in the world, so that if we were to establish a hypothetical continent in the middle of the Pacific, it would be relatively easy to predict, at least roughly, its various climates.

There are two parts of the world that we will make no attempt to classify; they are the oceans and the mountains. This does not mean

---

[1] C. W. Thornthwaite has presented a quantitative classification that has received increased recognition as a valuable tool in advanced scientific investigation. See C. W. Thornthwaite, "An Approach to a Rational Classification of Climate," *Geog. Rev.,* XXXVIII (1948), 55–94.

[2] The Köppen system is a quantitative approach to climatic classification wherein specific values are given to critical boundary lines and frequently formulas are employed to arrive at these values (the boundaries are subject to minor change as new data constantly become available). One difficulty for the beginner lies in the use of the Centigrade scale, not a familiar American tool, and translating into awkward fractional Fahrenheit degrees. Once established, a climate is assigned a series of letter symbols based on German words, each having its own particular value. (See Appendix A.)

Unquestionably, such an approach has a great deal of cogency for the serious student of climatology. An excellent description and analysis of the Köppen system may be found in W. Köppen and R. Geiger, *Handbuch der Klimatologie,* 5 vols. (Berlin: Verlagsbuchhandlung Gerbrüder Borntraeger, 1930). Vol. 1, Part C, 1936—most complete analysis in English.

that they do not have climates, but no long-time weather records are available at sea as they are at land stations on which to base our system. And mountains break down into what is essentially a mass of microclimates. Every 1,000 feet of elevation changes the temperature roughly 3 degrees, while shady slopes vs. sunny slopes, windward slope vs. lee slope, etc., introduce such myriad variations that it becomes impossible to integrate each individual valley's climate into the world pattern.

Climographs (Fig. 4–1)

A number of the basic characteristics of each of these climates, as we establish them, can be rendered visual by plotting the data of a representative station in graph form. These are called *climographs* and are condensed versions of the main features of each climate re-

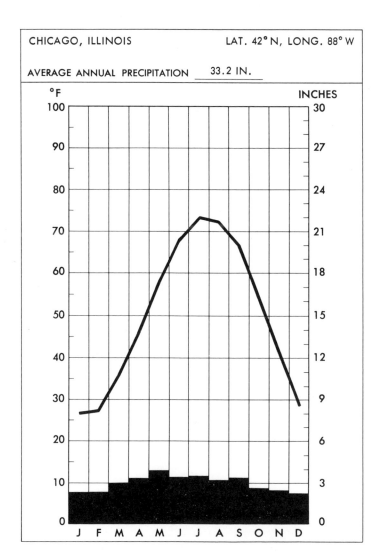

Fig. 4–1. Sample climograph of an actual station, illustrating the monthly temperature averages connected to form a curve, and the monthly precipitation shown in shaded columns.

gion. The graph is made up of twelve vertical columns corresponding to the twelve months of the year. They are always labeled starting at the left with January and following in sequence so that December is the right-hand column. In the Northern Hemisphere then, the middle columns will be summer and the outside ones winter, whereas in the Southern Hemisphere, the reverse will hold. Along the right margin of the graph, a precipitation scale is marked in inches and the normal monthly precipitation is plotted by blacking in each column from the bottom to the proper height as indicated by the scale. When this is done for each month, the total annual precipitation becomes visible at a glance, as does the typical distribution of that precipitation throughout the year.

Along the left margin of the graph is a Fahrenheit temperature scale. Related to this scale, the average monthly temperature is plotted by placing a dot in the middle of each column. When all months have been plotted, a line is drawn connecting the dots, and this curve makes apparent the average temperature for each month and the annual temperature range.

Because of their usefulness as immediate visual representation of the more important features of each climate, typical climographs of actual stations will be included for each region discussed in the following treatment.

Tropical Climates (Fig. 4–2)

The tropical climates approximate in their location that wide belt astride the equator that the Greeks called the Torrid Zone. As they looked south from the Mediterranean, the northern margin of the Sahara was obviously the outer edge of the excessively hot land and the beginning of a more moderate temperature regime. Others have suggested the Tropic of Cancer and the Tropic of Capricorn as the limits of the true tropics, but actually the Greeks were nearer to the truth when they selected the Sahara margin some 30 to 35 degrees from the equator. Köppen's selection of a cold month averaging 64° comes close to this as does the poleward limit of palms. Within this zone are three climates, all generally warm as the "tropical" would indicate, but differing markedly in their precipitation characteristics. They are: Tropical Rain Forest, Tropical Dry, and Tropical Wet and Dry.

Tropical Rain Forest. The major representatives of the Tropical Rain Forest climate occur within 10 degrees of the equator and therefore are roughly coincident with the Doldrums and at times with the

Intertropical Front. Thus, the Amazon Basin in South America, the Congo Basin and closely adjacent areas in Africa, and most of the East Indies are the chief land areas in the Doldrum belt and each exhibits a Tropical Rain Forest climate.

The words "Rain Forest" are a key to the precipitation characteristics of this climate. Heavy constant rainfall is required to support a rain forest vegetation. Probably 65 inches per year would be a minimum requirement, while 100 to 150 inches would not be uncommon. And the distribution of this moisture throughout the year must be even, at least to the extent that no real dry season is experienced. Köppen has suggested that in the tropics with its high rate of evapora-

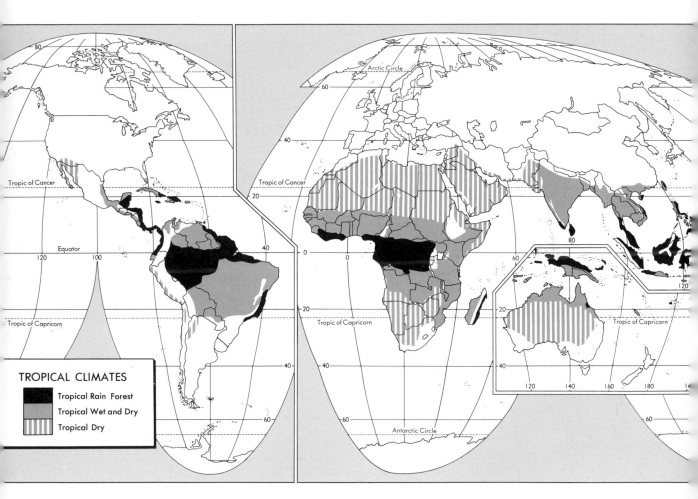

TROPICAL CLIMATES

- Tropical Rain Forest
- Tropical Wet and Dry
- Tropical Dry

Fig. 4–2. Tropical climates.

tion, any month receiving less than 2.4 inches of rainfall must be regarded as dry. So, any tropical situation where at least 65 inches of rain falls in a year and no month receives less than 2.4 inches of rain will support rain forest vegetation and must be classified as Tropical Rain Forest. Locally, the populace may speak of the wet season and the dry season. It is entirely possible that one season may experience double the precipitation of another, but if it is true Tropical Rain Forest, there is no dry season, and the reference is actually to a wet season and a *less wet* season.

The typical source of all this moisture is the almost daily convectional shower. Saturated equatorial air heated by a sun never far from overhead gives rise to this phenomenon that occurs in many places, virtually "on schedule" every day during the period of maximum heating—2 to 3 o'clock in the afternoon. In general, mornings are bright and fresh, but as the day wears on, the lower atmosphere, heated by conduction and radiation, becomes increasingly warm and sticky until relief arrives in the afternoon in the form of clouds and torrential showers. The violently ascending convectional column is topped by towering thunderheads and lightning, and thunder frequently accompanies the short but heavy rainstorm. For a while at least, as the rain descends in sheets and the runoff floods the ground, there is a welcome cooling, but the storm is of short duration and within an hour the sky clears, the vegetation steams under a high sun, and the heat returns, accompanied by even higher humidity than before the storm.

Occasionally, a weak tropical cyclone will move through, giving rise to several days of continual cloud cover and drizzle, but these are infrequent and by far the most important moisture source is the convectional shower. Since the heating is constant the year round as a result of equatorial location, and the showers regularly occurring, it follows that no dry season will exist and heavy forests will be the landscape feature.

Temperatures are, of course, generally high, but despite being so near the equator, world record high temperatures are not found in the Tropical Rain Forest. The daily clouds during the early afternoon cause the heat curve to level off so that 90° to 95° is the normal daytime maximum. This is, of course, warm, especially when combined with high humidity, and afternoons are enervating and uncomfortable. But it is a far cry from the over 100° that is typical of many locations much farther away from the equator. The worst thing about these 90° temperatures from a human comfort standpoint is that, since there are no seasons, every day is the same. The only real respite is at night when temperatures may drop to 65° to 70°. This is certainly not cold, but these are the coldest temperatures ever expe-

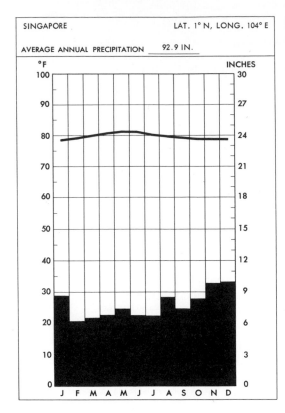

SINGAPORE LAT. 1° N, LONG. 104° E
AVERAGE ANNUAL PRECIPITATION ___92.9 IN.___

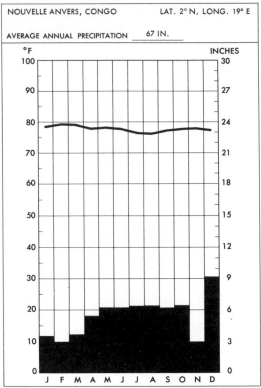

NOUVELLE ANVERS, CONGO LAT. 2° N, LONG. 19° E
AVERAGE ANNUAL PRECIPITATION ___67 IN.___

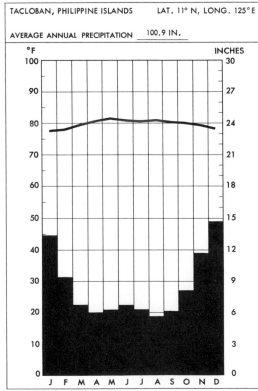

TACLOBAN, PHILIPPINE ISLANDS LAT. 11° N, LONG. 125° E
AVERAGE ANNUAL PRECIPITATION ___100.9 IN.___

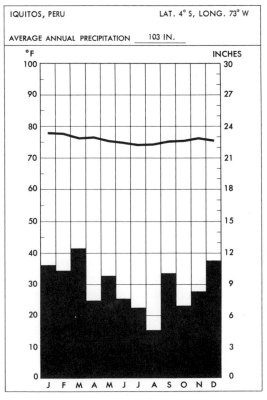

IQUITOS, PERU LAT. 4° S, LONG. 73° W
AVERAGE ANNUAL PRECIPITATION ___103 IN.___

Fig. 4–3. *Tropical Rain Forest stations.*

rienced here.   Lack of seasonal temperature change means that there is more than a kernel of truth in the old saying that "night is the winter in the tropics."

Notice on the climographs (Fig. 4–3) that the average monthly temperature (day and night both) never is far from 80° and that the temperature curve is virtually a straight line.   This is a visual expression of the annual temperature range that never varies more than a degree or two.   The daily range, which does not show on the climograph, is considerably larger, averaging as much as 25 degrees.

Having traced the chief characteristics of the Tropical Rain Forest climate, we will look again at the location map (Fig. 4–2) and notice that although the bulk of this climate occurs in the Doldrum belt near the equator, there are several narrow coastal strips of Tropical Rain Forest some distance from the equator.   These are all in the same latitude (20°–25°N and S) and all on east coasts: the east-central coast of Brazil, the east coast of Madagascar, the northeast coast of Australia, the east coasts of Central America, Hawaii, and most West Indian islands, and the east coasts of Vietnam and the Philippines.   (This last region in Southeast Asia is confused by local monsoon circulation, but generally fits the overall world pattern.)   These areas all have three climatic controls in common that are responsible for their climatic similarities.   First, despite their distance from the equator, they are still well within the tropics, and thus experience continuously high temperatures.   Second, they are all in the trade-wind zone and therefore are constantly exposed to moisture-bearing winds from off warm seas.   And third, each of the regions features uplands rising abruptly back of the coast.   So, as the oceanic air masses impinge upon these highlands, they are forced aloft and orographic precipitation bathes the mountain slopes.   On the coast proper, the heated oceanic air most often gives up its moisture via convectional showers.   The end result of all this is a climate that is characterized by continuously high temperatures, constant heavy rainfall the year round, and dense rain forest vegetation, all of which is very similar to that of the equatorial regions.   There is no alternative then but to classify this climate as Tropical Rain Forest despite the non-contiguity of these trade-wind coasts with the much more extensive Doldrum regions.   The causes are different but the result is the same, and in classifying climates, we are concerned primarily with results.

If we were to compare a population map of the world (Map VII, pp. 418–19) with a climate map (Map I, pp. 406–7), it would become immediately obvious that the Tropical Rain Forests have not been sought out by man as a preferred habitat.   Along with the deserts and the polar regions, the Tropical Rain Forests all through history have shown up as great blanks on the population map.   This is a difficult region, as many an American or European who has been forced to live there for any length of time will attest. The monotony of moist heat day after day has a distinctly enervating effect on the human body, and disease is difficult to control, especially those carried by hosts, such as yellow fever, malaria, filariasis, and liver fluke. Mildew and mold flourish, attacking and decomposing textiles and leather in a remarkably short time. Furniture secured with glue falls apart, and termites may honeycomb wooden houses and foundations almost overnight.

Most of these Tropical Rain Forest regions are occupied by small numbers of wandering tribes whose economy revolves about hunting, fishing, and gathering what the forest provides. Some have become sophisticated to the point of clearing small sections of the forest by fire and carrying on a rudimentary agriculture among the stumps and snags. Shortly, however, they are forced to move on and repeat the operation, for soils are typically lacking in soluble minerals near the surface because of heavy rainfall (*leaching*), and the forest, quick to regenerate itself, crowds out the clearing in a very short time with thick secondary growth that is too much for primitive implements to control.

Fig. 4–4. *Although the coconut grows widely throughout the tropics, it is most at home along Tropical Rain Forest beaches. Copra, the dried meat of the coconut from which oil is extracted, is the commercial product. Its manufacture requires few skills and only rudimentary equipment, and many thousands of farmer-fishermen are engaged in its production as a supplementary source of cash income. (Courtesy of Information Office, Government of India.)*

There are, however, some limited locations within the Tropical Rain Forest that have become the home of large numbers of people and have achieved an important economic position because of certain factors offsetting or complementing the basic difficulties of the climate. Some of these are: superior accessibility, occurrence of valuable minerals, above-average soil fertility, application of capital and technical skills (formerly in colonial holdings), or combinations of these. An excellent example is the island of Java in the East Indies. Here, because Java is in an archipelago, it is easily accessible from the sea, and by virtue of its location off the coast of Southeast Asia is near important shipping routes. Its mountain backbone made up of constantly active volcanoes has supplied fertile ash showers that are rejuvenated more rapidly than they can be leached. Economic deposits of minerals, petroleum in particular, have been found. And there has been the application of Dutch capital, direction, and development during the colonial period. All of this has resulted in Java becoming a highly productive region capable of supporting a population of many millions.[3]

Ceylon with her tea and coconut plantations, various West Indian islands with their sugar, Central America with its bananas, Malaya with its rubber and tin, Surinam with its bauxite, and Nigeria with its cacao plantations are other examples of Tropical Rain Forest areas that have progressed above the average because of one or more special factors. (Figs. 4–4 and 4–5.) But still, on the whole, Tropical Rain Forest areas remain sparsely populated.

Despite the backward position of Tropical Rain Forests today in terms of human habitation, there may be considerable potential there. Most of these remote areas have scarcely been touched by the geologist in search of economic mineral deposits. It is entirely possible, even likely, that New Guinea or the back country of the Amazon Basin may contain sizable ore bodies. And any place with continuous high temperatures, a year-round growing season, and heavy precipitation certainly has an agricultural potential. It has been suggested that since the Tropical Rain Forest is one of two of the world's remaining large forest reserves (the other being the subpolar regions) it may become in the not too distant future a major source of timber and wood products. At the moment, the middle latitude forests are adequate and much more accessible to the chief markets, but these sources are being depleted rapidly and at the same time demands are increasing. The basic advantage of the rain forest is its rate of regeneration —many times that of the middle latitude forests. And although the

[3] With independence, the Republic of Indonesia has encountered a good many difficulties, and productivity has slipped a great deal from its prewar peak.

Fig. 4–5. *Plantation agriculture featuring tree crops is typical of the more accessible parts of the Tropical Rain Forest. These six-year-old rubber trees on the Firestone plantation in Liberia are being prepared for their first tapping. (Courtesy of Firestone Tire & Rubber Co.)*

rain forest is characterized by hundreds of botanical species as opposed to the relatively pure stands occurring elsewhere, there does exist a tremendous volume of basic cellulose capable of reproducing itself at a very rapid rate.

Tropical Dry. All of the world's Tropical Dry zones are found in a broad belt at about the same latitude—roughly astride the Tropics of Cancer and Capricorn. Thus, they are in the region dominated by the trade winds and are often called trade-wind deserts. Also, without exception, they have a west coastal frontage. Some, notably in North and South America, are narrow coastal ribbons hemmed in by mountain ranges closely paralleling the coast. Others as in Australia and Africa, lacking this topographical control, extend for long distances inland.

The largest of the Tropical Dry regions by far is that continuous zone extending from the Atlantic Coast across North Africa, Arabia, and into northwestern India and adjacent Pakistan. Here it has been traditional to apply three different names to the various sections of this extensive desert. In North Africa, it is called the Sahara; between the Red Sea and the Persian Gulf is the Arabian Desert; and in India-Pakistan, the name Thar is applied. In virtually identical latitudes, the west coast of North America is also Tropical Dry. Baja California and the coastal strip across the Gulf of California are included here as well as the Imperial Valley and lower Colorado River section of California and Arizona. Frequently, the appellation Sonoran Desert is used to refer to the entire area.

The Southern Hemisphere exhibits the Tropical Dry climate too, every continent being represented. In the northern third of Chile and the entire coast of Peru is the Atacama, limited to a strip between the Andes and the sea. Also, astride the Tropic of Capricorn and on the west coasts of Africa and Australia are sizable dry regions extending far into the heart of each continent. These are the Kalahari and Australian deserts, respectively.

Deserts are hot and dry. This is scarcely news. But how hot is hot and how dry is dry, and more important why does this situation exist in these particular locations?

Except for the very high latitudes where evaporation is limited, any place receiving less than 10 inches of rainfall per annum is normally regarded as a true desert. Under these circumstances, there is little or no natural vegetation, only xerophytic shrubs at best, and this cover is widely spaced with considerable areas of bed rock, sand, or gravel interspersed. Actually, in the tropics where evaporation is exceptionally high, even 15 to 20 inches of rain each year is scarcely sufficient to support more than a skimpy bunch grass cover. And, although this may have some small value in good years for nomadic grazing of small flocks, it is so unreliable as to be legitimately classified with the true desert as too dry for more than sporadic human habitation. (Fig. 4–6.)

Unreliable rainfall is a characteristic of the world's dry regions. As a general rule, *the smaller the total precipitation, the greater the variability.* Lima, Peru, which averages 1.8 inches of rain per year, recently went over 13 years without any measurable precipitation and then had several storms that brought the average back to normal. Sudden violent storms are typical in the dry regions, resulting in heavy

Fig. 4–6. *Along the fringes of the true tropics, but still within the Tropical Dry climate, nomadic herding is a common occupation. These Karakul sheep in South Africa can browse as well as graze more closely than can cattle, and thus utilize this type of scant pasture. (Courtesy of Information Service of South Africa.)*

surface runoff of the hard baked earth. Arroyos or wadies are cut by raging torrents of short duration, adobe buildings melt, and people drown. In some parts of the desert, the rainfall, however unreliable, is concentrated in the winter, as in the northern Sahara or southwest United States. In other places such as the southern Sahara and the Thar, whatever rainfall is received comes in the summer. But the cohesive element that allows us to classify all of this as Tropical Dry is not *when* the rain comes, but the fact that the total is low and even that is usually unreliable. If the precipitation of an area is too little for continuous occupancy by humans, without resorting to irrigation or other artificialities, then we shall consider it as Tropical Dry.

Now, why should west coastal exposures at these particular latitudes be so dry? Kalama in the northern Chilean nitrate fields has never recorded even a trace of rain since records were begun over 80 years ago, and many other places are almost as dry. One cause appears to be the trade winds coming in off the sea from the east. Notice again on the map (Fig. 4–2) the Tropical Rain Forest trade-wind coasts. Here the Trades are forced up over highlands, precipitating most of their moisture at the east coast. In almost every case, the Tropical Dry regions are immediately opposite these trade-wind coasts, and thus are in the lee of the highlands and the continental masses. Also, at least the poleward parts of these Tropical Dry regions are strongly affected by the permanent Subtropical High cells offshore. Here the air is constantly sinking and warming and therefore antipathetic to condensation.

It may seem a bit strange that the world's driest regions should be in coastal situations. To be sure, the subsiding air masses of the Horse Latitudes discourage precipitation, but certainly local land and sea breezes must introduce moist oceanic air onto the heated land from time to time; and so they do except that an invisble barrier exists to intercept this air and remove its moisture just short of the coast. This is a cold ocean current, and there is one off the coast of every continent in these tropical latitudes. Further, the offshore drift of the general trade wind pattern tends to pull surface waters out to sea, allowing colder water from the depths to rise along the coast (*upwelling*).

Discounting minor counter and eddy currents, major ocean current circulation is essentially the same in every ocean basin. Whatever sets the basic currents in motion (and there are continuing discussions as to what all these factors might be and how they operate), once the currents begin to move, they respond to Coriolis force. Thus, in the Northern Hemisphere, they exhibit a right-hand or clockwise circulation, and in the Southern Hemisphere, a counterclockwise or left-hand motion. As to the temperatures of these currents, they are designated warm or cold not by having achieved any specific temperature, but simply by being warmer or colder than the water that they are flowing through. As an example, let us consider the current behavior in the North Pacific. Warm tropical water begins to move northward along the east coast of Asia. As it gains latitude, it invades continually cooler seas and thus is classified as a warm current (Japanese current). Obeying Ferrel's law, this stream of warm water gradually curves to the right until at about southern Japan it pulls away from the continent and pushes northeast into the Gulf of Alaska. The current is considerably cooler now than when it first left the tropics, but relative to the high latitude ocean it is flowing through, it remains warm. Still curving to the right, it moves eastward and then south along the coast of the Pacific Northwest, cooling still more but continuing somewhat warmer than the surrounding water and therefore remaining a warm current. Finally, as it continues south off the coast of Southern California and Mexico, it invades quite warm subtropical and tropical waters and relative to these is now cold. So the same current is alternately classed as both warm and cold, depending on its relative temperature, and this same pattern shows up in reverse in the Southern Hemisphere. Irrespective of hemisphere, *major ocean current circulation exhibits a warm current flowing poleward along east coasts and a cold current flowing equatorward along a large part of west coasts.* (See Chapter 9, "The Oceans.")

This means that since all Tropical Dry regions front on west coasts that cold currents are inevitable offshore. And in terms of intercepting moisture, a cold current can be almost as effective as a mountain range. Saturated air masses moving over a broad cold current will be cooled from the bottom, and condensation will occur. Often, it is in the form of dense fog, and as this drifts in over the desert coast, there is the curious anomaly of the air being filled with moisture much of the year in a place that has never recorded more than a fraction of an inch of actual precipitation. Chilling of the air at the surface in conjunction with warming via subsidence at the eastern end of the Horse Latitude anticyclone produces an inversion that makes normal convection virtually impossible. In South America, the Humboldt current (the largest of the cold ocean currents) plus the Andes paralleling the coast cause the Tropical Dry zone to extend to just a degree or two south of the equator.

Heat is another typical feature of the Tropical Dry climate. Here is where the world's record high temperatures are encountered, the current record being a recording at Azizia, Libya, in the Sahara of 136° (shade reading).[4] And yet the Tropical Dry region is at the outer edge of the tropics a considerable distance from the equator. But in the Tropical Rain Forest at the equator, the temperature almost never exceeds 100° even on the hottest day. The reason, of course, is cloud cover and rain. The sun is directly overhead at both places at one time or another each year, but in the Tropical Dry sum-

---

[4] Keep in mind whenever dealing with world records of heat, cold, rain, etc., that places with such extremes are very uncomfortable spots in which to live and therefore lightly inhabited. The cited world records simply mean that for some reason an observer lived there and had the official instruments. It is entirely possible that there are hotter places than Azizia, but for that very reason a good place not to be and thus the temperatures go unrecorded.

mer, the overhead sun and the lack of any clouds allow a continued buildup of temperature well into the late afternoon. Only along a narrow band of fog-bound coast is there any amelioration, and this fact has helped to make west coasts preferred locations for permanent habitation in the desert. (See Fig. 4–7 [Iquique].)

The foregoing emphasis on heat extremes refers only to the summer when the sun is high. Daytime maximums are regularly over 100° for two to three months. But in winter, the overhead sun is 45 to 50 degrees away, temperatures are mild, and clear sunny days and crisp nights prevail. Actually, where Tropical Dry regions are easily accessible to populated regions of more severe clime, they have become winter resorts—witness Palm Springs, Phoenix, or Tucson, and the major leagues' spring training program. The annual range of temperature then is sizable, the largest of any tropical climate. But the daily range is even larger. Remember, the control of daily range is moisture in the air. If the atmosphere is heavily charged with water vapor, then the radiation of heat from the surface of the earth will be intercepted and absorbed, with the moisture acting as a blanket to hold in the day's heat. Erase this blanket and the daytime accumulation of heat will be radiated off into space in only a few hours after sunset. So the Tropical Dry regions with their predominantly dry air will have a very large daily temperature range. Where summer daytime temperatures may go as high as 110° to 115°, they will drop to 60° to 65° at night. In winter, something on the order of 80° (daytime) and 45° (at night) is typical.

Consult the climographs (Fig. 4–7) and note that the average for the hottest month is in the neighborhood of 90°. This is the mean of both day and night for the entire month. Cool nights act to pull down the 100°+ daytime temperatures to this lower average. And similarly, the coldest month temperature is an average of the more extreme day and night maximums.

As has been pointed out previously, the Tropical Dry regions do not possess such climatic charms that people have flocked in to live there, and now, having checked some of the details, it is not difficult to see why. Water is the critical factor. Always where water is available in surface streams, springs, or underground strata, the desert sustains life. (Fig. 4–8.) A year-round growing season, maximum sunshine, *and water* make the oasis agriculturist a small-scale but extremely productive operator. Traditionally, the oasis has been one of two attractions for man in the desert; the other has been minerals. Given rich mineral deposits, a man will go anywhere and live under the most difficult conditions. On the whole, the deserts are no more productive of minerals than any other climatic region, climate having relatively little to do with the occurrence of ore-bearing formations.

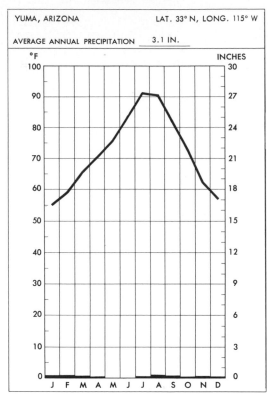

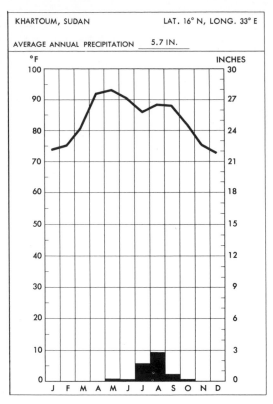

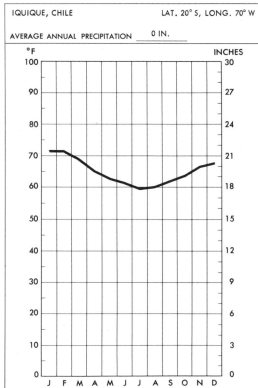

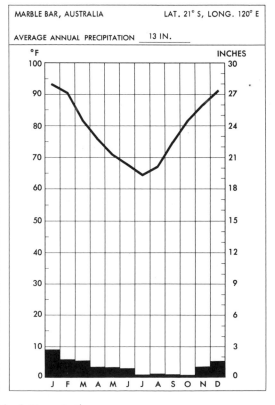

Fig. 4–7. Tropical Dry stations.

Fig. 4–8. *Water availability in the desert leads to tightly agglomerated population centers. This is the old oasis town of Qatif, Saudi Arabia, surrounded by its important date groves. (Courtesy of Arabian American Oil Co.)*

To be sure, such water soluble minerals as nitrates and borax could be found at the surface only in dry regions and they are usually the result of high evaporation, but the popular image of the desert prospector being more common than prospectors elsewhere is erroneous but easily understood. (Fig. 4–9.) He is the only fellow out there and thus commands attention. No large numbers of others have, of their own volition, selected the Tropical Dry regions as their home. But this may not always be the case. Air conditioning, new mineral strikes, or cheap ocean water desalinization—these things could mean a new deal for the desert.

Fig. 4–9. *Potash salts from the Dead Sea. Their concentration in economic quantities is directly attributable to accelerated evaporation in the Tropical Dry climate. (Courtesy of Israel Office of Information.)*

Tropical Wet and Dry. Located roughly between the excessively moist Tropical Rain Forest and the arid Tropical Dry are the regions experiencing the Tropical Wet and Dry climate and, as the name implies, exhibiting some of the characteristics of each of their neighbors. The map (Fig. 4–2) shows this intermediate location. Examine Africa first, for this latitudinal lineation is most apparent there unimpeded by major mountain ranges or coastal indentations. Between the Congo Basin and the Sahara, there is a narrow band of Tropical Wet and Dry climate broadly designated as the Sudan, while in the Southern Hemisphere, a comparable zone (the term "Veldt" is usually applied) shows up between the Congo and the Kalahari. In South America, despite the variations brought about by the Andean cordillera and the Caribbean, the same general pattern is again represented. North of the Amazon Basin, interior Venezuela and Colombia (Llanos) and parts of Central America and the West Indies make up the Northern Hemisphere Tropical Wet and Dry region, while most of southern Brazil (Campos), Paraguay, and sections of Uruguay, Argentina, and Bolivia are representative in the Southern Hemisphere. Much of Southeast Asia from South China to and including India is Tropical Wet and Dry, and the entire north coast of Australia and adjacent Indonesian Islands are of this climatic type.

The "Wet and Dry" places the emphasis in exactly the right place —the annual rainfall seasons. In the middle latitudes, we have a tendency to break the year up on a temperature basis, i.e., warm season (summer) vs. cold season (winter) because this is the most prominent seasonal change. However, near the equator where temperature changes are mild, the dramatic difference in seasons is wet vs. dry, and the local inhabitants invariably refer to them in this way. Now, we must account for this phenomenon and the reasons are varied, but generally there are two basic causes—one applying in Southeast Asia and Australia and the other in most of Africa and Latin America.

Let us begin in Southeast Asia. Why the alternating wet and dry seasons in this particular location? This is the region of the monsoon, the all-pervasive seasonal winds whose characteristic circulation is chiefly responsible for the distinctive rainfall regime in this part of the world. Whether it is a result of jet streams, upper-air frontal activity, deflected Trades, differential heating of land vs. water, or all of these operating in some sort of concert, the end product is a summer rainy and a winter dry season. Saturated air drifting onshore from tropical seas each summer readily gives up its moisture on the mountain flanks or via convection or frontal lifting. The amount varies with distance inland, latitude, exposure, etc., but the general tendency remains for oceanic air to invade the land during the warm months. Concomitantly, colder drier continental air begins to move offshore with the onset of winter, and although the details vary from place to place, precipitation ceases in large part and the cold season becomes the dry season. In the Southern Hemisphere, but still within the greater Asiatic realm, namely, northern Australia and parts of the African east coast, a reciprocal monsoon also operates as the dominating force. This monsoonal influence gives us then, throughout a sizable part of the world, a moisture regime featuring rainy summers and dry winters.

In the Tropical Wet and Dry regions of Africa and Latin America, the essential cause of rainfall seasons is something else again. You will recall that as the overhead sun makes its apparent annual migration from Cancer to Capricorn and back again, all of the world's standard wind and pressure belts tend to follow. Their change in position lags a bit behind the sun and the shift is small (on the order of 5 to 10 degrees of latitude), but to regions along the margins of these belts, even such minor changes can be pivotal in determining climate. The Tropical Rain Forest is almost wholly within the Doldrum zone, and the Tropical Dry is dominated by the Trades and Horse Latitudes, but the Tropical Wet and Dry has no such wind or pressure belt of its own; instead, it is located astride the boundary separating the Doldrums from the Trades. Thus, even slight latitudinal changes of the Trades or Doldrums will cause the Tropical Wet and Dry to be affected.

Consider the Northern Hemisphere summer when the overhead sun is at the Tropic of Cancer. The Doldrums, in shifting slightly northward, have lapped over the Tropical Wet and Dry region, and it is now under the influence of all the factors that give rise to the Tropical Rain Forest climate. At the same time in the Southern Hemisphere, the Trades have moved slightly north and are dominating that hemisphere's Tropical Wet and Dry region, bringing Tropical Dry conditions. As the sun moves to the Tropic of Capricorn six months later, this movement is reversed. So, in essence, the Tropical Wet and Dry zones have no real climate of their own but borrow their neighbors' in turn. The Sudan of North Africa, for example, experiences an imported Congo climate in the summer with the attendant daily showers and high humidity, while in the winter arid Sahara conditions move in. The result is a summer rainy season and a winter dry season very much like that of the monsoon. Undoubtedly, this same set of circumstances would prevail in Southeast Asia and Australia except for the local monsoon currents. They are so assertive as to wipe out any traces of the standard wind and pressure system, but climatically (monsoon or shifting belts), the results are the same, and we can logically class all these regions as Tropical Wet and Dry.

This characteristic distribution of precipitation throughout the year is more important than total amount in determining just which areas shall be included as Tropical Wet and Dry. The only limitation on amount is that if a region receives less than 20 inches, that region must be classified as Tropical Dry. Any place in the tropics receiving more than 20 inches in one year, any amount more, and with a winter dry season will be Tropical Wet and Dry. Actually, the highest annual recorded rainfall in history was 900 inches at Cherrapunji, India, a Tropical Wet and Dry station.

The natural vegetation will closely reflect the total rainfall and the length of wet or dry season. If we were to travel from the northern edge of the Congo to the southern margin of the Sahara, a regular

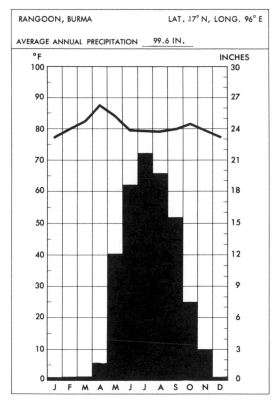

RANGOON, BURMA — LAT. 17° N, LONG. 96° E

AVERAGE ANNUAL PRECIPITATION 99.6 IN.

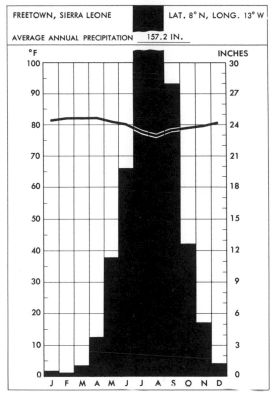

FREETOWN, SIERRA LEONE — LAT. 8° N, LONG. 13° W

AVERAGE ANNUAL PRECIPITATION 157.2 IN.

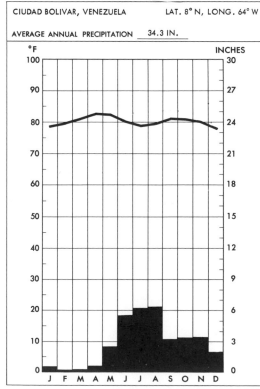

CIUDAD BOLIVAR, VENEZUELA — LAT. 8° N, LONG. 64° W

AVERAGE ANNUAL PRECIPITATION 34.3 IN.

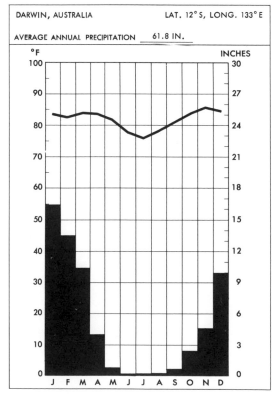

DARWIN, AUSTRALIA — LAT. 12° S, LONG. 133° E

AVERAGE ANNUAL PRECIPITATION 61.8 IN.

Fig. 4–10. *Tropical Wet and Dry stations.*

progression of vegetation zones would be apparent. Just north of the Tropical Rain Forest, a near rain forest prevails. The trees are more widely spaced and occasional open glades result from the short dry season. And near the desert where the dry season is dominant, short grass turf and stunted thorn brush are found. In between these two extremes is the savanna, extensive grasslands where the vegetation sometimes reaches a height of 8 feet. All of these regions are Tropical Wet and Dry because they have in common a winter dry season and a total precipitation of greater than 20 inches.

Temperatures, of course, are generally high in any tropical situation, and as might be expected in the Tropical Wet and Dry are closely related to those of its neighboring climates. The summer temperatures are a reasonable equivalent of those of the Tropical Rain Forest. A continual high humidity and afternoon cloudiness combined with 90° days and 70° nights are the average. Heat is greater near the desert margins and the daily range increases proportionately. Winter, being the dry season, displays temperatures that tend to be somewhat like the desert winters, roughly 75°–80° days and 55°–60° nights. (Fig. 4–10.)

Thus, it can be seen that a rather wide range of conditions prevails within the Tropical Wet and Dry regions, and similarly, variations in human occupancy and land use. In the Orient, this is a highly productive climate from an agricultural point of view. Southern China and India particularly support as many as 3,000 people per square mile in some places who are directly dependent on the land for their livelihood. Paddy rice and the monsoon are highly compatible as long as the rainfall is over 40 inches per year, and the climatic rhythm becomes the pulse of life. (Fig. 4–11.) Sugar cane too, as in the West

Fig. 4–11. The carabao (water buffalo) and the rice paddy are an inseparable couplet in the Tropical Wet and Dry portion of the Philippines. Coincidence of annual rainfall with the season of highest temperature dictates that millions of Oriental farmers adjust their pattern of livelihood to the monsoonal rhythm.

Fig. 4–12. *Sisal, a semidrought-resistant plant from which cordage is extracted, replaces the native scrub without recourse to irrigation during the dry season. This scene is from Angola. (Courtesy of Casa de Portugal.)*

Indies and India, is adaptable to the alternation of wet and dry seasons and allows these areas to produce a cash crop and sustain sizable numbers of people. Sisal and pineapple are similar in their ability to withstand partial drought (Fig. 4–12). But elsewhere, where the natural grasslands have been put to less-intensive use as pasture, much smaller populations are supported. The savannas have proved not to be the ideal grazing land that some have supposed them to be. Isolated, alternately parched and flooded, and plagued by disease, it takes a special breed of animal to survive here, and more often than not such a rugged animal does not produce particularly tender steak. Only in Australia has any sort of commercial grazing proved successful, and even there, despite continued efforts, losses are high and profits small. (Fig. 4–13.)

But there are always possibilities. Again, mineral strikes such as copper in Zambia (Northern Rhodesia) and iron in Venezuela will draw large numbers of people and pay for the construction of modern transport, which will help to defeat isolation. New crops and new agricultural techniques may also help. At Humpty Doo in northern Australia, a joint United States–Australian venture in large-scale mechanized rice culture has been attempted, although with less than complete success.

Fig. 4–13. *In northern Australia, the largest commercial cattle grazing industry anywhere in the tropics is carried on, but not without a great many tribulations. Not the least of these is water availability during the extended winter dry period. Here a government bore, tapping underground resources, has ameliorated the local problem. (Courtesy of Australian News & Information Bureau.)*

And here and elsewhere, peanuts, cotton, and other tropical crops have shown varied results. With world population continuing to rise at a rapid rate, the relatively empty portions of the Tropical Wet and Dry do have a potential as a productive home for man.

Subtropical Climates (Fig. 4–14)

Transitional between the tropics and middle latitudes, and reflecting some of the characteristics of each, are the subtropical climates. They are two in number, one occurring in regions facing out on west coasts and the other on east coasts; and this opposing coastal orientation introduces some sharp divergencies in climate despite their generally identical latitude.

Mediterranean. Here is the west coast subtropical climate, the name deriving from its typical location along the margins of the Mediterranean Basin. There has been some criticism of the use of the term "Mediterranean" to denote this particular climate in that it is merely a geographical location and inconsistent with the other climatic names which refer to vegetation or some outstanding feature of the climate. But it does aid the student in location and through long use has become traditional.

Since Mediterranean climatic regions are always west coastal, and because they are subtropical and immediately adjacent to the tropics, they must then, wherever they occur in the world, share a common boundary with the tropical dry climates, for these are the most poleward of the tropical climates and always appear on west coasts too. In the Old World the west coast immediately north of the Sahara Desert is breached by the Mediterranean Sea and the coast extended greatly, so that almost the entire fringe of this inland sea is considered

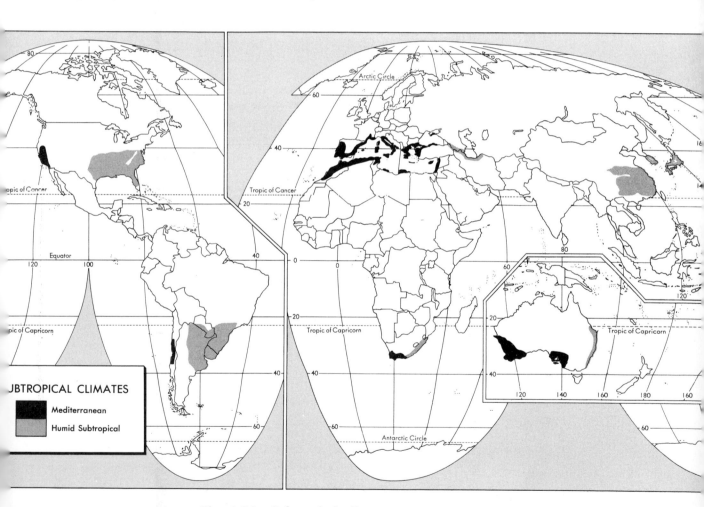

Fig. 4–14. Subtropical climates.

representative of the Mediterranean climate. Normally however, if the continental west coast is straight, regions exhibiting a Mediterranean climate will be rather limited, for they must be near the sea and their latitudinal extent is not great. So, if there were no Mediterranean Sea, only the coasts of Morocco and Portugal would be so influenced. But with the Mediterranean Sea multiplying the length of the coastline many times, we find here the largest area of Mediterranean climate anywhere in the world. Involved are the coasts of Spain, southern France, peninsular Italy, Yugoslavia, Albania, Greece, Turkey, the Levant states, Libya, Tunisia, and Algeria. The Sahara reaches the Sea from southern Israel to Libya, but elsewhere the Mediterranean climate completely encircles the Mediterranean Sea and even pushes into the Black Sea littoral in Turkey and the Crimea.

On the west coast of North America, in the same latitude as the Mediterranean Sea, is another Mediterranean climate region. It includes the California coast from the Mexican border, where it abuts with the Sonoran Desert, northward to just beyond San Francisco Bay, and also the greater part of the Central Valley. In South America, the central one-third of Chile occupies a similar position. And in South Africa, the southern margin of the Kalahari Desert, in the vicinity of Cape Town, displays a Mediterranean climate. Presumably if Africa were longer, the region would be more extensive, but South Africa barely reaches subtropical latitudes and its Mediterranean representative is the world's smallest. An unusual situation exists in Australia in that the Great Australian Bight (bay) indents the south coast so as to present two west coasts in these latitudes, and thus Australia has two Mediterranean climate areas, one in the Perth region of West Australia and one involving Adelaide and environs in South Australia.

Among the outstanding features of the Mediterranean climate is its rainfall peculiarities. Not only is the total annual receipt low, averaging about 15–20 inches, but it is highly concentrated in the winter, while the summer is almost absolutely dry. Frequently, the arid season is dominant, reflecting the adjacent situation of the Mediterranean to the tropical deserts. So once again, as in the Tropical Wet and Dry, we find a climate where the year is broken up into two distinct seasons on the basis of rainfall, except that this time winter is the rainy season and summer is dry.

In accounting for such a distinctive rainfall regime, we must analyze the wind and pressure systems of these particular latitudes and recognize again their slight north-south shifting with the seasons. First, dominating the tropical deserts are the Trades, which exert a particularly drying influence on west sides of continents. Then, poleward of the Trades are the Horse Latitudes, regions of sinking air and thus warming drying air. They show up particularly as permanent cells at sea, the Hawaiian High off the North American West Coast being representative. And finally, poleward of the Horse Latitudes are the broad Westerlies, characterized by their many eastward-moving cyclones following the Polar Front. These are the wind and pressure systems affecting the Mediterranean regions and, as they shift with the advance and retreat of the summer sun, are responsible for the alternating wet and dry seasons.

As an example of a representative area, let us examine the California Mediterranean region. In the summer, when the sun is overhead near the Tropic of Cancer, the northern fringes of the Sonoran Desert move northward to affect California. Offshore the Hawaiian High has shifted to the north also, forcing the storms from the Gulf of Alaska to skirt its poleward edge well north of California. An imported Tropical Dry climate results for the duration of the summer months. But when the overhead sun moves into the Southern Hemisphere, the Hawaiian High tends to follow it south, and the westerly storms from an increasingly active Aleutian Low begin to swing farther south. All of these do not move across the southern half of California but many of them do, and their low stratus clouds and drizzle rain are typical of winter conditions. Occasionally, cyclones will stagnate (blocked by a combination of mountains and a continental high inland) and heavy precipitation will result. At other times, quite violent storms will develop from polar maritime air detouring far south over subtropical seas and thus becoming increasingly unstable as it is warmed at the bottom. But between storms bright sunny weather prevails, so that a winter in California is not quite the same as a winter in Oregon, yet frequent cyclones are characteristic and the full year's rainfall is received during the cold half of the year, frequently in just a few midwinter months. This pattern is essentially the same on all continents in both hemispheres, and its net result is a Mediterranean winter rainfall regime on every continent immediately poleward of the tropical deserts.

Because it is limited to a narrow coastal zone, the high summer temperatures that should prevail at these subtropical latitudes are considerably ameliorated by oceanic influences. Particularly, the cold current (the same cold current that is found off the coast of Tropical Dry climates) is an effective moderator of daytime temperatures. Land and sea breezes bring cool air onto the land, and of particular influence are the advection fogs drifting ashore from off the current and shielding the coastal regions from the direct rays of the sun until almost noon each day. Making for even more comfortable living conditions are the cool nights, for summer is the dry season and the accumulated heat of the day is radiated off into space very rapidly during cloudless

Fig. 4–15. *The sunny Mediterranean climate is a distinctly salable item. Everywhere along its pleasant beaches, resort facilities, catering to both tourists and the local populace, are highly developed. This view of Viña del Mar, Chile, is representative. (Courtesy of Panagra.)*

nights. On the average, summer-month daytime temperatures reach only about 75°–80°, and they seem even cooler because of low humidity; and nights are a comfortable 50°–55°. No wonder the Mediterranean regions have been renowned as resort and tourist areas with long rainless summers and brilliant sunny afternoons, yet mild daytime temperatures and cool nights. (Fig. 4–15.)

There are exceptions. The Central Valley of California, insulated by the coast ranges from the cooling effects of the sea, closely approximates the inland temperatures of the Tropical Dry climate. Nights are cool but summer daytime temperatures average near 100° throughout. Latitude has little effect, as Redding in the far north and Fresno in the south display a good deal of similarity—it is distance from the sea that is important. The question arises, "Should the Central Valley be classified as Mediterranean climate?" In all respects, it is typical except for summer daytime temperatures, and since the only alternative is to establish a separate climatic classification to accommodate it, the Valley is usually included with the Mediterranean. But one should be aware of this single variation.

To a somewhat lesser degree, most of the Old World Mediterranean also deviates from the typical in the same way. The Mediterranean Sea lacks a cold current and, as a landlocked sea, is warmer in any case than the open ocean. Therefore, its cooling influence on the adjacent littoral is less effective than elsewhere. Palermo, for instance, in Sicily, is at approximately the same latitude as San Francisco, yet the average temperature for the month of August (both day and night included) is 79°, while fog-bound San Francisco reaches only 60°.

Winters are moderate. Frosts are not unknown but temperatures seldom drop much below 30°, and then only on infrequent winter nights. Such mildness might seem to be expected in the subtropics, but Northern Hemisphere locations in the interior of the continents at equivalent latitudes experience much colder temperatures because they are invaded by outward moving polar continental air masses. However, the Sierra Nevada forms a high barrier against such cold air in North America, and comparable mountain chains ringing the northern Mediterranean Basin are equally effective in blocking out continental air. Occasionally the cold air will spill over a low spot in the mountains and flow, frequently at high velocity, down the Mediterranean slope. The dreaded *Bora,* at the head of the Adriatic, is a gravity wind of this type originating in the Danube Basin, but as it loses altitude, it is warmed adiabatically so that when it arrives at the sea, its temperature is a great deal warmer than when it started. It still seems cold relative to the normal temperatures and may be well below freezing, but this type of phenomenon is rare and winter-month averages are usually on the order of 50°. (Fig. 4–16.) In the Southern Hemisphere, continental cold air masses in the middle latitudes are unknown.

Short, mild winters and long, warm, sunny summers with virtually a year-round growing season would appear at first to be an ideal agricultural climate, especially for those who are conditioned to regarding California as the great national garden spot. But there is a serious flaw in this agricultural paradise—water. Rainfall is a little short in any case, but more importantly, it comes at the wrong time of the year. The summer growing season is the water-short period, and crops must be limited to those that have the ability to withstand prolonged drought. The natural vegetation reflects this condition in its sparseness and the special adaptation of grasses, brush, and occasional

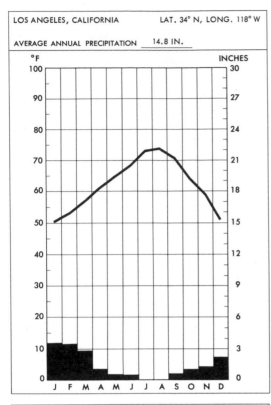

LOS ANGELES, CALIFORNIA   LAT. 34° N, LONG. 118° W

AVERAGE ANNUAL PRECIPITATION   14.8 IN.

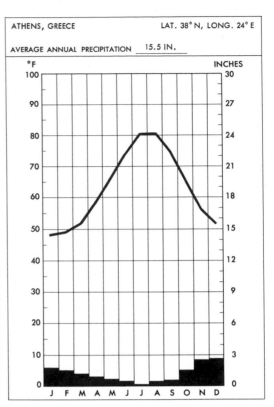

ATHENS, GREECE   LAT. 38° N, LONG. 24° E

AVERAGE ANNUAL PRECIPITATION   15.5 IN.

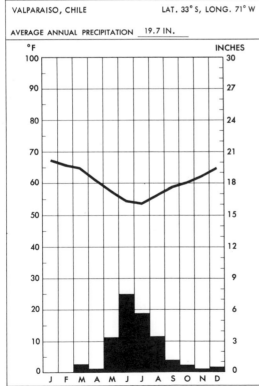

VALPARAISO, CHILE   LAT. 33° S, LONG. 71° W

AVERAGE ANNUAL PRECIPITATION   19.7 IN.

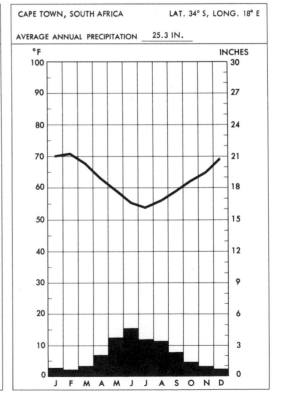

CAPE TOWN, SOUTH AFRICA   LAT. 34° S, LONG. 18° E

AVERAGE ANNUAL PRECIPITATION   25.3 IN.

Fig. 4–16. *Mediterranean stations.*

trees to survive aridity.   It is no accident that anywhere one travels in the world among the Mediterranean climates olives, grapes, figs, and wheat are common.   These are the standard drought-resistant crops and their numbers are not great.   To a large degree, the rural poverty of the Old World Mediterranean Basin stems from a numerous agricultural peasant population attempting to make a living from the land in the face of this inherent climatic defect.

But, given summer moisture, the Mediterranean climate can become highly productive.   With irrigation, as in the California Central Valley where exotic streams are fed by melting Sierra snows, the long growing season and bright summer sun can be taken advantage of. Now the land, which had been utilized only for sparse grazing or low-yielding dry-field crops, can produce citrus, cotton, sugar beets, and a seemingly endless range of profitable products.   (Fig. 4–17.)   How-

Fig. 4–17.   The highly regarded Jaffa orange is an important Israeli export, but like so many crops grown in the Mediterranean climatic regions, these groves on the Plain of Sharon must be irrigated. (Courtesy of Israel Office of Information.)

ever, the normal river in the Mediterranean climate, reflecting the
seasonal rainfall, carries water only during the winter; yet even here,
given sufficient capital, a dam can be erected to save the winter's water
in a reservoir for utilization the following summer. Many would
claim that from the standpoint of human comfort, the Mediterranean
climate is the world's finest, but without irrigation, it is far from the
finest climate for agriculture.

Humid Subtropics. On the east coast of every continent, almost
opposite the Mediterranean regions, is the Humid Subtropic climate.
It too is on the margin of the tropics and shares a common boundary
with a tropical climate—in this case, the Tropical Wet and Dry. So,
if we apply these locational criteria to the United States, we find the
Humid Subtropics in the southeastern states. Since the climate, unlike the Mediterranean, is not confined to the seaboard and there are
no limiting high mountain ranges, a rather sizable area is encompassed,
including all of the so-called "Old South"—from central Texas to the
Atlantic and from the Gulf to a line roughly along the Ohio River to
Chesapeake Bay. Comparable to this on the east side of the Eurasian
continent is a large part of central China centering on the Yangtze
River, and southern Korea and Japan. The same pattern holds in the
Southern Hemisphere where southern Brazil, Paraguay, Uruguay, and
the Argentine Pampas make up a large contiguous area. But in South
Africa and Australia, mountain ranges parallel the coast and limit the
Humid Subtropics to the coast. The representative in Africa is very
small for this reason and also because Africa scarcely pushes into the
subtropics, but in Australia the coastal strip extends from Brisbane
in the north to almost the southern tip of the continent.

The name "Humid Subtropics" points up the major difference between this climate and the Mediterranean, that is, moisture. Not only
is the annual total roughly double that of the Mediterranean, averaging 40 inches, but there is no dry season. We are dealing here with
the identical wind and pressure systems that we were on the west coast
but their effect is different. The Trades, for instance, which in the
summer contributed to west coast aridity, are onshore here, coming
off a warm sea and crossing a warm current. And not merely are the
Trades onshore, although they do not migrate far enough poleward to
affect the entire subtropics, but the general flow of air into the summer
continental low brings moist air off the sea. In the Far East, we use
the term "summer monsoon"; however, every continent, even those
in the Southern Hemisphere, has a summer monsoon-like tendency and
sucks in air from offshore. This air is heated by conduction and the
typical warm season precipitation comes in the form of frequent afternoon convectional thundershowers. Heat plus moist air equals con-

vectional precipitation, and the Humid Subtropics meet these requirements each summer. Intermittent weak cyclones of continental origin produce some clouds and rain, and to add further to late summer–early fall precipitation totals, it should be remembered that with the exception of South America, these latitudes are affected by hurricane-typhoon influences. The coastal regions especially receive moisture from this last source simply because these storms are in the general vicinity. So, while the west coast Mediterranean is experiencing a protracted dry season, the east coast Humid Subtropics are receiving significant rainfall, often, as in the Far East where the monsoon and typhoon are well developed, a definite summer maximum.

Winters are much like those in the Mediterranean. Polar Front cyclonic disturbances swing farther equatorward with the retreat of the overhead sun, and frontal activity gives rise to gray skies and drizzle rain. Only in the Orient is there a variation on this pattern, for North Atlantic spawned storms do not always survive the trip across Asia in the winter. They are compensated for to a degree by new storms generated along the Polar Front in the vicinity of the upper Yangtze Valley, but generally winter precipitation fails to match that of the summer.

In the Northern Hemisphere, some of this winter precipitation is in the form of snow as the great continental cold air masses surge out of the interior. They do not dominate the Humid Subtropics by any means, but occasional cold spells are a definite element of the winter climate. Lack of mountain barriers in North America, at right angles to the flow of Canadian air, allows invasions of cold all the way to northern Florida and the Gulf for short periods most winters, and the more northerly locations such as Virginia and Arkansas receive several minor snowstorms every year. Asiatic Humid Subtropic regions, although protected to a greater degree by high mountains, are subject to a more vigorous winter monsoon pushing Siberian air far out of the interior, so that with few exceptions, periodic snow and cold are encountered everywhere. Tokyo, Shanghai, and Seoul all have several cold spells each year with snow a regular winter feature.

However, the average temperatures for the winter months, as shown on the climate charts (Fig. 4–18) do not always reflect the few days of freezing weather each month, for they are offset by many relatively mild days. In comparing the averages of Northern Hemisphere stations with those of the Southern Hemisphere, where there are no large middle latitude continents to develop cold air masses, there appears to be no great differences. But the cold spells should be recognized. An excellent example of their effect in limiting agriculture is a comparison of the northernmost limit of frost-touchy citrus on a commercial scale in Florida vs. southern California. The lake country of

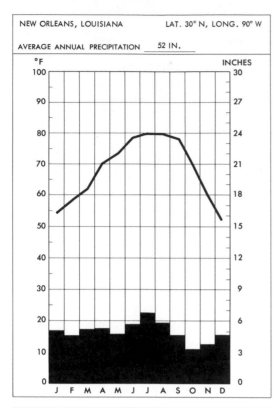

NEW ORLEANS, LOUISIANA   LAT. 30° N, LONG. 90° W

AVERAGE ANNUAL PRECIPITATION   52 IN.

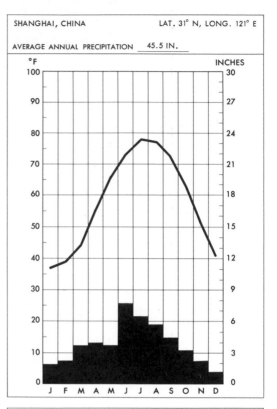

SHANGHAI, CHINA   LAT. 31° N, LONG. 121° E

AVERAGE ANNUAL PRECIPITATION   45.5 IN.

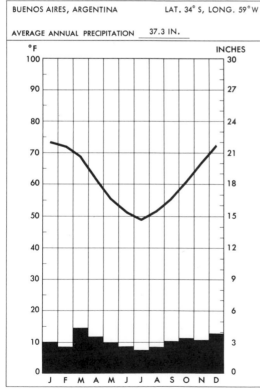

BUENOS AIRES, ARGENTINA   LAT. 34° S, LONG. 59° W

AVERAGE ANNUAL PRECIPITATION   37.3 IN.

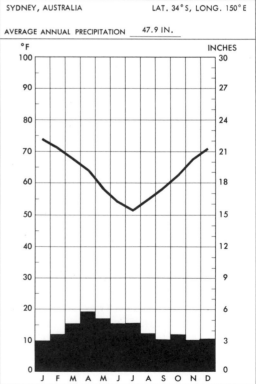

SYDNEY, AUSTRALIA   LAT. 34° S, LONG. 150° E

AVERAGE ANNUAL PRECIPITATION   47.9 IN.

Fig. 4–18. *Humid Subtropic stations.*

central Florida is the heart of the industry in the Humid Subtropics with a northern limit of perhaps Jacksonville. While in Mediterranean California, sizable orchards are common in the San Joaquin Valley at least as far north as Fresno. There is a discrepancy of 6–7 degrees of latitude here, reflecting the frequency of killing frost, yet the coldest month average for both the Mediterranean and Humid Subtropic regions in general is much the same—in the vicinity of 45°–50°.

Summers are hot—several degrees warmer than the same latitudes on the west coast—for there is no cooling current offshore and no fog. Moreover, the humidity is constantly high because tropical maritime air is dominant, so that sensible temperatures are uncomfortable, even at night. New Orleans, for instance, features four midsummer months averaging close to 80° and almost daily convectional showers. This is a very near approximation of Tropical Rain Forest conditions and without air conditioning can be an enervating season. Days are often in the 90's and the hottest month anywhere in the Humid Subtropics is seldom below 75°. Florida beaches may be very pleasant as the local land and sea breezes keep the air moving, but only a few miles inland, it becomes hot and sticky.

Thus, the Humid Subtropics differ in several ways from the Mediterranean climate:

1. Greater total precipitation distributed more evenly throughout the year
2. Higher summer temperatures
3. Similar mild winter temperatures, but interspersed with occasional cold spells

But where this climate suffers a bit relative to the Mediterranean in terms of human comfort, it is basically much more productive agriculturally. A long growing season combined with adequate rainfall in midsummer is the chief advantage, and because the summer precipitation is derived from afternoon showers of short duration, days remain bright and sunny. Everywhere in the world, man is engaged in agriculture in the Humid Subtropics.

Intensive rice culture supports a numerous population throughout the Far East (Fig. 4–19), and farming has been a way of life for generations in the U.S. Cotton Belt (Fig. 4–20). Lesser population pressures have led to a more extensive land use in South America and Australia, yet the agricultural potential remains. Where excessive slope or soil inadequacies are a problem, forests often make the land productive and regenerate themselves rapidly, once cut, under the influence of a benign climate. The thirteen states of the old Confederacy produce more wood products today than any other section of the country.

Fig. 4–19. *Harvested rice hangs on racks and poles to dry in southern Japan. Rice as a major crop invades the Humid Subtropics in South Korea and central China as well as Japan. (Courtesy of Pan American Airways.)*

Fig. 4–20. *The cotton economy of the South, although diversifying broadly into livestock and industry, is still with us as evidenced by this photo from east Texas. Cotton requires a long growing season, great summer heat, and over 20 inches of rainfall, conditions that are met in the Humid Subtropic climate. (Courtesy of Texas A. & M. College.)*

Middle Latitude Climates (Fig. 4–21)

Largely dominated by the Westerlies, the middle latitude climates occupy a broad belt between the subtropics and the high latitudes. Along west coasts, they extend, in some cases, almost to the Arctic Circle, while their dry representative pushes equatorward to abut with a tropical climate. The basic characteristic, as might be expected, is strong seasonality, although there is an important exception; and the middle latitude climates are most widely represented in the Northern Hemisphere where the continents become larger as opposed to their very limited extent at these latitudes in the Southern Hemisphere.

Marine West Coast. The climate of the entire west coast of every continent in the middle latitudes is called Marine West Coast. The third of a west coast series of climates stretching from well within the tropics to the poleward limits of the middle latitudes, the Marine West Coast shares a common boundary with the Mediterranean at the margin of the subtropics and it in turn merges into the Tropical Dry. Chile is a neat yardstick illustrating this inevitable series: the northern one-third is Tropical Dry, the central one-third Mediterranean, and the southern one-third Marine West Coast. Only Africa, of all the continents, misses out, for it does not push into the middle latitudes in either hemisphere. Australia barely does with only Tasmania and the southern tip of Victoria in the vicinity of Melbourne being represented. And New Zealand, in much the same latitude, can be included here with Australia.

The Northern Hemisphere, where the greatest land masses are in the middle and high latitudes, exhibits the most extensive regions of Marine West Coast climate. Along the west coast of North America, the climate is essentially the same from northern California to southern Alaska. The belt is narrow, between the fringing mountains and the sea, but fully 20 degrees of latitude are involved. Western Europe is similar in this respect in that the entire coastal zone, from northern Spain to just short of the Arctic Circle in Norway, is classified as Marine West Coast. Included here are northern Spain, western France, the Benelux countries, the North Sea Coast of Germany, Denmark, southern coastal Norway, and, of course, Great Britain and Ireland. However, unlike North America, only in Norway is there a mountain range closely paralleling the seaboard, and the inland climatic boundary is much more difficult to determine. As the word "Marine" implies, regions involved in this climate must be closely oriented to the oceans, so that where no mountain barrier exists to sharply demark marine from continental influences, as in Western Germany and France, we must recognize a zone of subtle transition.

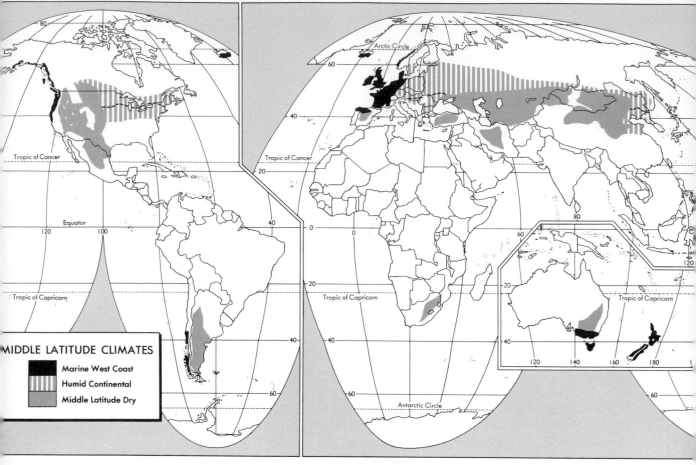

Fig. 4–21. *Middle Latitude climates.*

MIDDLE LATITUDE CLIMATES

- ▮ Marine West Coast
- ▥ Humid Continental
- ▨ Middle Latitude Dry

Probably the most striking feature of the Marine West Coast climate is the mildness of the winters at these relatively high latitudes. One measure of this is the average temperature of the coldest month, which is typically above 32°—often in the low 40's. Another measure is length of growing season (number of days between the last frost in the spring and the first frost in the fall), which averages well over 200 days, and at such locations as Valencia, Ireland, and Cape Flattery, Washington, is over 300 days. This is almost tropical. In the southeastern United States, a 200-day growing season is regarded as the minimal limit for growing cotton, so in essence, other things being equal, subtropical crops such as cotton can be grown in, say, British Columbia. Other things are not equal, of course, but it is nonetheless remarkable that such mild temperatures should prevail. Freezing temperatures, if not common, occur every winter and snow is not unknown, although nearly always in short-lived flurries and the fall melts rapidly. But, compared with North Dakota or central Siberia at exactly the same latitude, the Marine West Coast is a virtual hothouse.

The oceans are responsible. These great water bodies to the west change their temperature only slightly from season to season, and the air masses above them reflect this moderation. Of equal importance is the fact that the prevailing winds in the middle latitudes are from the west, constantly bathing the west coasts with oceanic air. These keep the excessively cold continental air masses of the interior at bay, and if reinforced by protective mountain chains, as in North America, or the cold air is lacking, as in the Southern Hemisphere, the west coasts display very moderate temperatures indeed. Western Europe is the least typical in that Eurasia develops the largest and coldest winter air mass in the world (with the possible exception of Antarctica), and there is no continuous mountain barrier to block its occasional invasion of the west coast. But even here, this is relatively rare.

Also a definite warming factor, although probably of secondary significance to the basic oceanic influence, is the occurrence of a warm current impinging on these west coasts. This is the same current that was classified as cold off the coasts of the Mediterranean and Tropical Dry climates, but at these higher latitudes, flowing through colder waters and retaining somewhat more of its residual tropical temperatures, it is considered warm. Its effect is to exaggerate the already moderating influence of the oceanic air masses, adding perhaps 3–5 degrees to the winter temperature average. In the North Atlantic, where a lesser branch follows the Norwegian coast into the Arctic Ocean, ports are kept ice free all the way to Murmansk, and the Marine West Coast climate is pushed northward almost to the Arctic Circle.

So, in the winter, the sea is the source of heat and the continent of cold, and the moderation of this middle latitude climate is directly related to its nearness to the sea. Cold-season isotherms depart radically from their normal east-west trend upon crossing west coasts, especially in the Northern Hemisphere, and align themselves almost north-south; in this part of the world, latitude is of lesser importance as a temperature control than is coastal orientation.

Summer temperatures are cool, the hottest month usually averaging in the 60's. In this season, the imported oceanic air masses exert a cooling influence that, although not as striking as the winter warming, is readily apparent when compared with summer temperatures in the interior of the continent. The general tendency of the sea to maintain much the same temperature the year round is reflected in the limited annual range of the Marine West Coast climate. Warmed in winter and cooled in summer, the annual temperature range is no more than 15 degrees in many places and seldom greater than 20–25 degrees. There are tropical locations with a range greater than that, and it is about the same as the average annual temperature range in the Mediterranean climate. Such a lack of seasonality is one of the chief features of the Marine West Coast climate and is particularly startling when encountered in the middle latitudes where strong seasonal differences are to be expected.

Despite these very pleasant temperatures, the Marine West Coast regions have not rivaled the Mediterranean in attracting tourists and resorts; they have had a reputation of having constant rain and a generally dark and gloomy aspect—a reputation not wholly unearned. It is inevitable that a narrow coastal strip with prevailing winds onshore should experience a good deal of precipitation, particularly if it is backed up by high mountains forcing saturated oceanic air masses aloft. And there are many places where the mountain slopes receive in the neighborhood of 200 inches each year. But even where the mountains are lacking, persistent rainfall results from the frontal activity of the many cyclones that frequent the Westerlies. This is usually in the form of light but constant drizzle, a great deal of low-hanging cloudiness, and mist and fog interspersed with actual rain. The end product is a great many rainy days each year but a total receipt of less precipitation than might be expected. London, for instance, enjoys a deserved reputation of being a very dank and drippy city. Virtually every day is a rainy day, the ground is always wet, the air saturated, and umbrellas and raincoats are in order for all seasons. Yet London receives only 25 inches of rain each year. In some parts of the world, this would be considered semiarid. But, because so much of London's rainfall is in the form of drizzle or mist, it requires about 200 rainy days to produce these 25 inches. And because of the saturated air and high rate of cloudiness, evaporation is kept to a minimum and 25 inches is more than adequate for agriculture. Seattle only gets 33 inches of rain per annum; Portland, 44; and Melbourne, 26. These totals are scarcely exorbitant, yet to live in any of these cities is a wet and dreary experience, mainly because of excessive cloudiness. All Marine West Coast regions receive well under 50 per cent of the possible sunshine each year. Scotland, for example, receives less than one hour of sunlight per day in December and only five and a half hours in June despite the very long summer days. It is this cloudiness that accounts for the general gloom that appalls the casual visitor, but it also is responsible for the lessened evaporation, so that a little moisture goes a long way and maintains the lush greenness of the landscape and the permanent snowcaps on even fairly low mountain peaks.

So precipitation totals may vary widely within the Marine West Coast climate, from a low of 23–25 inches to over 200, but in terms of human occupation, there appears to be a maximum limit of about 60 inches. All the large cities and densely populated lowlands are in regions of under 60 inches of rainfall, while those areas with more are

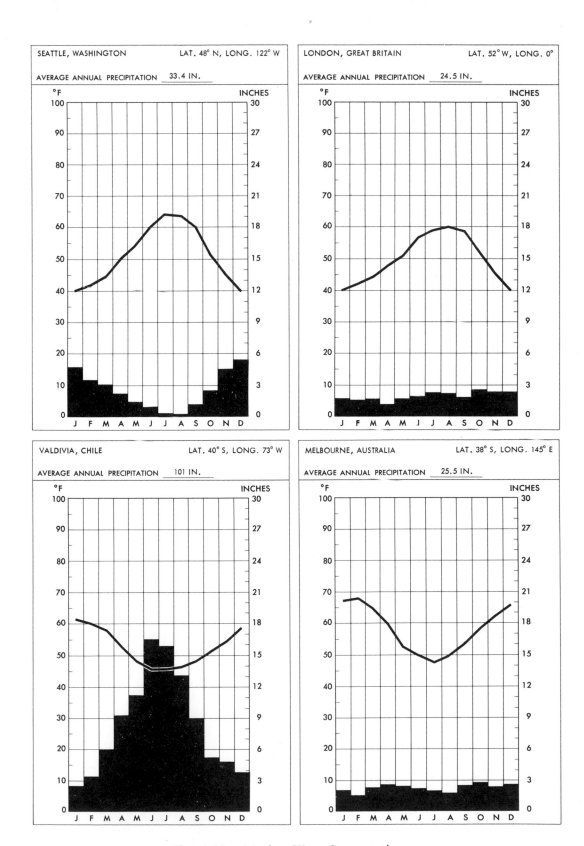

Fig. 4–22. *Marine West Coast stations.*

virtually uninhabited. A part of this may be simply that normal drainage cannot cope with over 60 inches and marshes and moors prevail, but in order for a region to receive these high totals, it must have steep mountain slopes immediately adjacent to the sea, and such a coast allows little room for man to find a toehold. The British Columbian Coast, western Scotland, much of Norway, and southern Chile are all empty, or at most support only tiny villages of fishermen or lumbermen.

Normally, there is a slight tendency toward a winter precipitation maximum, although the summers are by no means dry, because there is a general lessening of cyclonic activity during the warm months. However, there is one small area that deviates enough from the average situation to merit mention. This is the North American Coast from northern California to southern British Columbia. Here there is a distinct, if limited, summer dry season lasting from about mid-July to mid-September. It is a beautiful time of year with a great deal more sunshine than is usual, and daytime temperatures are seldom out of the 70's. Lawns and pastures require some irrigation and forest fires are a problem, but generally the dry season is of such short duration that the countryside remains green and the mountain snow caps glisten without melting away. This unusual situation seems to be the result of a general weakening of the Aleutian Low with a lessened ability to produce vigorous storms, while at the same time the offshore Hawaiian High cell migrates strongly northward, shielding this part of the coast from the few storms that do move eastward. But all of this does not last long. By mid-September, the rains begin and, although somewhat sporadic at first, shortly settle into a 9–10 month pattern of clouds and drizzle. (Fig. 4–22.)

Where flat land exists and the rainfall is below 60 inches, the Marine West Coast regions have attracted man. Agriculture is possible, although not ideal, the greatest drawback being lack of sunshine rather than temperature. In many parts of the world, grass has been the best crop and it is so treated. Certified seeds are sown on well-prepared soil, and it is top-dressed and rejuvenated by repeated feeding so that it flourishes under conditions of moderate temperatures and misty half-light. Then animals are pastured year round and convert the cheap grass into profitable dairy and meat products. (Fig. 4–23.)

It is no accident that most of our domesticated animal breeds are of Western European origin and have been introduced successfully into the Pacific Northwest, New Zealand, and Chile—Hereford, Dorset, Shropshire, Percheron, Holstein, etc. Other crops besides grass are grown, but many of them such as oats and potatoes have the special ability to produce well with lack of sunshine.

Fig. 4–23. *Although this view is in the North Island of New Zealand, the dairy animals feeding on lush pasture and the mountain backdrop could easily be in the Pacific Northwest or southern Chile. The lack of sunshine and the constant rain frequently lead to the cultivation of grass as a major "crop." (Courtesy of New Zealand Government Travel Commission.)*

Forests are the natural vegetation in the Marine West Coast climate regions, and their exploitation is an important industry where they are reasonably accessible. In Western Europe, most of the trees are gone, being cut off long ago; but in southern Chile and Canada–Alaska, virgin forests remain untouched. (Fig. 4–24.)

Fig. 4–24. Forests are an important resource in the uplands and less densely populated parts of the Marine West Coasts. These are Douglas fir logs being efficiently handled by modern forestry equipment in western Washington. (Courtesy of Weyerhaeuser Co.)

Wood for ships, often rugged terrain, excellent harbors, and a warm current offshore conducive to the growth of sea life: all of these factors have conspired to force men to go to sea as fishermen, and the fishing industry and the maritime heritage as evidenced in extensive merchant marines and seaborne foreign trade are well represented. Today, trade is tied intimately to manufacturing, and Western Europe particularly stands out as one of the world's great industrial and commercial leaders.

To a degree, the broken coastlines of typical Marine West Coast climate regions are a result of climatic similarity. All of these regions with the same climate today are characterized by fiorded coasts. Here is evidence that in the past, all must have had a similar climate, which was cold enough to support ice at sea level, for fiords are a result of ice erosion. It is a rare situation where in examining a present-day physical map, we can find evidence of climatic similarity by merely looking at the coastal character. Alaska, British Columbia, Puget Sound, Scotland, Norway, southern Chile, Tasmania, and the South Island of New Zealand all have fiords, evidencing past climatic similarities, and all display a Marine West Coast climate today.

Middle Latitude Dry. The Middle Latitude Dry climate is very similar to the Tropical Dry, so similar in fact that many classifiers lump all the dry climates together as one. Furthermore, the areas involved in the Tropical Dry climate and those of the Middle Latitude Dry are adjacent and merge almost imperceptibly one into the other so that there are inherent difficulties in deciding exactly where to separate them. But, aside from the obvious locational differences between the Tropical Dry and the Middle Latitude Dry, they are the results of entirely different causes and there is one major difference between the climates. We will regard them as separate climates, although we must recognize their many similarities.

Since the middle latitudes are essentially the Westerly belt, any dry climate occurring here must be away from the west coast. The North American representative comes very close to the west coast but is east of the high and continuous Sierra Nevada–Cascade chain, so that it is in a rain-shadow position and the moisture off the sea is precipitated in heavy amounts on the Marine West Coast seaward slope of the mountains. Here is one of nature's sharpest lines: up to 200 inches of rainfall on the windward slope, while such places as Wapato, Washington, immediately in the lee of Mt. Rainier, and the Owens Valley, California, in the rain shadow of Mt. Whitney, receive 5 inches. The entire area between the Sierra Nevada–Cascades and the Rockies averages only 10–15 inches. But this is only half the total dry region, for although the Rockies attract some increased moisture through orographic lifting, in their rain shadow on the high plains, it is dry once again. It has been traditional to regard the 100th meridian running through the Great Plains as the 20-inch rainfall line in the United States; that is, west of this line, the precipitation is less than 20 inches. To the early pioneers, here was the beginning of the Great American Desert, and it is so labeled on many old maps. We know now, of course, that the true desert lies much farther west, but in our classification here as in the Tropical Dry, we will include the semiarid regions with the true desert, since water is the critical factor in both. Thus, it becomes convenient to designate the 20-inch rainfall line as the eastern margin of the Middle Latitude Dry climate.

A second and even larger Middle Latitude Dry region is encountered in interior Eurasia. It is in the same general latitudes of that in North America but much farther removed from the west coast. In Europe, it will be recalled, no continuous mountain chain parallels the coast to sharply limit all the moisture to a narrow littoral. Consequently, the Marine West Coast in northern Europe merges into somewhat drier climates farther inland, but the decreased receipt of Atlantic moisture with distance eastward is such a gradual process that a 20-inch rainfall line is far back into the interior of the continent. The western margin of the Middle Latitude Dry is in the southern Ukraine, and from there it stretches eastward into the Caspian Basin and Russian Turkestan, interior China north of the Tibetan Plateau, and even into parts of Manchuria and the North China Plain, almost to the east coast.

The only part of the Southern Hemisphere where a significant landmass is encountered in the middle latitudes is in South America, and even here the area is limited. But Patagonia (the southern half of Argentina) finds itself in the rain shadow of the Andes, which isolate the Marine West Coast region of southern Chile. Here is a close parallel to the situation in North America with the Middle Latitude Dry climate closely approaching the west coast.

Aridity is, of course, the chief cohesive factor in allowing us to classify all these regions together. It does not matter whether the moisture arrives in the summer or the winter, we make no distinction; the important thing is that there is not enough. A good deal of the Middle Latitude Dry is true desert, i.e., less than 10 inches per annum, but the fringing semiarid regions receiving up to 20 inches of precipitation are also included. One reason that a district with 15–20 inches of rain can be legitimately classified here is because of the typical erratic nature of its occurrence. As in the Tropical Dry zones, *the drier the climate, the less reliable the rainfall,* and this often means great difficulty in carrying on any reasonably sustained and coherent human land use. Yet all these precipitation characteristics

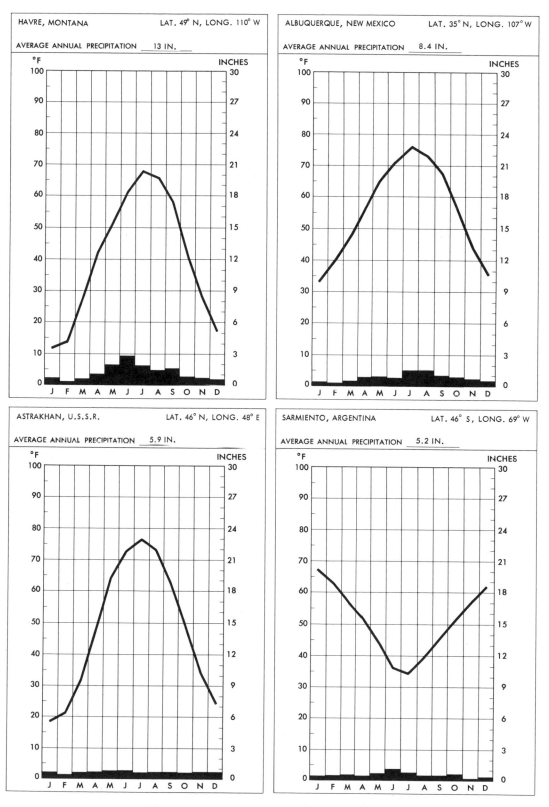

Fig. 4–25. *Middle Latitude Dry stations.*

fail to help us find a means of separating the Middle Latitude Dry regions from those of the Tropical Dry, for they are essentially similar. It remains for a certain dichotomy of temperature to aid us in this endeavor.

Winter temperatures in the heart of the Middle Latitude Dry regions, especially in the Northern Hemisphere where continental air masses dominate, are well below freezing, and precipitation is in the form of snow. This is a far cry from the Tropical Dry where cold-month averages are typically in the 50°–60° range. In eastern Montana or Chinese Sinkiang, winter days are frequently far below zero. Here is what makes the middle latitudes a different world from the tropics. On the other hand, summers are hot, often excessively so; but in the Middle Latitude Dry, they are neither as hot nor of as long duration as in the Tropical Dry. Averages run in the neighborhood of 75° for the hottest month. Nights are cool, reflecting the low humidity; and even in the winter, days may be a great deal warmer than the nights. (Fig. 4–25.)

Temperatures then, particularly in the winter, are the strong divisive element between the Tropical Dry and the Middle Latitude Dry, yet in the zones where these two dry regions merge, there is an extensive area where temperatures take on a median character somewhere between the extremes of the tropics and the middle latitudes. In northern Mexico–southern New Mexico, Iran, Iraq, Syria, northwestern Argentina, and in parts of southern Africa and Australia, we encounter a dry climate, but one whose temperature characteristics are not quite typical of either Tropical Dry or Middle Latitude Dry. Winters, for instance, average just above freezing and summers are in the low 80's. This is further complicated by upland plateaus, as in Chihuahua and Iran, while not high enough to be disregarded as mountains yet slightly affect temperatures. Classifiers have always had difficulty drawing a separating line through this territory. One solution is to establish an entire new classification and call it "Subtropical Dry." The problem is that this is an "almost but not quite" region, and such a climate lacks character of its own to strongly distinguish it from its neighbors. The plan followed here is simply to draw a line at a midway point through this zone of merging. Recognize that such a line is somewhat arbitrary, and although this border region is often thoroughgoing desert, it is a transitional band between Middle Latitude Dry and Tropical Dry.

As in all dry regions, water is the critical factor in allowing human habitation on any significant scale. To a large degree, the geography of the western United States, for instance, is oasis geography. (Fig. 4–26.) Yakima, Salt Lake, Reno, and the lower Colorado are all densely populated oases, but in between these limited and widely

Fig. 4–26. *An oasis in the Middle Latitude Dry region near Boise, Idaho. The canal in the foreground carries irrigation water to a limited valley area. Notice the contrasting aridity of the hills. (Courtesy of U.S. Bureau of Reclamation.)*

scattered favored spots are extensive regions essentially unpopulated, although here and there rich mineral deposits support some activity despite a lack of water. But the semiarid desert margins, unlike most comparable regions in the tropics, have been made reasonably productive. Grazing has been traditional (Figs. 4–27 and 4–28), but large-scale grain farming, especially wheat, has taken over extensive areas. The reasonably good accessibility to the middle latitude urban markets is probably largely accountable for the greater development of agriculture, relative to the roughly similar tropical situations, but this is far from ideal agricultural land. Both the high plains of North America and the "virgin lands" in the U.S.S.R., as examples, have suffered from recurrent drought, and they have had a continuous history of all too frequent crop failure. There are those who claim that these regions are not agricultural land at all and should be maintained in permanent grass with even grazing controlled to conform to the inevitable rainfall cycles.

Fig. 4–27. *Semiarid grazing in Argentine Patagonia. (Courtesy of Panagra.)*

Fig. 4-28. *When the winter range is frozen and snow-covered, as here in eastern Colorado, supplementary feed must be distributed to the animals to assure survival. (Courtesy of Union Pacific Railroad.)*

Humid Continental. The third middle latitude climate is the Humid Continental, in much the same latitude as the Marine West Coast and the Middle Latitude Dry. It is encountered, however, only in the Northern Hemisphere, for even South America does not exhibit sufficient mass for its full development in the Southern Hemisphere. In North America, virtually the entire northeastern quarter of the United States and adjacent Canada is involved. Its southern boundary is the Humid Subtropic, its western boundary is the 20-inch rainfall line or the Middle Latitude Dry, and its northern border is essentially the northern limit of agriculture dictated by shortened growing season. There is a finger of the Humid Continental that pushes far to the west, north of the Middle Latitude Dry. Lesser evaporation offsets the slightly lesser precipitation, allowing this region to be classified as humid.

In Europe, the Humid Continental is found immediately east of the Marine West Coast and it extends well into the interior of the U.S.S.R. The area involved is in the shape of a triangle with its broad base to the west. Southern Sweden, all of Germany except the North Sea Coast, Czechoslovakia, Hungary, and the Po River Valley of northern Italy form this base, while to the east, southern Finland, Poland, Romania, and much of European U.S.S.R. are included. The tip of the triangle is north of the Middle Latitude Dry region and pushes as far east as Lake Baikal.

There is another smaller triangle-shaped area classified as Humid Continental in the Far East; this one has its base along the sea. Most of North China and Manchuria east of the Middle Latitude Dry is included, as are North Korea and the northern one-half of Japan. The triangle's tip is north of the Middle Latitude Dry region and follows the Amur Valley inland to Lake Baikal.

The word "humid" in connection with this climate means an average precipitation of about 30 inches, although there are variations from 20 inches at the fringe of the semiarid to over 50 inches near the sea. But nowhere is the receipt of rainfall during the growing season too slight for agriculture. In the winter, the bulk of the precipitation is of cyclonic origin from the usual frequent westerly storms and much of it is snow. Summer rainfall, on the other hand, occurs most commonly as convectional showers. There is a general tendency for summer and winter precipitation to be approximately equal near the coast (except the Far East), but for both lesser totals and a greater concentration in the summer with increased distance inland. This is explained by the winter dominance of the dry cold continental air masses of the interior from which only limited amounts of moisture are derived. The Far East, even this far north, still strongly reflects the influence of the monsoon, so that strong summer maximums are the rule and winters are almost dry despite occasional winter cyclones. However, Japan, because of its insularity, receives heavy winter snowfall. This pattern of winter cyclonic precipitation and summer convectional showers with no well-defined dry season is reminiscent of the Humid Subtropics, but the annual totals are somewhat less and a good deal more snow is involved.

The word "continental" appearing in the climatic title has definite temperature implications. It is the opposite of "marine," which means amelioration by the sea of both summer and winter temperatures and a resulting small annual range. Continental has inherent within it the concept of continental control of temperatures—radical cooling in the winter and heating in the summer. And the air masses reflecting this large annual range give their character to the temperatures of the Humid Continental climate. Summers are hot and often sticky, as monsoonal influences bring in tropical oceanic air; nights cool off very little. These are the times when the Iowa farmer must rationalize that his corn is growing nicely even if conditions are far from ideal for human comfort. It may be a good deal cooler along the Baltic seafront or in Nova Scotia, and in the far interior the heat may be less trying because of drier air despite the high temperatures. But generally, the Humid Continental summers average 75° and are quite warm for their latitudes.

Winters are even more uncomfortable. Cold month temperatures must average below freezing in order to qualify as Humid Continental, and although near the coast, they may not be far below freezing, the humidity makes for a penetrating sort of cold. Inland it is drier but temperatures fall to averages of 10°–12° with a good many days below zero.

Basically, there are only two pleasant months each year—May and October, the transition periods. Indian summer is a glorious time and can be counted on virtually every October, but spring is often a transient affair so that if you wake up late some May morning it is entirely possible to miss spring altogether.

Because of its size and the relatively great variation within the region we call Humid Continental, it has become common to subdivide it on the basis of its agricultural potential. This was first done in the United States because of a very obvious "crop line" running east-west across much of the Middle West. The chief crop utilized as a climatic indicator was corn. South of a line drawn through southern South Dakota, southern Minnesota, southern Wisconsin, southern Michigan, the Ontario Peninsula of Canada, northern New York, and southern New England, the growing season is long enough for corn to come to full maturity in the field. (Fig. 4–29.) The line is very

Fig. 4–29. Modern equipment such as this harvester in Nebraska allows the American Middle West to achieve the highest yields and most efficient production of corn in the entire world. (Courtesy of International Harvester Co.)

Fig. 4–30. A bumper crop of spring wheat in the Humid Continental Short Summer climate of southern Saskatchewan. (Courtesy of Canadian Government Travel Bureau.)

sharp to anyone driving northward across, say, southern Minnesota and observing the fields. Winter wheat, too, adheres reasonably well to the same northern boundary, for its ability to survive in the field (already sprouted) through the winter is closely related to the severity of the winter temperatures. Spring wheat, planted in the spring, must replace it if winters are too cold for survival. (Fig. 4–30.) The line then largely depends on the length of growing season and, to a degree, severity of winter temperatures. We have given the names (subdivisions of the Humid Continental) "Humid Continental Long Summer" to the region south of the line and "Humid Continental Short Summer" to that part north of the line.

In Europe, although corn is less common, an identical line may be recognized separating the Danube Basin, northern Italy, and the southern Ukraine from the remainder or more northerly portion of the Humid Continental. And in the Far East, it runs through southern Manchuria, North Korea, and between Honshu and Hokkaido in Japan. (Figs. 4–31 and 4–32.)

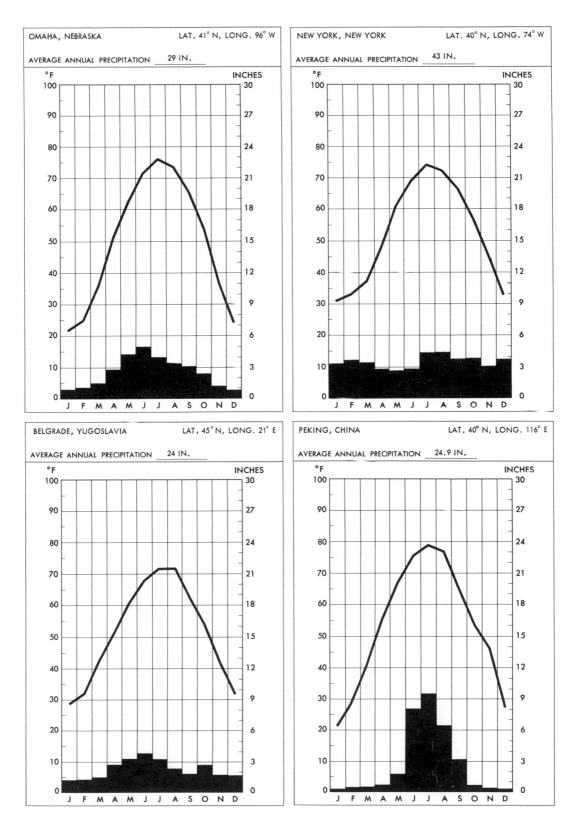

Fig. 4-31. *Humid Continental Long Summer stations.*

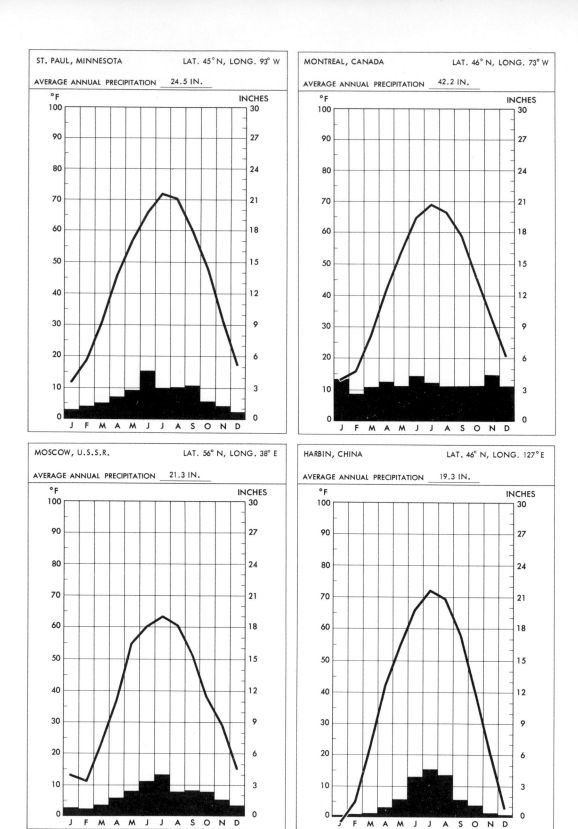

Fig. 4–32. *Humid Continental Short Summer stations.*

Agriculturally, this is a permissive climate, but mere permissiveness is not enough to account for the general large-scale development that has taken place. There is a close relationship to the rise of urban markets and their increasing needs for food. Sea frontage in North America and especially Japan in the Far East has encouraged the growth of large cities based on foreign trade, and in maritime Europe, a similar development has drawn large parts of the adjacent Humid Continental region into its hinterland. But trade is not the only impetus to urbanization; industry too has played a leading role—industry based in large part on coal. It appears that at some period in the distant past, the entire middle latitudes was under the influence of a wet tropical climate, and the accumulation of thick beds of decomposing vegetative material built up in numerous swampy situations. This was embryonic coal, and subsequent pressures eventually formed this into extensive deposits of high-quality coking coal. Not all of today's good coal fields are within the Humid Continental climatic regions but many are: the Appalachians, East Germany, Poland, the Ukraine, Kuznetsk (Siberia), and southern Manchuria. Others are nearby, and this coal availability has led almost inevitably to the establishment of large-scale manufacturing. (Fig. 4–33.)

Fig. 4–33. Attempting to hurry spring a bit, iron ore ships push their way through the ice on Lake Superior. The long cold Humid Continental winters completely disrupt the normal flow of traffic by icing up the lakes for several months. (Photo from Dwight Boyer, Cleveland Plain Dealer—courtesy of U.S. Steel Corp.)

Some have said that the fluctuating temperatures and humidity of the Humid Continental climate are invigorating and responsible for a particularly vigorous human response, as opposed to the enervating effects of the tropics. Others have held that the undeniable development within this region has been accomplished despite a thoroughly uncomfortable climate. Whatever the cause, some parts of the Humid Continental, especially in North America, must be counted as among the most advanced regions in the world.

High Latitude Climates (Fig. 4–34)

In the high latitude climates, we are essentially beyond the limits of agriculture and practically beyond the limits of human occupation as well. These are virgin lands, almost untouched except in a few particularly favored spots. In this aspect, the high latitudes are not unlike large parts of the world's dry regions and the Tropical Rain Forest, and the climate is largely responsible. Long, cold winters are the basic restrictive factor. Because of their unattractiveness to man

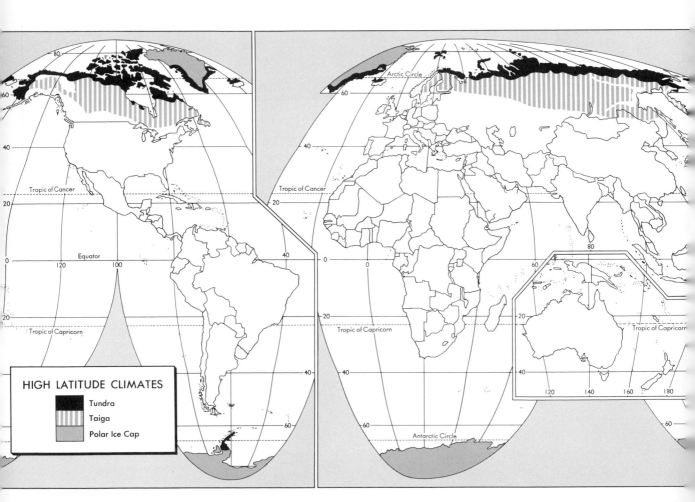

Fig. 4–34. High Latitude climates.

and their general inaccessibility, the high latitude climates have not been studied with any degree of thoroughness. Recording stations are completely lacking over huge areas, and thus data are limited. Only recently has there been any organized effort to understand these climates, and an immense amount of work remains to be done.

We recognize three high latitude climates; the first two of them are largely restricted to the Northern Hemisphere. They are (1) the Taiga, (2) the Tundra, and (3) the Polar Ice Cap.

Taiga. "Taiga" is a term referring to the distinctive type of vegetation that is characteristic of this climate just as Tropical Rain Forest was used earlier. It is an open forest made up of a distinctly limited group of conifers, and its occurrence is exactly coincident with the boundaries of the climate. Details of the forest makeup are discussed in Chapter 5, but its importance here is to emphasize that only a highly specialized vegetative complex is capable of survival within a region dominated by the rigorous Taiga climate.

The North American representative of the Taiga is a long, relatively narrow, band extending clear across the continent between roughly 50° and 60°N latitude. But, although it closely approaches the west coast in Alaska, it does not quite reach it, nor does it touch the north coast anywhere except along the margin of deeply indenting Hudson Bay. Only at the Atlantic shore, in Labrador, does the Taiga reach the sea. Thus, it is a continental climate and exhibits typical continental tendencies.

At very similar latitudes, a comparable belt of Taiga extends across the much larger Eurasian continent, again touching the sea only at its eastern extremity. From northern Sweden and Finland to Kamchatka on the Pacific Coast, the Taiga region stretches for over 5,000 miles, and for most of that length shares a common southern boundary with the northern edge of the Humid Continental climate as it does in North America.

Outstanding in the Taiga is the dominance of winter. Not only is it long (eight to nine months) but for many years the Taiga was thought to be the coldest region on earth. Verkhoyansk, a mining community in east-central Siberia, has recorded a minimum temperature of −92°; however, just a few years ago an even colder temperature was recorded at the South Pole, and it may be equally cold at the top of Mount Everest. Notwithstanding, winters are excessively cold in the Taiga, averaging far below zero. In contrast, summers are surprisingly warm despite their short duration. Fairbanks, Alaska, experiences a few daytime temperatures in the 90's nearly every year. Generally, the hottest month average throughout the Taiga is close to 60°, making at times a 100-degree annual range, by far the largest in the world. (Fig. 4–35.)

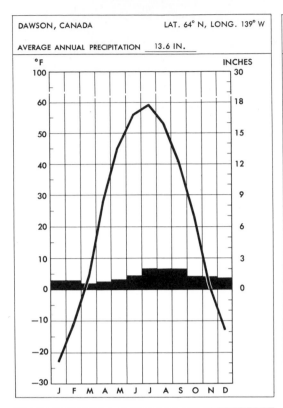

DAWSON, CANADA — LAT. 64° N, LONG. 139° W

AVERAGE ANNUAL PRECIPITATION   13.6 IN.

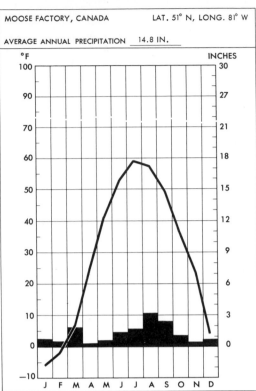

MOOSE FACTORY, CANADA — LAT. 51° N, LONG. 81° W

AVERAGE ANNUAL PRECIPITATION   14.8 IN.

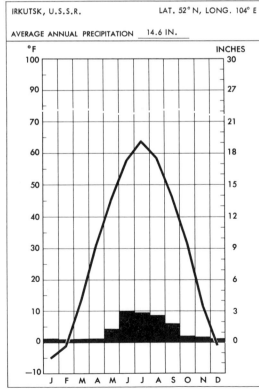

IRKUTSK, U.S.S.R. — LAT. 52° N, LONG. 104° E

AVERAGE ANNUAL PRECIPITATION   14.6 IN.

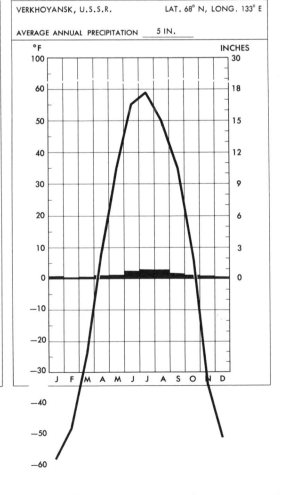

VERKHOYANSK, U.S.S.R. — LAT. 68° N, LONG. 133° E

AVERAGE ANNUAL PRECIPITATION   5 IN.

Fig. 4–35. *Taiga stations.*

Because these far northerly continental interiors are the home of polar continental air, there is very little moisture available throughout much of the year. Snow falls in limited quantities, but it is dry and powdery. There is an illusion here regarding total amounts; actually, snowfall is very modest. But since no melting occurs for months at a time, the entire winter's receipt is visible all at once, a situation that does not prevail in many areas where snowfall is much heavier. In addition, dry snow is readily picked up and whirled around by high winds, so that blinding blizzards may actually be contributing very little new snow. Drifting, too, against obstructions of any kind in the path of the wind is common. So, although snowfall is not excessive, it is difficult to convince a man who is forced to dig his way through an 8-foot drift to get out of his house that this is the case. Actually, when the total annual fall of this powdery snow is melted down to be measured in inches of moisture, it amounts to very little. By far, the greatest moisture comes in the form of rain from widely scattered summer convectional showers. Precipitation totals average 5–15 inches, which would indicate desert areas in most parts of the world, yet this precipitation supports forests here. But the greatly decreased evaporation at these high latitudes plus the fact that the bulk of the rain is concentrated during the short growing season allows tree growth.

Who would choose to live in a climate like this? Apparently not very many, for it is populated only thinly and sporadically. The agriculturalist is conspicuously absent, but the miner is there. Iron in Sweden, gold in Siberia, and uranium in Canada—these attract people. And the forests, although the trees are not large and regenerate themselves very slowly, can be exploited. So far, only in a few places is forestry profitable, and this is chiefly along the populated fringes as in Scandinavia and Quebec. (Fig. 4–36.) One indication of the remoteness of the Taiga is that it is the last stronghold of the fur trappers; cold winters produce fine pelts. But if animals still abound, there cannot be many people.

Tundra. Once again, we have a vegetative title drawing attention to the specialization involved in plants that are able to grow and flourish under the restrictive influences of this high latitude climate. Trees, for instance, are absent, making the boundary between Taiga and Tundra the poleward limit of trees. Only certain sedges, wild flowers, low bush, and the primitive mosses and lichens are represented. These are all shallow rooted so that the permanently frozen subsoil is of no hindrance, can remain dormant during a long cold season, and can mature and produce their seeds with great rapidity once the short cool summer commences.

Fig. 4–36. Winter is the lumbering season in northern Sweden. Compare the size of these logs with those being taken out of the Washington forests. (Courtesy of American Swedish News Exchange.)

The Tundra is a coastal climate never extending very far inland. It involves the entire north coast of North America, including the Canadian Arctic Islands as well as the ice-free shores of southern Greenland. In Alaska, it is also found facing westward on the Bering Sea, and although the Aleutians and Alaska Peninsula are not highly representative, they are usually classified as Tundra since they lack trees. The Alaskan south coast, however, in the vicinity of Anchorage and Cordova, is neither Tundra nor Taiga and is probably best included with the Marine West Coast, although much too cold to be typical. A similar merging with the Marine West Coast takes place in northern Norway, and from there the Tundra fringes the entire north coast of Eurasia.

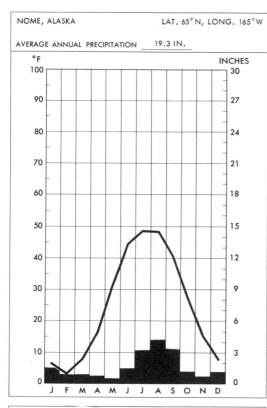

NOME, ALASKA — LAT. 65° N, LONG. 165° W

AVERAGE ANNUAL PRECIPITATION   19.3 IN.

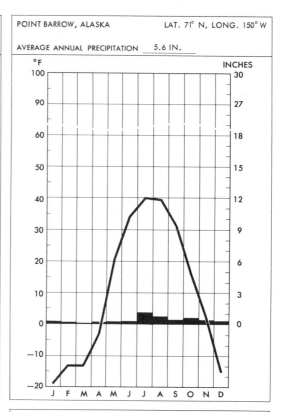

POINT BARROW, ALASKA — LAT. 71° N, LONG. 150° W

AVERAGE ANNUAL PRECIPITATION   5.6 IN.

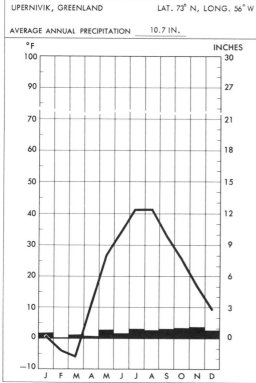

UPERNIVIK, GREENLAND — LAT. 73° N, LONG. 56° W

AVERAGE ANNUAL PRECIPITATION   10.7 IN.

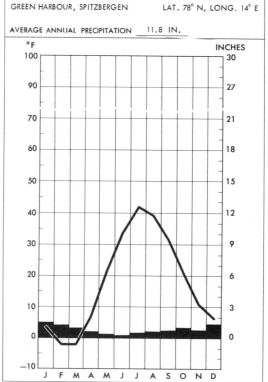

GREEN HARBOUR, SPITZBERGEN — LAT. 78° N, LONG. 14° E

AVERAGE ANNUAL PRECIPITATION   11.8 IN.

Fig. 4–37. Tundra stations.

Because of this coastal orientation, the Tundra displays certain marine characteristics. Marine has meant mild temperatures as opposed to continental in our previous usage, but in the Tundra the temperatures are far from benign. However, we must remember the latitudes involved here. Relative to these high latitudes and particularly when compared with the somewhat lower latitude but continental Taiga, the temperatures encountered in the Tundra are really quite moderate. The coldest winter month averages only a little below zero despite the fact that offshore waters are frozen much of the time. This may seem cold, yet the Taiga winters are usually a good deal colder. And summers are comparably cool, reaching a warm-month average of about 40°, approximately 20° less extreme than interior locations.

These short cool summers produce a phenomenon peculiar to the Tundra called *permafrost,* a permanently frozen subsoil; following the long winter, the hard frozen soils thaw to a depth of only a foot or so. With inadequate surface drainage, as is often the case in the flat to rolling Tundra terrain, and the solid ice beneath blocking any loss of moisture downward, the soil becomes a soupy mud. Alternating shallow ponds and quaking bogs, where tangled roots and matted vegetation "float" on the mud, make the summer tundra landscape a difficult one to traverse. Water is everywhere despite a low receipt of annual moisture amounting to only 5–15 inches. As in the Taiga, most of this comes as summer rain, some as convectional showers, but some from Arctic Front storms that are also probably responsible for the occasional winter blizzards. (Fig. 4–37.)

Obviously, this is a difficult habitat for man, and traditionally the Lapp reindeer herders of Scandinavia (Fig. 4–38) and scattered groups of Eskimos, living chiefly off the sea, have been the only inhabitants. But today, a few scientific and military installations are intruding into the Arctic solitude and attempting to solve the problems of modern living under unique and adverse conditions.

Polar Ice Caps. The Polar Ice Caps are found in Antarctica and Greenland, the only high latitude land areas permanently covered by masses of ice of sufficient size to induce a distinctive climate. The Arctic Ocean too, in the immediate polar region, is frozen the year around and undoubtedly displays a similar climate, but we have agreed not to attempt a classification of oceanic climates, so this must be ruled out. By the same token, we have not classified highland climates, and much of interior Greenland and Antarctica is well over 5,000 feet; so, in the interest of consistency, only the relatively low parts of these ice-covered lands should be considered. Actually, however, so little specific data are known that it has been usual simply to make a few generalities and ignore the variations caused by elevation. Gradually,

Fig. 4–38. These Lapps in northern Scandinavia have adapted their way of life to the rigorous Tundra environment. They are wholly dependent on their herds of reindeer that manage to find browse on the ground moss, even when they must paw their way through the snow to get to it. (Courtesy of American Swedish News Exchange.)

climatic data are being gathered and eventually we will be able to introduce greater detail. (Figs. 4–39 and 4–40.)

Primarily, we know that the Polar Ice Caps are very cold. The old Little America station established by Admiral Byrd on shelf ice at the Antarctic continental margin has recorded a coldest month average of −34°. But more recently, a temperature reading near the South Pole indicated −127°. Since this is a minimum figure rather than an average and since the South Pole is nearly 10,000 feet in elevation,

Fig. 4–39. *Scientific establishments, such as this Navy outpost at Mc-Murdo Sound, occupy the empty wastes of Antarctica. Mount Erebus, an active volcano, is in the background. (Official U.S. Navy photo.)*

Fig. 4–40. *Only the whistling wind disturbs the eerie solitude of interior Antarctica. (Official U.S. Navy photo.)*

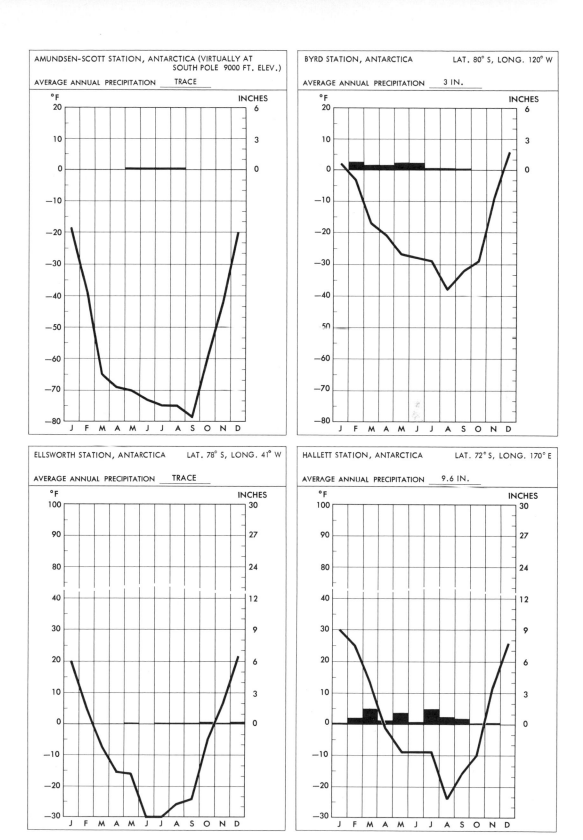

Fig. 4–41. *Polar Ice Cap stations.*

such a reading is scarcely typical. Probably, a winter average somewhere between the Little America and the South Pole figures would
be about right—colder than the Tundra and possibly even colder than
the Taiga. But of greater significance than the winter cold is the fact
that the warmest month averages do not reach as high as 32°. Even at
relatively mild Little America, the summer average is only 23°. This
means, of course, minimal thawing and a maintenance of the ice mass
despite low precipitation, and only slight possibilities of vegetation
even if soil were exposed.[5]

Precipitation has not been accurately measured, but it is unlikely
that the cold air masses are capable of giving off more than 10 inches
per annum, and this is in the form of dry snow and minute ice
crystals. (Fig. 4–41.) But since there is a constant loss of ice as these
great continental glaciers move out toward the sea, discharging bergs
at their periphery, there must be sufficient replacement through precipitation to sustain them. High winds and blizzard conditions are
more frequent here than in the Tundra, as accelerated air drainage
causes high-velocity gravity winds to blow down from the elevated
interiors.

[5] Certain lichens have been encountered on rocky outcroppings, so even here vegetation
is not absolutely lacking.

5

Natural Vegetation

Virtually the entire land surface of the earth supports some sort of vegetative cover. To be sure, ice fields, barren rocky outcroppings, sterile sand dunes, and alkaline salt flats are occasionally completely devoid of any growing plants, but these situations are relative rarities and excite some comment, for vegetation is the norm. And even here a close examination will often reveal that many rocks support mosses and lichens; certain salt tolerant plants will grow, albeit thinly, in highly saline soils; and the seemingly driest desert will, after a rare shower or even heavy fog, display a rapid flowering of long dormant but still viable spores. It is this natural vegetation that gives a certain distinction to our landscape so that we think not only in terms of terrain or climatic variation from place to place, but vegetational variation as well. Grassy plains, forested hills, or impenetrable jungle are part of our standard vocabulary in describing and transmitting to others the character of a given region.

The earth as a habitat for man is the prime concern of geography, and natural vegetation as an element in man's physical environment has long played an important role. For example: When the Spanish first attempted the occupation of central Chile, they found familiar Mediterranean open grassy and low brush country that reminded them of home. They understood a grazing economy based on this type of vegetation, and they discovered that the vine, grains, and olive introduced from Iberia flourished here. But as they pushed south into the increasingly forested littoral of southern Chile, they were repelled by the unfamiliar character of the country (and the Indians occupying it), and without the spur of gold to urge them on, they stopped abruptly at the forest edge. Many years later, German immigrants, familiar with a forest environment and the skills to cope with it, moved readily into the accessible portions of southern Chile and developed its latent resources. Their potato and dairy economy and their knowledge of forestry combined to make them feel very much at home in a region that appeared to the Spanish extremely inhospitable. Today, the high-gabled frame homes in forest clearings contrast strongly with the tile-roofed stucco and adobe dwellings in the villages of central Chile.

This is not to say that other factors are not as important, or even more so, as vegetation in controlling where and how man shall live. The very fact that vegetation can be removed or altered makes it a less-compelling determinant than climate or terrain, but it is a factor everywhere and a highly visible one, and certainly a part of the total physical environment that cannot be ignored.

In attempting to analyze and classify the vegetation of the world under the title "Natural Vegetation," we are, of course, immediately synthesizing the situation, for there is very little *natural* vegetation remaining. Everyplace that man has laid his hand, the original vegetation has been changed. He has cut the forests, plowed the prairies, drained the swamps, and introduced extensively new and alien vegetative varieties. There are sizable regions in China, India, and Europe where dense human occupation has been of such long standing that no general agreement has been reached today as to precisely what the original vegetation must have been. Even in lightly populated or wholly unpopulated areas, the balance of nature has been upset by the destruction of animals which were a part of the total ecological environment, or by the introduction of exotics (Australia's rabbits are a well-known example). Fire too, frequently of human origin, has caused noticeable variations. Nonetheless, we will make an attempt at classifying natural vegetation, partially because to catalog the pattern of farm crops around the world takes us out of the realm of strictly physical geography and into the myriad ramifications of economic geography, and more importantly because of the concept of *climax vegetation.*

CLIMAX VEGETATION

The idea behind the term "climax" is that, given a particular plant environment (especially climate and soil), the vegetation association that develops will display a certain character that represents an equilibrium with that environment and will continue unchanging indefinitely. However, if the original vegetation is destroyed or altered by man or nature, a rapidly growing secondary association of an entirely different type will spring up to replace it. But this is not permanent. These plants will establish a local environment that will encourage their replacement by a second series and these in turn a third, until finally this evolution of succeeding associations will culminate in the original climax vegetation which, if the basic environment continues static, will maintain itself. An example might be the destruction of a climax Douglas fir forest by fire. Almost immediately among the blackened snags and ashes, there will appear fireweed, rank grass, and bracken fern to be in turn replaced, as their very growth fosters conditions favoring them, by alder, willow, and blackberry. These too will establish a local environment that will allow still others to take their place, and so on through several stages until the Douglas fir complex is re-established. (Fig. 5–1.) This may take many years, but if the overall environment remains unchanged, the climax vegetation must reassert itself. Thus, if man and his influences were to disappear from the face of the earth, theoretically the original climax vegetation would take over everywhere. This, of course, is not absolute, and there are many places where man's work could not be undone entirely—and then too, no natural environment is wholly static. Nature is, in the long run, dynamic and changes are constant. However, it is the pattern of the initial natural vegetation, some substantially unchanged, elsewhere largely erased, that we will classify, describe, and analyze.

VEGETATIVE ASSOCIATION

All natural vegetation occurs in plant communities or "associations," each species mutually dependent on the others. In some associations, one species is strongly dominant and only a few others are represented, while elsewhere literally hundreds of species will occur. It may appear that a grassy savanna or a high latitude pine forest represents only a single species, but close examination will reveal that in the savanna, despite the dominance of rank grasses, many other plants grow among and below them, and that other trees and undergrowth are represented among the pines. There is a strong tendency toward storied or tiered vegetation:

1. Tall plants or trees requiring light
2. Those of intermediate height requiring somewhat less
3. Those hugging the ground and able to survive only in deep shade (Fig. 5–2)

This is universal in natural vegetation. Only in the case of planted field crops, where men expend great effort to eradicate weeds and competing plants, do large-scale stands of a single species prevail.

Fig. 5–1. *These four photos illustrate several of the stages involved in the evolution of a Douglas fir forest, destroyed by lumbering and fire, to the climax. In (A), the old stumps and snags are still visible amidst the tangle of two-year-old secondary brush. The return of the conifers, which are gradually crowding out the willow and alder, is shown in (B). The conifers are well established in (C) and are rapidly approaching sawtimber in size. And finally, in (D), the mature climax forest has fully re-established itself. (Courtesy of U.S. Forest Service.)*

(A)

(B)

(C)

(D)

(A) (B)

Fig. 5–2. *Both the association of several species and the common tiered character of vegetative communities are visible in these interior photos of two quite different forests. In (A), the largest boles and the tallest trees are Douglas fir, with white pine and western hemlock forming the second story of this Washington forest. Younger members of all these make up a third level, with several varieties of brush and fern at the floor. The same characteristics are apparent in an Indiana forest (B) where poplar and hemlock dominate. (Courtesy of Weyerhaeuser Co. [A] and U.S. Forest Service [B].)*

CLASSIFICATION OF NATURAL VEGETATION

There is an obvious very close relationship between the distribution of natural vegetation over the world and the distribution of climatic regions. It will be recalled that the climatologist Köppen utilized vegetation as perhaps his most important criterion in establishing climatic boundaries. Soil fertility too, as we will shortly discover, is largely a product of climate, and whether we regard vegetation as strongly reflecting the character of the soil in which it grows or the soil as being effectively modified by the vegetation growing in it (both being true), the fact remains that in terms of world distribution, a comparison of the climatic, natural vegetation, and soils maps will reveal striking similarities. Once again, we will make no attempt to classify the vegetation of the world's major mountains for the same reasons that we ignored them in the climatic classification—not because they are without vegetation, but because of the multitudinous variation. There is a general tendency for high mountains to display a vertical zonation of vegetation somewhat analogous to the latitudinal zonation that is typical of the rest of the world. But the complications introduced by windward slope vs. leeward slope, sunny slope vs. shady slope, etc., become so detailed that it is beyond the scope of this general treatment to do more than group them altogether as undifferentiated mountain vegetation.

The definitive lines on the map marking the boundaries of one vegetative type from another may be misleading, for there are few sharp lines in nature. Rather, as in climate, there are zones of transition or merging wherein one vegetative association changes gradually into another. Also, it should be kept in mind that in the interest of rational classification, although the actual botanical genus and species may vary widely from one continent to another, they can nonetheless be classified within the same vegetative category; that is, desert vegetation, wherever it is found, is sparse and has the special adaptations of root and leaf, allowing it to conserve a limited water supply. So, whether it is the sage brush of North America or the blue bush of Australia, we will include it within one grouping.

Basically, there are three types of vegetation associations: (1) forest, (2) grasslands, and (3) desert plants. It should not be startling news to anyone to be informed that forests are made up of trees. They may be evergreen or deciduous (dropping their leaves during one season of the year), broadleaf or needleleaf. Generally speaking, coniferous (cone bearing) trees are needleleaf and evergreen, while broadleaf trees may be either evergreen or deciduous. But as long as the vegetative type has a woody bole and grows to some height, it is a tree, and if trees are dominant in occurrence over other members of the association, it is called a forest.

Grasslands feature grass as the dominant. Bunch grass, short grass, long grass, rank grass (bamboos and canes), or sedges—they are all grass, and probably as a group are as widely represented as some member of a plant community as any vegetative type in existence.

The third category, desert plants, is made up of a wide variety of vegetative types, but whatever family or genus they may belong to, they must have special adaptations of moisture conservation and use to allow them to survive under conditions of limited moisture.

We probably can add still a fourth grouping here called Tundra. As will be described later in this chapter, these many species of plants, somewhat like those of the desert, must display certain special adaptations to deal with the particularly stringent environment that they occupy.

Vegetation Regions

Tropical Rain Forest (Selva).   As the name implies, the Tropical Rain Forest climate and the vegetative complex called Tropical Rain Forest are virtually identical in location. The Amazon Basin, Congo Basin, Guinea Coast, Ceylon, Malaya, most of the East Indies, and the large islands of Melanesia constitute one of the largest zones of nearly unmodified climax vegetation anywhere in the world, and certainly the greatest area of dense forest vegetation. In addition, the east coasts of continents and islands in the trade-wind zone and minor lesser regions are also clothed with this type of forest. It should be explained that in these minor lesser regions, the typical Tropical Rain Forest climate is not always absolutely necessary for the growth of a true Tropical Rain Forest. The galeria forest is of this type and is discussed a little later in this chapter. And in parts of the Guinea coast of west Africa, southeast coastal India, and the west coast of Burma and adjacent Pakistan, there is a dry season, and climatically these regions are classified as Tropical Wet and Dry. However, the rainy season is so very wet (200 or more inches of rain each year) that the soil never dries out, thus allowing the growth of Selva despite a definitely rainless period.

Stimulated by constantly high temperatures and heavy precipitation, vegetative growth is unceasing, and the resulting forest is of a particular type duplicated nowhere else on earth. Tall (150–200 feet) straight trees growing close together and reaching for the light, form a solid canopy far above the ground as their foliage coalesces. (Fig. 5–3.) In shadowy half-light below, branches fail to develop so that typically the bole is a featureless shaft flowering and producing leaves only at its upper extremity. The base is often buttressed or fluted to support the tree erect in the absence of a deep root system that does not have to search for water. (Fig. 5–4.) Lacking climatic seasons of any kind and supplied abundant moisture, these trees are broadleaf evergreens that continually regenerate their foliage and drop dead leaves. But the forest floor is remarkably clean because the hot moist climate fosters microbiotic decomposition at a rapid rate. Even fallen timbers are disposed of with dispatch by decay and a large array of termites.

Well beneath the dominant canopy, there is normally a sparse second story of shade-tolerant trees averaging only 25–50 feet in height.

Fig. 5–3. *Here, in the New Hebrides, only the coalescing crowns of the Tropical Rain Forest are visible from the air. (Courtesy of U.S. Navy.)*

This is their preferred habitat and they cannot survive if exposed to direct light. The common cacao from whose beans chocolate is made is one of these, and when it is planted in commercial plantations, great care must be exercised to assure it continual shade by retaining many of the taller trees when the forest site is prepared for plantation use. And finally, at the ground where the shade is deepest, few plants can survive. There is no underbrush as we know it in the middle latitude forests, and there are considerable expanses of bare soil. Rattan, a woody vine that runs along the ground, and a few low fernlike plants are the typical light vegetation. Lianas or climbing vines, which have the ability to cling to trees, can make their way upward to the light of the upper canopy, and one of the features of the forest interior is the many hanging lianas, like great ropes, draped among the trunks of the tall trees.

But notwithstanding this great frenzy of continued vegetational growth, the interior of the Tropical Rain Forest is relatively open

Fig. 5–4. *Flanged roots impart stability to a tree whose habitat is the wet tropics where it is not forced to develop deep tap roots to find adequate moisture. This is a kapok tree in the Virgin Islands. (Courtesy of U.S. National Park Service.)*

country and a distinctive world unto itself, with perpetual gloom, a dank and moldy odor, and still moist air. The active life zone is remote in the high canopy where arboreal animals and birds spend their entire life cycles and the trees flower and fruit. At the ground, where deep shade inhibits growth, there is no great difficulty in moving about from place to place, and the great myth of thousands of square miles of impenetrable jungle is just that, a myth. There is such a thing as a jungle and it is highly impenetrable, but it is merely a phase of the rain forest, limited to certain favored localities, and by no means dominant.

Jungles come about when light is allowed to reach the forest floor. If a storm or fire removes some trees causing a break in the canopy or, as is more frequent, if man opens a clearing to plant a garden, the ensuing light brings to life countless dormant seeds. Grasses, saplings, bamboo, and low brush take over very rapidly, and within just a few years the region is a dense tangle of interlocking vegetation. (Fig. 5–5.) Often, elements of the original planted garden, abandoned by migratory agriculturalists as the secondary growth becomes too rapacious to cope with, are found competing with the other species for survival. Left to itself, such a jungle will evolve eventually back to the original climax Selva. But if fire is utilized to repeatedly clear a given plot, it will usually develop into a semipermanent rank grass Savanna.

Fig. 5–5. *Bamboo is one of the most common of the many varieties of rapidly growing secondary vegetation that almost immediately choke any clearing in the Tropical Rain Forest.*

Many parts of Southeast Asia and Africa are visually distinctive because of the great frequency of these grassy openings in the forest. The dense grass strongly suppresses the establishment of tree seedlings, but presumably, given time, even this will finally revert to the climax vegetation as the rain forest slowly encroaches from all sides. This sort of thing is, of course, merely a temporary jungle, but given a situation such as a fairly steep slope where the trees at various levels do not have interlocking crowns, more light than normal will find its way to the forest floor and a permanent jungle will result. More common than this are riverine jungles which develop along the banks of streams wide enough to cause a rift in the overall canopy. Such dense vegetation, merely fringing the stream course for many miles, has given rise in the past to reports of dense jungle over extensive areas. Early explorers utilizing the waterways as the easiest means of penetrating the interior observed nothing but the densest of jungle from their craft and quite naturally assumed that the back country was of the same character. Even greater misconceptions came about when these travelers, still clinging to the streams, journeyed well beyond the margins of the rain forest proper. Here a dry season each year results in a much lighter, more open vegetation, but fringing the rivers where water is available to tree roots even during the annual rainless period is a continuation of the riverine jungle called a *galeria forest*. A true picture of the situation can be seen from the air during the dry season. The brilliant green of the galeria, only a narrow band faithfully following each turn of the river, pushes long fingers into the more open, brown-colored vegetation of the surrounding countryside. But voyagers on the river have no means of knowing that they have left the Tropical Rain Forest far behind.

Also permanent in nature are the coastal jungles where a dense wall of trees and underbrush faces out to sea at the inland margin of the beach sands. Many of the usual forest species are represented here, supplemented by vegetational varieties whose seeds have the ability to remain viable for long periods of time when immersed in seawater as they are transported longshore, or whose root systems can cope with some mild soil salinity, such as a number of the palms and casuarina. A variant on the coastal jungle is the frequently encountered amphibious mangrove. Its habitat is along swampy shorelines and extending, often miles out to sea, on gently shelving alluvial bottoms. The mangrove actually requires brackish water, preferably a few inches to 3 feet deep, and thus flourishes offshore, making it difficult to determine the exact point where land meets water. Its seeds are readily distributed by water currents, and the plant is equipped with aerial roots so that wherever the tips of drooping branches touch the water, they become rooted and establish a new trunk. The man-

Fig. 5–6. Mangrove is an important source of firewood on the island of Samar, Philippine Islands, where this photo was taken, as it is in many tropical regions. Here the tangled knees have been exposed to view at low tide, after the trees have been cut away.

grove can literally march out to sea and form the densest of jungles in a very short time. A further addition to this impenetrable tangle are the stilted roots or knees that push up a foot or two above the water to allow aeration of the root system. (Fig. 5–6.) A particularly favored site for the propagation of extensive mangrove swamps is at the mouth of a heavily silted stream. Here the shelving outer delta (if strong currents or high tides are not frequent) forms an ideal environment. The stream course itself is fresh water and thus maintains itself clear of vegetation, but the saline alluvial flats with their mangrove cover trap the new sediments in the quiet water of the swamp. Thus, mangrove jungles help to build new land above sea level. Having done so, they have destroyed their ideal environment and are gradually replaced by more orthodox land plants on the landward margin of the delta, while at the same time they push new growth continually out to sea. Also, because it draws its moisture requirement from the sea, mangrove is less dependent on the natural rainfall and like the galeria forest may expand well beyond the limits of the Tropical Rain Forest climate.

Aside from its amphibious habits, the mangrove is atypical of the Tropical Rain Forest in another respect—the entire jungle is made up of a single species. This may not seem particularly odd to those of us familiar to middle latitude forests where a single type of tree is often strongly dominant until we recall that the plant community is almost universal. And in the Selva, the number of individuals making up a community are likely to number in the thousands. There is probably no other widespread plant association with as many different species represented as the Tropical Rain Forest. So the mangrove is especially unique in this respect. One of the many difficulties in attempting to exploit the great economic potential of the Selva, be it rubber, Brazil nuts, or mahogany, has been the fact that none of these valuable trees grow in even small groves, much less forests.

The greatest area of untouched virgin Tropical Rain Forest is to be found today in the still lightly populated and inaccessible upper Amazon Basin. Elsewhere in the world, its occurrence is somewhat more spotty. Southeast Asia and much of Africa display the effects of man's hand to an increasing extent. Generally, where population pressures are heavy or along the great river valleys and accessible coastlines, secondary growth or permanent plantation development have changed the original vegetation. But in the backcountry, such as interior New Guinea, upper Amazonia, or Borneo, the virgin forest remains intact.

Tropical Deciduous Forest and Scrub. The climatic limit of the Tropical Rain Forest is, in nearly all cases, the beginning of a winter dry season. When its severity becomes sufficient to interrupt plant growth for even a short period each year, it is reflected in the character of the natural vegetation. Widespread tropical grasslands are the usual resultant of an extended annual dry period or erratic and unreliable rainfall from year to year. But where the moisture receipt is too great for continuous grass yet insufficient to support a true Selva, a variety of intermediate associations develop as a transitional phase, grouped rather loosely here under the general heading of Tropical Deciduous Forest and Scrub. The outstanding features of this broad classification are the continuing dominance of woody trees, a tendency toward more open country than in the Tropical Rain Forest, and a loss of foliage during the dry season indicating dormancy. (Fig. 5–7.)

In large parts of Southeast Asia and to a lesser extent in South America, Africa, and Australia, where rainfall is heavy and reliable, considerable forests of large trees occur. They are more widely spaced than in the Tropical Rain Forest and since their crowns do not coalesce into a continuous canopy, there is a fairly heavy development of bushy undergrowth. Brown and barren during the winter and admitting light to the forest floor, these deciduous woodlands have an altogether different appearance from the nearby Selva. Also, despite having represented among them some of the same species as in the Selva, there is a much greater tendency for the Tropical Deciduous Forest to display large stands of a single specie. Teak has been outstanding in this respect in Burma, Thailand, and adjacent regions, and because it is a valuable cabinet and construction timber, this has led to widespread forestry and some alteration of the climax plant community. Fire too is a hazard during the dry season and is believed to

Fig. 5–7. *This view in northern Transvaal shows an involved plant community featuring both evergreen and deciduous scrub. (Courtesy of Information Service of South African Railways.)*

have been a factor in limiting the occurrence of this type of forest over much larger areas of Africa and South America.

In regions of lower precipitation or where the dry period is more extended, true forest gives way to a great variety of scrub associations. To dignify such vegetation by the term "forest" despite the dominance of trees, as is sometimes done, is to evoke an image of something much more lordly than actually exists, for the trees are stunted and seldom reach heights of more than 25 feet. Most display the deciduous character in response to the dryness of their environment, but others develop xerophytic (moisture preserving) tendencies such as thick bark, small pulpy leaves, and protective thorns and maintain their leaves

the year round as evergreens. (Fig. 5–8.) Some trees, such as the flat-topped acacias of east Africa, spread out rather thinly with grass intervening and no brushy undergrowth. Some group themselves in groves with sizable grassy openings separating one grove from another. While still others, although fairly widespread as individuals, develop a dense thicket of thorny undergrowth. In northeastern Brazil, such an association called *caatinga* extends for hundreds of miles and is virtually impenetrable. The remarkable evergreen eucalyptus family of Australia (of which there are several hundred varieties adapted to nearly every climate on the continent) is found, along with acacia, in a virgin scrubby woodland that encompasses the whole of the north coastal region.

Altogether, the entire category of Tropical Deciduous Forest and Scrub represents a gradual change from the dense Selva of the Tropical Rain Forest climate region to the Savanna grasslands that occupy the heart of the Tropical Wet and Dry climate region. (Fig. 5–9.) Based on this concept of decreasing size of tree and denseness of undergrowth with increase of length of dry season, it would appear that the various types of deciduous tree and scrub vegetation should be arranged in bands parallel to the outer margin of the Selva. To a certain extent, this is the case, but less so than might be expected. Causative variables include: total amount of annual precipitation (not merely length of dry season), reliability of rainfall from year to year and season to season, terrain, soils, and, of course, the activities of man, particularly with respect to fire. The distribution map (Map II, pp. 408–9) illustrates these variations and emphasizes the difficulties

Fig. 5–9. *Here is still another of the many variations of South African tropical scrub. The palmlike trees in the foreground are cycads. (Courtesy of Information Service of South African Railways.)*

involved in assessing with any real integrity what the climax vegetation of large areas might actually be once man has occupied that region.

Savanna. The Savannas are tropical grasslands representing the drier phase of the Tropical Wet and Dry climate. Where moisture is insufficient to support, as the dominant plants, woody trees and bushes, the grasses take over. Only in a few places, however, are trees of one sort or another entirely absent, the Savanna normally featuring scattered acacia, palm, brush, or even giant cactus-like plants along the desert margin. In this respect and several others, the tropical grasslands are somewhat different from the more familiar middle latitude prairies. (Fig. 5–10.) The grass is taller and coarser, sometimes reaching heights of 10–12 feet, and during the long dry season, these sharp-edged blades become parched and harsh. Neither does the Savanna form a turf, but more typically is arranged in tufts or bunches with patches of soil visible in between. The sharply divisive wet and dry seasons control a vegetative rhythm, alternating between the tall rank brownish mature grass and the rapid growth of new green shoots with the onset of the summer rains. If adequate surface drainage is lacking,

Fig. 5–10. Tall savanna grass in the Llanos of interior Venezuela. The line of trees in the background is a dense galeria forest marking a stream course. (Courtesy of Venezuela Ministry of Development.)

this same rhythm is also reflected in an annual change from a dry drab landscape to one of flood and seasonal marsh. Late winter and spring are the fire season, usually deliberately set by the graziers and thereby encouraging a full and early sprouting of the new grasses. This common use of fire has made it difficult once again to precisely determine the boundary between the Savannas and the forest and scrub country —no two distribution maps are exactly alike. But authorities are in rather general agreement that the grasslands are expanding at the expense of the trees.

Much the greatest extent of unbroken Savanna occurs in a wide latitudinal band in northern Africa between the Congo Basin (where in places it abuts with the Selva) and the southern margin of the Sahara where short bunch grass begins to grade into Desert Shrub. The general term for this region is the "Sudan." Comparable zones, though somewhat smaller, are found in much of the veldt country of southern Africa, the Campos of interior Brazil, the Llanos of central Venezuela and adjacent Colombia, and a broad belt just south of the north coast of Australia. Lesser widely scattered pockets of tropical grasses, including even the Florida Everglades, are difficult to show at the scale of our map. (Fig. 5–11.)

In comparing the map of world vegetation distribution with the map of world climate regions, you will note that although only one type of vegetation (Selva) coincided with the Tropical Rain Forest climate, two distinctive vegetation complexes (Tropical Deciduous Forest and Scrub and Savanna) occupy the region of Tropical Wet and Dry climate. Once again, this serves to point up strongly the transitional character of this region between the very wet and the very dry within the tropics.

Desert Shrub. All desert plants must be equipped to withstand the vicissitudes of a harsh and stringent environment, and as a result they do not grow in any great profusion, individuals being widely scattered and nowhere forming a continuous mantle. It is amazing that a great variety exists throughout the world's desert regions. But nature has provided these plants with a number of special mechanisms to achieve survival in an almost waterless habitat, and there are only very limited regions that fail to support some kind of vegetative cover. (Fig. 5–12.)

The true desert begins where grass ceases to be dominant, but in the better watered regions and where precipitation is reliable, bunch grass persists, intermingled with shrubby vegetation. Many of the bushes and shrubs exhibit deciduous characteristics as a means of survival when rainfall is distinctly seasonal, and a large number of flowering annuals display the ability to mature and produce seeds within a very short time following periodic showers. But the largest

Fig. 5–11. *A marsh variant of tropical Savanna is shown near the northern limit of the tropics in the Florida Everglades. (Courtesy of U.S. National Park Service.)*

Fig. 5–12. *Emaciated eucalyptus, wizened wattle (acacia), and sturdy saltbush are all visible in this desert panorama in the Macdonnell Ranges of central Australia. Note the extensive areas of bare earth. (Courtesy of Australian News & Information Bureau.)*

group of desert plants is xerophytic, with special adaptations to conserve moisture or to get along on very little. The succulents, of which the many cacti are representative (Fig. 5–13) store water in their tissue, while other woody plants are equipped with small shiny leaves with hairy undersides to inhibit evaporation. Special root systems, thick bark, and salt tolerant capacities are means evolved by still others to combat aridity. Since we are including here the natural vegetation of both the tropical deserts and the middle latitude deserts, still another ability must be possessed by many of the plants—that of surviving severe winter frost.

Fig. 5–13. *An Arizona landscape featuring succulents and deciduous shrubs. (Courtesy of U.S. Forest Service.)*

Fig. 5–14. *This South African thorn bush has managed to find sustenance via its deep root system well out into the Kalahari Desert. (Courtesy of Information Service of South Africa.)*

Despite the popular image of endless vistas of rolling sand dunes as typical of deserts everywhere, the sandy regions without a vestige of vegetation make up only a very tiny part of the total desert area of the world. Most of it supports some kind of plant cover, and often in much richer variety than is generally appreciated, ranging from the spectacular saguaro cactus and Joshua trees which may grow up to 50 feet tall and appear from a distance as forests, to the simple lichens giving color to rocky outcrops. (Fig. 5–14.)

The Sahara and contiguous deserts extending through Arabia and the Middle East into Central Asia form what is much the largest dry zone in the world supporting Desert Shrub vegetation. Other, but lesser, regions include all continental west coasts in the trade-wind belt, pushing far inland in Australia, Patagonia (southern Argentina), and the Great Basin of North America.

Mediterranean Scrub Forest.   The rainfall of the Mediterranean climatic regime is adequate to support a fairly dense vegetation, even sizable trees, when it is remembered that it is heavily concentrated during the winter season when evaporation is low. But the summer dry season is long and often quite warm so that plants and trees taking advantage of the winter moisture must adapt themselves to withstand extended drought to assure survival. The deciduous habit and complete dormancy is a means of combatting seasonal aridity in the Tropical Scrub Forest, but the Mediterranean Forest is broadleafed and evergreen and cultivates a variety of xerophytic adjustments to resist drought. The cork oak with its thick bark, the eucalyptus with its deep tap root, and the California oak with its tiny leathery leaves are examples. (Fig. 5–15.) The entire plant community has a gray and

Fig. 5–15. An oak park, typical of much of non-agricultural California. This is the slow-growing live oak, adapted to the dry Mediterranean climate by its deep roots and tiny waxy leaves. (Courtesy of U.S. Forest Service.)

dusty appearance during much of the year as it continues to grow, but only very slowly, during the long summer. But with the coming of the winter rains, new shoots appear and the landscape takes on a somewhat greener aspect as the rate of plant growth accelerates. Winter frosts are not unknown, but they are usually mild and of short duration and seldom cause damage to the tender new buds.

Trees, although common in the Mediterranean Scrub Forest, are not dominant. They are usually encountered widely spaced or, in certain specially favored areas such as draws or seasonal water courses where deep roots can reach a higher water table, in limited groves. Moderate height and gnarled trunk and branches are typical. Oaks of many kinds are native to both North America and Europe and have been introduced successfully into the Southern Hemisphere. Conversely, the Chilean pepper tree with its grotesque bole and weeping habit, and several of the Australian eucalypti have been very popular in California and many parts of the Mediterranean Basin. These last trees grow taller, straighter, and more rapidly than most Mediterranean trees and are an important source of timber in western Australia. A few of the trees of the scrub forest, notably the olive, fig, and chestnut, have been removed from their native context and cultivated as important sources of food. Still another representative of the trees, found in small numbers in the scrub community, is the needleleaf evergreen. These trees, such as the digger and Bishop pines, giant redwood, and Lebanon and Aleppo cedars, are usually encountered along the slightly wetter foothill margins. Others, like the Monterey pine and cypress (pre-ice relicts) and the coast redwood, require the special environment of the low temperature and high humidity of the foggy coasts to survive in the Mediterranean climate.

But despite the wide occurrence of trees in the scrub forest, the dominant member of the plant community is a low woody brush understory, generally called chaparral (United States) or maquis (Europe and South Africa). (Fig. 5–16.) The many shrub varieties which make up this complex are beautifully adapted to their environment, with both deep roots to tap the summer water table and wide-spreading shallow roots to take immediate advantage of winter rains. They also spread themselves through sucker propagation from the roots and thus expand their domain in all directions. (Fig. 5–17.) In the mallee (scrub eucalyptus) country of southern Australia, they have proven almost impossible to eradicate short of the monumental task of digging out every involved root system. This scrub, often a tangled intertwined mass, is, however, very susceptible to summer fires, and if it is burned repeatedly may be succeeded eventually by grass. Large parts of California, especially the drier hills, are grass covered—brown in summer and green in winter with the colorful California poppy and blue lupine intermixed.

Fig. 5–16. *A* maquis *mantle caps the dry rocky slopes of the French Maritime Alps. (Courtesy of French Embassy Press & Information Division.)*

Inasmuch as the Mediterranean climate is limited in its distribution to mere coastal regions of the Mediterranean Basin and tiny west coast exposures poleward of the tropical deserts, the Mediterranean Scrub Forest is not a widespread association. And even within the Mediterranean climate regions, man has been in residence for such an extended period of time that a typical scrub forest in its virgin state is difficult to reconstruct or to encounter today.

Subtropical Coniferous Forest. There is only one locality in the world where coniferous trees are the dominant species within the subtropics; that is in the southeastern coastal United States. An extensive region forested almost exclusively by several varieties of pine is found here. Stretching from Chesapeake Bay in the north, along the coast in an ever-widening band into eastern Texas, the coniferous forest appears to be strongly coincidental with the sandy soils of the low-lying coastal region. The deep alluviums of the Mississippi bottoms

Fig. 5–17. *French maquis goes by the name of* chaparral *in California. This dense thicket is 6 feet high. (Courtesy of U.S. Forest Service.)*

and the heavier soils of the interior support a mixed or broadleaf forest and, since these develop under what is essentially an identical climate as that of the coniferous forest (Humid Subtropic), the soil factor is almost certainly the basic determinant; that is, the vegetation is edaphically rather than climatically controlled. Furthermore, although the Humid Subtropic climate is found in every continent, only in a couple of these areas is there any hint of a true coniferous forest. In southern Brazil, there are some limited stands of Araucaria pine that may have been more extensive at one time. Today, they are found only at moderate elevations that slightly ameliorate the subtropical climate. South of this region, the grasslands of Uruguay and much of the Argentine Pampas are sufficiently wet to support trees, although they have not within historic time. Very probably, they did at one time before repeated fires wiped them out, but there is no way now of knowing whether or not these speculative forests were coniferous.

In Norfolk Island in the Southwest Pacific, the Norfolk Island Pine is found, and in the Auckland Peninsula of New Zealand, the famous huge Kauri pine. But these are scarcely forests.

Fig. 5–18. *A 65-year-old stand of loblolly pine in coastal North Carolina. The wide spacing of the trees and their limited girth are typical. (Courtesy of U.S. Forest Service.)*

Within the pine forest area of the southeastern United States, loblolly, yellow, and shortleaf pine are all represented, often mixed one with another. They grow fairly widely spaced and mature into a medium height tree of less than 150 feet tall. (Fig. 5–18.) Grass and occasional evergreen shade-loving broadleaf shrubs such as rhododendrons occupy a remarkably clean forest floor where heat and moisture promote the rapid decay of fallen needles and litter. One of the features of the subtropical evergreen forest has been its reproductive ability after the trees have been removed. And with the advent of technologies allowing the utilization of southern pine forest for a wide range of wood products, the regrowth of mature timber trees within 30 years after cutting (less for pulpwood) has given the southern lumberman a real advantage over his competitors. Much of this area has been in crops at one time, but impoverished soils and increasing demand for timber has led to extensive plantings of farm woodlots and reforestation of wastelands. Today, probably more of this region is in timber than at any time in the last 100 years.

Middle Latitude Coniferous Forest. Like the Subtropical Coniferous Forest, the Middle Latitude Coniferous Forest occurs only in North America. It appears to be a product of the Marine West Coast climate and is limited to a narrow coastal strip from northern California to southern Alaska. But there are other areas in every continent, except Africa, exhibiting a Marine West Coast climate, and although they are forested, conifers nowhere constitute the dominant species. Possibly the short summer dry season that shows up only in North America is responsible, but whatever the cause, our Pacific Northwest and adjacent Canada and Alaska support some of the world's heaviest forests. Not only are the trees huge, coast redwood and Douglas fir reaching over 200 feet in height and 30 feet in girth, but they grow very close together. (Fig. 5–19.) On the west side of the Olympic Peninsula and Vancouver Island, what might well be described as a Middle Latitude Rain Forest exists, with as heavy a vegetation growth as any Tropical Rain Forest. Under conditions of 150 to 200 inches of rainfall and mild year-round temperatures, the giant Douglas fir grows mightily. Below, an understory of western hemlock, dwarfed by the Douglas fir but a sizable tree in its own right, fills in the narrow intertrunk spaces. In some places, the ground cover is bracken fern that on occasion reaches 6–8 feet in height, or scattered fern is often interspersed with huckleberry, rhododendron, and other low herbaceous growth. In the less well-drained areas, western red cedar supplants the Douglas fir; and beneath the cedar-hemlock association, devil's club and skunk cabbage are common. This tangle of growing vegetation is rendered even more impenetrable by the accumulation of

Fig. 5–19. *Many of these virgin redwoods in northwestern California are over 200 feet high. (Courtesy of U.S. Forest Service.)*

moss-covered downed trees and windfalls that fail to decompose as rapidly as in the tropics. (Fig. 5–20.)

By no means does all of the North American northwest coast support this heavy a growth or even all of these specific plants and trees, but only minor variations on this are the rule. For instance, northern California features the redwood, while the Douglas fir fades out north of Oregon and Washington and spruce and hemlock take over. Also, since the mountains very closely approach the coast throughout most of the region, the forest changes its character in a regular sequence with gain of altitude. But remember, we are not classifying mountain vegetation and must draw an upper limit to the typical coastal forest,

Fig. 5-20. *One of the world's densest rain forests occurs along the excessively moist western slope of Washington's Olympic Peninsula. (Courtesy of Washington State Department of Commerce and Economic Development.)*

probably well below 1,000 feet. Certain portions of the Middle Latitude Coniferous Forest have been removed permanently as in the Willamette Valley and Puget Sound country, but in less accessible regions and the steeper hillsides, millions of board feet of timber remain despite commercial cutting and frequent summer fires. (Figs. 5–21 and 5–22.)

Fig. 5–21. *Mt. St. Helens looms over an extensive stand of old growth Douglas fir. The clean-block logging operation in the foreground is deliberately limited so that the surrounding trees will naturally reseed the cleared area. Helicopter seeding occasionally aids nature. (Courtesy of Weyerhaeuser Co.)*

Fig. 5–22. *Fire is always a threat during the summer dry season in the Pacific Northwest. (Courtesy of Kenneth S. Brown.)*

Middle Latitude Broadleaf and Mixed Forest. This type of forest, displaying many variations, occupies regions exhibiting three different climates—Humid Subtropic, Humid Continental, and Marine West Coast. All of these have in common relatively heavy precipitation, thus allowing the development of trees as the dominant vegetation.

In the United States, much of the South, inland from the sandy coastal plains, supports a deciduous broadleaf forest featuring an oak-chestnut association that in turn merges into, in the Middle Atlantic States and the Middle West, a quite similar oak-hickory or walnut-poplar woodland. (Fig. 5–23.) These are trees of considerable girth but only moderate height and, although they grow quite close together, do not form a canopy after the fashion of the broadleaf Selva.

Fig. 5–23. *Black walnut and yellow poplar, shown here in Hoosier National Forest, Indiana, are representative of the original Middle Latitude Broadleaf Forest in North America. (Courtesy of U.S. Forest Service.)*

A fair amount of light can reach the forest floor, especially since this is a deciduous forest, and the growth of saplings and young trees is thus encouraged. Brushy undergrowth is not dense, but windfalls and the accumulation of several inches of leaves, twigs, and general forest debris are typical. In poorly drained areas, swamp associations such as the cypress–red gum of the southern Mississippi River flood plain replace dry land forest and may cover many square miles with their jungle-like tangle of supporting brush and vines. (Fig. 5–24.)

Fig. 5–24. *The cyprus knees, a device to allow aeration of the roots for trees whose normal habitat is shallow water, in this South Carolina swamp are reminiscent of the tropical mangrove. (Courtesy of U.S. Forest Service.)*

North of this broadleaf deciduous forest, in the region of the Great Lakes and New England and roughly coincident with the Humid Continental–short summer climate, there is a gradual change to a mixed forest; that is, conifers begin to appear as individuals or in sizable groves or clumps among the broadleaves. Birch, beech, and maple take over from the oak and hickory; and various pines, spruce, and fir show darkly among them. (Fig. 5–25.) Sandy or rocky soils often are responsible for extensive stands of conifers, as in northern Michigan, New Jersey and Maine, while elsewhere they are much more generally intermingled.

Europe is somewhat a counterpart to North America in terms of correlating climatic regions to vegetative type except that the Marine West Coast climate here supports a broadleaf deciduous forest and the Humid Subtropic climate is lacking. Unlike the Marine West Coast climate of North America where coniferous forests predominate, western coastal Europe from northern Spain to southern Norway had an original, deciduous forest on the order of that of the eastern United States. Frequent conifers seen today are either at some elevation or (with the possible exception of the Landes region of southern France) have been planted to replace the slower-growing hardwoods. But the Humid Continental–long summer climate of northern Italy and much of the Danube basin corresponds to that of the United States in producing a broadleaf deciduous forest, and the Humid Continental–short summer regions of northern Europe are mantled by a mixed forest.

China, Korea, and Japan demonstrate quite clearly the general progression from broadleaf deciduous and semideciduous in the south to mixed forests in the north with increased severity of winter and shorter growing season.

Broadleaf and mixed forests are represented in the Southern Hemisphere although to a more limited degree. The narrow coastal strip of southern Chile, with its Marine West Coast climate, displays a dense broadleaf deciduous forest where beech is the dominant species, while along the Humid Subtropic coast of southeastern Australia, the ubiquitous eucalyptus, broadleaf but evergreen, is much the most common tree. (Fig. 5–26.) Pines, cedars, and a few deciduous species vary the dominance of the eucalyptus in Tasmania. New Zealand too, except for the grass-covered Canterbury Plain, supports a mixed forest of evergreens and deciduous trees, ranging all the way from the tremendous Kauri pine to tree ferns. (Fig. 5–27.)

Without a doubt, man has destroyed the Middle Latitude Broadleaf and Mixed Forest more thoroughly than any other vegetative type in the world—in places so successfully that the character of the original climax vegetation is mere conjecture. In northern China, where for

Fig. 5–25. *A beech-hemlock mixed forest in Pennsylvania. (Courtesy of U.S. Forest Service.)*

Fig. 5–26. *A mature stand of Australian gum (eucalyptus) in Victoria. (Courtesy of Australian News & Information Bureau.)*

Fig. 5–27. *The dank rain forest on the west coast of New Zealand's South Island develops under conditions almost identical to that of Washington–British Columbia, but the conifers are not represented here. (Courtesy of New Zealand Government Travel Commission.)*

centuries not only the forests have been cut again and again but the roots systematically grubbed out for fuel, not a vestige remains. Soil erosion is, of course, inevitable unless some sort of crop or substitute vegetation is introduced to intercept the surface runoff. Reforestation is being pushed with considerable success in many parts of the world, not only to minimize soil erosion, but to make productive those steep slopes and rocky or sandy areas that are not used for other purposes. Northeastern United States, Europe, and China are heavily populated and timber-short and have long had to import wood products from other parts of the world or go without. Since the original forest was slow growing, replacement is usually with more rapidly maturing conifers. Even lightly populated New Zealand faced a recent timber shortage because her accessible forests would not reproduce themselves rapidly enough after cutting. They solved their problem and became a wood products exporter in a remarkably short time by planting heavily in the North Island with Monterey pine from California. (Fig. 5–28.) Curiously, in its native habitat, this tree has never been even remotely regarded as a timber tree, and yet halfway around the world, in an entirely different climatic setting, whole forests of merchantable trees developed in 20–30 years.

Fig. 5–28. *The fast-growing California Monterey pine has been planted widely in northern New Zealand to furnish sawtimber. (Courtesy of New Zealand Government Travel Commission.)*

Middle latitude steppe and prairie. Once again, here in the middle latitudes as in the tropics, grasslands show up as transitional vegetation between the climates that are moist enough to support vigorous tree growth and the deserts with their moisture deficiency. The tall grass prairie is adjacent to the forest, and they frequently interdigitate with fingers of tree-lined streams pushing well out into the prairie, while grassy openings become common along the forest margin. The prairies themselves feature grass averaging 2 feet high, although in places reaching well over that, with the root systems merging into a solid turf. Many lesser herbaceous plants are represented in the prairie also, some of them with showy annual flowers, but woody growth is distinctly lacking, and a prairie landscape is one of endless vistas of waving grass. (Fig. 5–29.)

Fig. 5–29. Tall grass prairie in Nebraska. (Courtesy of U.S. Forest Service.)

Fig. 5–30. *Low bunch grass interspersed with sagebrush near Big Butte, Montana, marks the margin between steppe and desert. (Courtesy of U.S. Forest Service.)*

As the margin of the desert is approached, the height of the grasses decreases to 6 or 8 inches and the species change, but the turf continues. This short grass prairie is commonly called steppe.[1] Generally, when bunch grass and woody scrub with bare soil between make their appearance and the continuous turf no longer is in evidence, the dry margin of the steppe has been reached. (Fig. 5–30.) Such grasses as the distinctive American buffalo grass are typical of the steppe, although if overgrazing is allowed, they often are gradually replaced by a less-nutritious secondary growth that does not change the appearance of the grassland but is not the climax vegetation.

[1] Obviously, in the tropics too, the height of the grass is lower as precipitation lessens and a kind of steppe develops, but since the term was first applied in Russia to describe a middle latitude short grass prairie, its use has been confined to that particular type of vegetation.

In North America, the prairie coincides with the drier western part of the Humid Continental climate region, while the adjoining steppe is found in the moister eastern fringe (chiefly east of the Rockies) of the Middle Latitude Dry climate. This gives us the world's largest continuous middle latitude grassland from Alberta and Saskatchewan south almost to the Gulf. Minor outliers occur in the Washington Palouse country and in eastern Texas. Almost as large a region is found stretching from Hungary through the Ukraine and vicinity and north of the Caspian Sea in a long narrow band far into central Siberia. Sizable outliers occur in Anatolia and Manchuria. The situation in Argentina, Uruguay, and southern Brazil has already been discussed, but this has been prairie as long as western man has known it and must be so classified. Australia exhibits a large region of middle latitude intermixed scrub and grassland in the interior southeast (chiefly New South Wales and Queensland) and small areas of prairie occur in the Orange Free State of South Africa and in New Zealand. (Fig. 5–31.)

Fig. 5–31. *The snow-capped New Zealand Alps form a backdrop for a "mob of woolies" enjoying the lush tussock of the eastern foothills. (Courtesy of New Zealand Government Travel Commissioner.)*

Fig. 5–32. *The Taiga of northern Sweden sweeps endlessly past the horizon. (Courtesy of American Swedish News Exchange.)*

The long grass prairie has proved to be a highly productive agricultural region since man has acquired the implements to break the heavy turf. As might be expected, the food grasses, chiefly corn and wheat, predominate. The steppe, on the other hand, with both its lesser total moisture and cyclic precipitation pattern has been traditionally a grazing area, although with improved techniques, small-grain agriculture is at least partially successful. This means that in terms of existing unmodified steppe and prairie today, there are few places in the world where either the plow or overgrazing has not wrought considerable change.

Taiga (boreal forest). The Taiga is the world's greatest forest, at least in terms of area involved, for it stretches in a wide band the entire breadth of North America from Alaska to Labrador and across the much greater breadth of Eurasia from Scandinavia to Kamchatka. And it is virtually a virgin forest, partially because of its remoteness from major population centers and partially because of the character of the trees as potential sawtimber. Only along its periphery has commercial lumbering modified the climax forest to any significant degree. (Fig. 5–32.)

The Taiga is basically a coniferous evergreen forest made up of a relatively small number of species. Extensive stands of spruce, fir, and pine are common in North America, while pine dominates the Eurasian forest except for a large area in northeastern Siberia where larch, a rare deciduous conifer, prevails. The extremely long cold winters and limited growing season are not an ideal habitat for trees, and those few species that do exist are simply the ones that have demonstrated their ability to survive. As a result, the trees are small, even stunted, seldom reaching over 50 feet in height and 8–10 inches in diameter. Widely spaced, the pointed conifers do not form a high canopy, but the receipt of light at lower levels allows the development of branches and foliage well down the bole, and these skirts tend to coalesce and form what amounts to a low canopy effectively cutting out light at the forest floor. Thus limited by lack of light and cold temperatures, undergrowth is very sparse. A thick carpet of needles and many dead branches and downed trees demonstrate the very slow rate of decay of organic material in the absence of high temperatures. (Fig. 5–33.)

Fig. 5–33. A few paper birch appear among the white spruce in this interior forest view near Fairbanks, Alaska. The small size and wide dispersion of individuals are characteristic of tree growth in these northerly latitudes. (Courtesy of U.S. Bureau of Land Management.)

This accumulation of trash plus the resinous character of the trees make the Taiga highly susceptible to fire, and each summer forest fires burn over extensive areas. Secondary growth of aspen, alder, and birch appears out of place among the dark conifers and, if left undisturbed, will eventually be succeeded by them. But growth is slow, relegated to just a few summer months each year, and the rate of replacement in the high latitudes forests contrasts strongly with that in the tropics.

Bogs too are common: the famous quaking muskegs. Much of the region has been glaciated, and ponds resulting from disrupted surface drainage are slowly filled in by mosses and aquatic plants growing toward the center from the periphery. As their roots entwine and accumulate silt, amphibious sedges and bushes find a foothold and gradually solidify the whole. At this stage when one steps onto such a vegetative island, the entire mass trembles, hence the quaking muskeg bog.

In some other places, notably the Ob River Valley of western Siberia, northward flowing streams that are frozen during the winter maintain the ice at their mouths long after the upper courses have thawed. The blocked mouth thus causes the river to overflow each spring and the formation of seasonal swamps over large areas which prevents the establishment of normal forest. Coarse grasses, sedges, and spotty low brush are the result.

Also, in the regions that have suffered severe glaciation, as in much of Quebec, bed rock has been exposed at the surface. Although the trees display remarkable tenacity in attempting to establish their roots in cracks and crannies where even a little soil may be available, true forest occurs only in scattered pockets between the expanses of barren rock. This is a patchy forest, if a forest at all, and locally breaks up the general Taiga landscape of endless trees extending out beyond the horizon.

Within the Taiga, the largest trees and the better-developed forest are found along the southern fringe, gradually deteriorating until in the far north trees fade out or mature into mere saplings. This is not because the winters are colder, for the trees are dormant in any case and whether the temperature is 30° below zero or 50° below zero makes little difference. Rather, the controlling factor is length of growing season and summer heat. Both of these decrease with distance north and it is reflected in the vegetation.

Tundra. Now we have gone beyond the tree line, roughly analogous to climbing a high mountain, through the forest to its upper margin. Between this tree line and the permanent snows of the mountain peak is a vegetation zone that is very similar to and developed under condi-

Fig. 5–34. *A closeup view of typical low Tundra vegetation. Notice the lichens on the rock in the right foreground. Trees in the background indicate that here, in Swedish Lappland, we are near the margin between Tundra and Taiga. (Courtesy of American Swedish News Exchange.)*

tions much like that of the Tundra. (Fig. 5–34.) The two-month summer season with its low temperatures, even occasional frost, is simply inadequate for trees. The botanist will tell you that there are trees in the Tundra and produce examples of alder or juniper, but they are 6 inches tall and likely to be recumbent in character and to most of us these are not trees. Woody plants of all kinds are rare, and Tundra vegetation is a highly specialized association of species which have the ability to withstand (or produce seeds which can withstand) long bitter winters, high winds, constantly cold moist soils, low-nitrogen soils, and to rapidly come to maturity and reproduce themselves during a short, cool summer. Such conditions rule out most plants.

The ever-present grasses are represented, chiefly in the form of rank sedges, and some mosses and the simple primitive lichen are everywhere. These, with sundry other low herbaceous plants, some flowering briefly, many reproducing through buds or shoots from their perennial root systems, make up the Tundra vegetation. (Fig. 5–35.)

It is a low, ground-hugging vegetation on a flat to gently rolling terrain. Surface drainage is inadequate at best, and vertical soil drainage is lacking entirely as a result of permafrost, often less than a foot underground in midsummer. So, despite only an average of 5–10 inches of precipitation per year, the surface is constantly wet and boggy during the growing season. Corridors of low trees may push out from the Taiga along stream courses in response to better drainage and lower permafrost levels, for paradoxically, flowing streams mean drier surface conditions.

During the summer, from seemingly out of nowhere, come great clouds of gnats and mosquitoes that somehow have survived the killing winter cold, and they can literally eat alive man or beast who attempts to inhabit the Tundra. Winter is the time to travel here, despite the bitter cold, for the insects are gone and the surface has frozen solid and is no longer one great bog.

Fig. 5–35. *Romping reindeer in the turgid Tundra near Teller, Alaska. (Courtesy of U.S. Bureau of Land Management.)*

The Tundra is a north coastal vegetation and is found in a virtually unbroken series along the north coast of North America and Eurasia. It is non-existent in the Southern Hemisphere except in a few tiny high latitude islands. The Falkland Islands off Patagonia and the Aleutians in the North Pacific are commonly included in the Tundra grouping despite their relatively low latitudes, for they do not support trees, although grass is more extensive here than in true Tundra. High winds and cool summers with occasional frost are probably the deterrents to trees.

6

Soils

Don't shrug off soil as "just dirt." It is an important element in man's physical environment. Certainly its ability (or inability) to produce living growth impinges upon his effective utilization of the earth as a habitat. So we should not only be interested, but at least rudimentarily informed as to its character. But what is soil? Merely rock broken into tiny fragments? If we were to take a rock and crush it mechanically, we would not have achieved soil, no matter how fine the particles. We would have the raw material from which soil is formed, for this breakdown of rock by natural means is the first step in the development of soil, but other steps must follow, and other elements, beyond simple rock fragments, must be present before true soil evolves.

It is traditional to regard soil as the result of the interaction of four elements: (1) mineral (rock fragments), (2) organic (both plant and animal), (3) gas, and (4) water. The mineral constituent not only suplies the great bulk of the soil, but is one of the basic determinants of fertility and contributes importantly to soil texture (size of particle from fine clays to coarse sands) and structure (the arrangement of particles from granular to blocky). Organic influences involve the breakdown of dead plant and animal remains and their integration into the soil, as well as the probing of plant roots and burrowing animals, the changes involved in the passage of soil materials through the digestive tracts of earthworms, and microbiotic activity in general. Growing plants require a certain root aeration and most soils, depending on density and drainage, have some air in them. But gases are also produced by decomposition and chemical change, and many of these, including air, further facilitate and encourage the activity of microorganisms and chemical reactions. But of all these soil-forming elements, water is singularly important. Without water there would be no vegetation, virtually no chemical reactions, and a paucity of microorganisms. And since water in soil is a direct result of climate, it can be said without equivocation that, given the initial broken rock as raw material, climate is the chief determinant of soil character. Compare the map of world soil distribution (Map III, pp. 410–11) with that of climate (Map I, pp. 406–7) and note the basic similarity.

This intimate relationship between soils, their fertility and formation, and climate is a closer relationship than was generally recognized for many years. It appeared in the early days of soil science (pedology) that a knowledge of the geology of a region would lead to an understanding of the soils, for after all, soil appeared to be fundamentally nothing more than decomposed rock. To a degree this sort of logic proved out, but it shortly became apparent that there were major flaws in this reasoning. Extensive areas of quite similar soils were found to overlie and have been derived from many dissimilar parent rocks, and conversely, in comparing several different regions, soils differing markedly were demonstrated to have originally derived from the same type of parent material.

Eventually, a Russian researcher put forth the suggestion that possibly climate had an important effect on the development of soil characteristics, and his subsequent soil distribution maps of parts of Russia were found to coincide almost perfectly with the climate maps of the same area. Modern soil science now recognizes this close relationship between soils and climate. Slope, drainage, and parent material are among the many other factors contributing to the final end product that we call soil, but climate, especially precipitation, is of prime importance in determining the fertility of most soils. And in geography where the emphasis lies on soil's utility by man, fertility is of paramount significance.

MINERAL COMPOSITION

Since nearly all known elements occur in the rocks of the earth's crust, it follows that these elements will be represented in the soils derived from this crust. The chemical composition of a typical soil should reflect initially something of the average proportions of the elements in the crust. There are about eight rather common ones: oxygen, silicon, aluminum, iron, calcium, sodium, potassium, and magnesium. All others may be regarded as trace elements, although several, notably phosphorus and nitrogen, are of great importance in the ability of a soil to support plant growth. The critical quality here is that the minerals constituting the vegetative nutrients in the soil must be soluble in water, for *a plant receives its nourishment through its roots in solution.* With a few unusual exceptions, such as plants that catch flies or feed directly from the air, this is universal. So if we check the common elements in most soils with regard to their solubility, we find that silicon, aluminum, magnesium, and iron (and their various compounds) are not readily soluble or soluble only under certain conditions. On the other hand, calcium, sodium, and potassium along with nitrogen and phosphorus are highly soluble in clear water. These then must be the chief plant foods, and if you were to read the list of chemicals on the label of any common garden fertilizer, you would discover that these elements make up the bulk of the product that is used for feeding plants. This is not to say that iron, aluminum, or many of the minute trace minerals are not required for vegetative growth; most plants need small amounts of even such minerals as copper and cobalt. But the nutrients that are required in large quantities must be readily soluble.[1]

LEACHING VS. EVAPORATION

Let us assume a region of heavy rainfall. As the moisture falls to the ground, some of it evaporates and some of it runs off as surface drainage, but always a certain amount of it enters the soil as groundwater and percolates downward in response to gravity. This constantly downward moving groundwater takes into solution the plant foods of the topsoil and carries them beyond the reach of normal root systems, thus, over a period of time, washing out the bulk of the nutrients and leaving only the non-solubles. This process is called *leaching,* and when carried to an extreme results in generally infertile soils. In relatively dry areas, leaching is cut to a minimum and, assuming a normal complement of minerals present, the soluble mineral content and fertility of the topsoil is correspondingly higher.

There is a factor, however, that tends to offset leaching by causing groundwater and its accompanying minerals in solution to move upward in the soil in opposition to gravity. This is evaporation from the surface. As the top layer dries from evaporation, it sets in motion *capillary action* (a blotter-like effect) that pulls the groundwater up-

[1] The actual mechanics of a soil's moisture-holding capacity and the ability of soil water in turn to take minerals into solution and transfer them to plant roots, is closely tied to the size of the individual soil particle. Both organic and inorganic particles eventually become reduced by normal soil-forming processes to submicroscopic dimensions. Chemical changes at this point lead to the formation of *colloids,* tiny particles that, when combined with water, become gelatinous in consistency. These colloids display an ability to absorb ions from the soil solution and then release them in exchange for other ions (termed "base exchange"). They act as a type of fertility bank, releasing stored nutritive ions as the soil solution balance is destroyed by plant withdrawal.

ward. If evaporation is roughly equal to precipitation, there is little or no loss of fertility from leaching. And if evaporation somewhat exceeds precipitation, not only are the surface solubles replaced as rapidly as they are leached, but in addition the salts from deep in the soil are brought up to within reach of the roots, thus increasing the natural fertility. (Fig. 6–1.) In the United States, a north-south zone in the

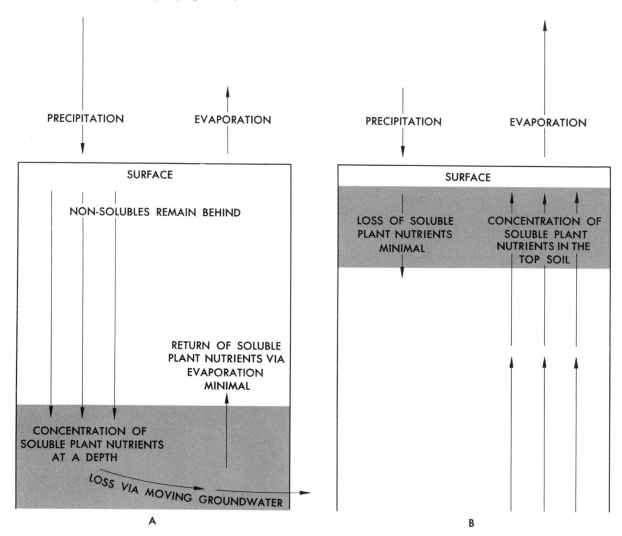

Fig. 6–1. *Leaching vs. the effect of capillary action. A situation where precipitation exceeds evaporation and the soluble plant foods are leached from the topsoil is illustrated in (A). In (B), the reverse is shown. Capillary action offsets leaching when evaporation is greater than precipitation and the solubles are concentrated near the surface.*

Fig. 6–2. *A saline flat near Uvalde, Texas. This low spot collects surplus moisture during infrequent rainy periods, and the excessive evaporation of the long hot summer draws alkalies to the surface. (Courtesy of U.S. Soil Conservation Service.)*

central plains states receiving about 15 to 20 inches of precipitation per annum and experiencing high temperatures has the ideal balance of precipitation and evaporation. Farther west in the desert and its margins, soil fertility is frequently excellent, but there is a danger that the evaporation potential may be so high that following infrequent storms (or inadequate irrigation), capillary action will operate so efficiently as to concentrate all the soluble salts on or near the surface in sterile alkali flats. (Fig. 6–2.)

So it would seem that, generally speaking, *the humid regions exhibit infertile soils because of leaching, and dry areas possess fertile soils*—the ideal being just short of the desert where evaporation somewhat exceeds precipitation.

ACIDITY VS. ALKALINITY

Soil water in humid regions is likely to be acid. Rainwater may absorb small quantities of carbon dioxide from the atmosphere, more contaminants will be acquired as it filters through a rotting mat of vegetative debris, and finally it absorbs acidic end products of rock decomposition in the soil itself. Attempting to neutralize these acid tendencies are the alkalies, but unless the parent material is particularly rich in calcium, sodium, or the like, alkalies are seldom in adequate supply. Not only are many alkalies readily soluble and therefore susceptible to reduction by leaching, but once a soil becomes acid, acid-tolerant vegetation such as conifers begin to flourish, and they drop their acidic needles to further sour the soil and complete an acid perpetuating cycle.

In drier areas where there is less vegetation, slower decomposition of both organic and inorganic materials, reduced leaching and an increasing dominance of evaporation, soils exhibit more alkaline tendencies. And here, grasses rather than trees respond to the sweeter soil conditions and in turn contribute their alkaline remains to be integrated back into the soil.

A good general statement that recognizes the prominent influence of leaching on soil acidity and the easy solubility of most alkaline minerals is that *humid regions generally display acid soils and dry ones alkaline.* (Fig. 6–3.) Both these tendencies can be overdone since most normal field crops prefer a reasonably neutral soil, if anything a little on the alkaline side. But, overalkalized soils, so typical of many desert regions, can be managed. The salts are soluble and can usually be washed out by heavy applications of irrigation water —always assuming, of course, adequate soil drainage. And the excessively acid soils of the humid areas can be made productive too by the addition of fertilizers containing proportionately large amounts of lime.

SOIL COLOR

The color of soil is one of its most obvious characteristics, and there is considerable temptation to attempt to relate certain vivid or striking colors to fertility. Locally, this may be possible, but there are few rational generalizations that can be made establishing such a relationship. The farmer of the Deccan district in India recognizes that his black soils are much more fertile than those of the surrounding areas because they have been derived from dark alkaline volcanic parent material, but Japanese farmers have learned to shun a dark volcanic

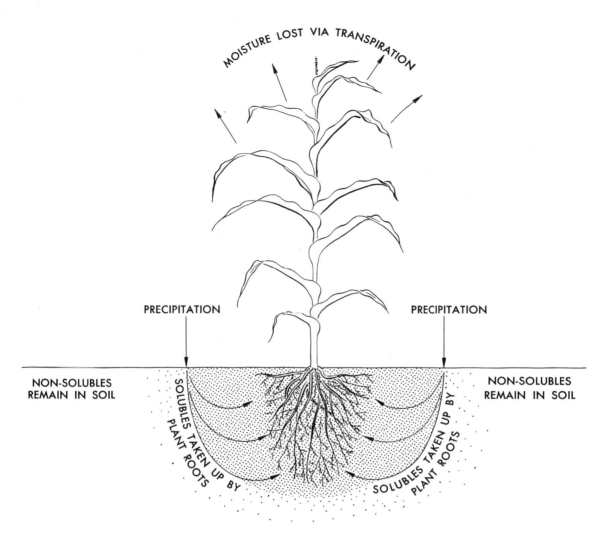

Fig. 6–3. *Soil fertility. Plants can obtain nutrients only via their roots and in solution.*

ash soil that is highly acid in character despite its color and the popular conception that volcanic soils must be fertile. The wheat farmer of the Ukraine finds his black prairie soil to be somewhat alkaline; the bog farmer of the Sacramento Delta finds his to be black but acid. And desert alkali wastes may be either black or white. In Brazil and South Vietnam, certain bright red soils (terra roxa and terra rouges, respectively) have a reputation for great productivity, while elsewhere in the tropics a reddish hue often means excessive leaching, and the darker alluvials of the river bottoms are preferred. And so it goes; color can be a clue to fertility, but only if the peculiarities of a certain local situation are known.

One very common source of dark color in soil is fixed carbon, an end product of organic decomposition. In the prairie, for instance, the grassy turf with its myriad hair roots dies each year, and this vegetable matter, immediately attacked by microorganisms, becomes a part of the soil. In the *partially decomposed* state, this material is called *humus,* and as it breaks down it releases carbon to color the soil. It would appear that a plant of any kind, receiving its nutrition from the soil, would return exactly that which it had removed when it died and once again became a part of the soil. This is not exactly the situation, however, for humus is in large part colloidal and thus becomes an important seat of topsoil base exchange. Further, nitrogen, an important nutritive element for most plants, is generally not available to the soil directly from the air, but nitrogen-producing microorganisms thrive in the presence of decaying vegetation, and humus thus aids in supplying this vital element. Light colored desert soils, being unleached, are often very fertile, but their inability to produce a significant vegetation because of lack of rainfall denies them humus and therefore nitrogen. To be made useful for agriculture, desert soils usually require nitrogenous fertilizers. And finally, humus improves the structure and texture of the soil (makes it crumbly or friable and easy to work), aids aeration in dense soils, and spongelike, adds greatly to its water-holding capacity. (Figs. 6–4 and 6–5.) So, the darker the color, the greater amount of humus. But, remember, dark coloration may come from other sources than humus, perhaps parent material, and black soil and fertility may not always go hand in hand.

Red color means iron in soils. It could be that the parent material was high in iron content and passed its coloration on to the soil formed from it; but, more commonly, oxidized iron in the soil under conditions of high temperature and heavy rainfall is responsible. This means, of course, that reddish to yellowish soils will be most characteristic of the humid tropics and subtropics and will display at least mildly acidic tendencies as a result of heavy leaching.

Probably, all things considered, the finest agricultural soil in the world is a series first identified in the eastern Ukraine and adjacent central Asia called *chernozem* (from the Russian, meaning black soils). In the United States, these soils are found in a band from Canada south through the central Dakotas into Kansas, and they also occur in similar climatic situations in Argentina, Australia, and South Africa. Here is the previously described region of ideal evaporation-precipitation ratio and, in addition, since the natural vegetation was prairie, a high humus content. Yet only low-yielding grains are grown in these places despite their agricultural potential because the very moisture factors that are required for this soil to develop are insufficient for most agriculture. Thus is seen the unhappy reality of natural soil

Fig. 6–4. The clods in this plowed field reflect a lack of humus and a poor soil structure. Among other things, humus improves structure and makes soil friable. (Courtesy of U.S. Soil Conservation Service.)

Fig. 6–5. This soil in a Columbia Basin potato field lacks humus entirely and is subject to wind erosion as a result. (Courtesy of U.S. Bureau of Reclamation.)

*fertility vs. agriculture—where enough rainfall exists for successful
general farming, the soils suffer through leaching, and where it is dry
enough for evaporation to balance leaching, not enough rain is present
to allow any but limited agriculture.*

THE SOIL PROFILE

It has been said that a soil is not deserving of the name "soil" until
it has developed some sort of profile (Fig. 6–6.) Only then has it
evolved into a proper life-supporting material, and the profile is the
measure of its maturity. Such a theory is subject to question, but
undoubtedly all soils are living things and do exhibit an evolutionary
progression that usually culminates, sooner or later, into a climax
stage and profile development. So, one clue, and a reasonably reliable
one, to a soil's character is its profile.

A vertical cut through most soils, from the surface to bedrock, will
display a cross-section with prominent horizontal bands called horizons. At the top is the A horizon or zone of *eluviation* (leaching).
This is the topsoil that experiences the greatest loss of both soluble
minerals and finer soil particles through washing, and thus tends to
have a somewhat coarser texture and lighter color than the adjacent
horizon. However, often at the immediate surface, there is a narrow
band, designated as the A_1 horizon, which is made up of the partially
decomposed leaves, stems, and general litter of the covering vegetation,
and this is black to brown in color.

The B horizon, below the A, is the recipient of the minerals and
clay particles leached out of the topsoil and is called the zone of *illuviation* (accumulation). It tends to be basically more fertile because of
this and is also more darkly colored and denser in structure, even to
the point of developing into a virtually impermeable hardpan.

Still farther down is the C horizon, which is only one step removed
from solid rock and is thus not yet true soil. It is made up of weathered and broken rock particles and will eventually, as time goes on,
become at its upper margin a part of the B horizon. Below this is the
parent material itself, sometimes called the D horizon.

Obviously, no two soils will have identical profiles, and it is by the
recognition of these differences that soil types can commonly be sorted
out and boundaries drawn between them. The A_1 horizon, for instance, is frequently lacking where vegetation is minimal, as in the
desert, or where decomposition is so rapid as to preclude its development, as in the humid tropics and subtropics. But the chernozem
soils are so dominated by the A_1 horizon that the remainder of the A
horizon is not recognizable. In some soils, the margin of each horizon
is sharply defined, while in others it is blurred and amorphous. Yet

most soils have some kind of a profile, and it is a recognizable feature of soil development. Only in newly formed or transported soils, or where some influence such as a steep slope or poor drainage interrupts their proper formation, do soils entirely lack profiles.

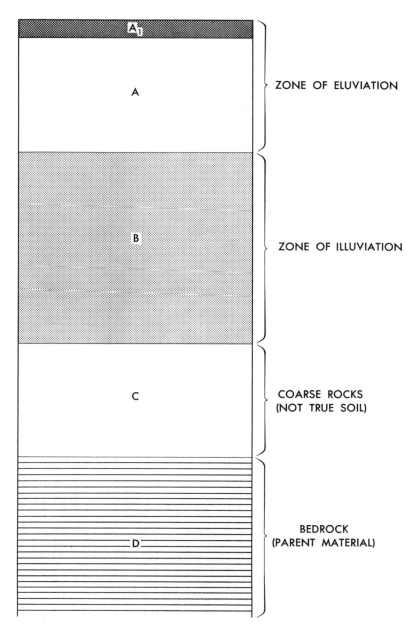

Fig. 6–6. *Idealized and simplified soil profile. These four horizons are found, at least to a degree, in nearly every mature soil.*

THE INFLUENCE OF TEMPERATURE

So far, emphasis has been on the precipitation factor in climate, since soil moisture is undoubtedly the major control of soil fertility. But temperature too has some effect, as in the determination of the rate of evaporation. Temperature is also a partial control of vegetative decomposition in humid lands and thus affects the soil. As an example, let us compare the forest soils of northeastern United States and southeastern United States. In both areas, heavy precipitation results in forest vegetation and leached soils, but in the north the winters are much longer and colder than in the south, and the rate of microbiotic activity in the vegetative litter on the forest floor is quite different. In the northeastern United States, there is a permanent mantle of needles and leaves which accumulates more rapidly than it decomposes. This means that precipitation entering the soil as groundwater must filter through this rotting litter and becomes strongly acid. It dissolves the readily soluble plant food and removes it, but also attacks and removes at a slower rate the iron and aluminum, leaving in the topsoil a concentration of silica. Such a soil, fully developed, displays a light colored and relatively thin A horizon, reflecting the absence of soil-coloring elements, although a brownish A_1 horizon, tinged by the carbon of incompletely decomposed ground litter, is always present. It is called a *podzol* or *podzolic* (from the Russian, meaning ash colored) and the process is called *podzolization*. These soils are typical of the middle and high latitude forested lands of North America and Europe.

In the humid southeast, where temperatures are not only higher but winters are shorter, decomposition of forest litter is more rapid and continuous. Consequently, the forest floor is clean and precipitation can reach the soil as clear water with a high oxygen content. Such groundwater removes the normal solubles and also slowly attacks the silica, so that after an extended period, the topsoil becomes high in iron and aluminum and the oxidizing iron frequently gives it a reddish color. Carried to its extreme, these soils are called *laterites* or *lateritics* and the process is called *laterization*.

Another extensive area where temperature is an important soil-forming element is northern Canada and Siberia where the Tundra climate is dominant. During the long cold winter, vegetative decomposition is held to a minimum and spongy masses of muskeg develop to a depth of a foot or more. Beneath this, the subsoil is permanently frozen, impeding normal drainage and giving these tundra soils a peculiar character duplicated in lower latitudes only above the timberline in high mountains.

IMMATURE SOILS

The foregoing discussion has revolved about *mature* or *zonal* soils, soils that have been in one place long enough to react to and reflect local soil-forming influences, especially climate—in other words, a climax soil just as we had climax vegetation. But there is also a general category of *immature* or *azonal* and *intrazonal* soils that, for one reason or another, have not yet reached an equilibrium with these soil-forming influences of the local environment, and here the previously developed generalizations do not always hold true. Newly formed soils, that is, rocks that have only recently decomposed through weathering and erosion, are likely to have a moderate alkaline content for a while despite heavy rainfall, simply because they have not existed long enough to be thoroughly leached. Or swampy conditions with their lack of groundwater movement will impede the normal development of the soil. Probably the largest group of immature soils owe their characteristics to the fact that they have been transported recently out of the region in which they originally developed. They may have been mature soils there, but now, in their new environment, they no longer reflect the local conditions. Running water is an effective agent of transportation, carrying quantities of silt from an exotic region and depositing it in deltas and flood plains. For instance, the Missouri River, called "The Old Muddy," too thick to navigate and too thin to cultivate, transports an immense load of silt from the dry regions of the west into more humid areas. Its lower valley and the flood plain of the Mississippi immediately south of St. Louis have high fertility ratings because of these imported soils. Carrying dry-land soils into adequate rainfall regions (or the reverse, taking irrigation water into the desert) accomplishes agricultural production miracles by combining sufficient moisture for crops with fertile unleached soils. Similarly, wind-transported soils called *loess* (Figs. 6–7 and 6–8) are immature and renowned for their ·fertility since they are frequently derived from the desert and deposited in better watered areas. (A further discussion of loess will be found in the section dealing with wind erosion in Chapter 7.)

In north China, the upper Hwang Ho or Yellow River traverses a region containing the world's largest deposits of loess. Here on the leeward side of the deserts of central Asia, prevailing winds have piled up a great plateau of fine silt. The river, cutting easily through these unconsolidated materials, becomes heavily laden with yellow sediment and carries it off to the sea. Through the centuries, the continuous deposition of this silt at the continental margin has built up the extensive North China Plain. The fertile soil is immature, having

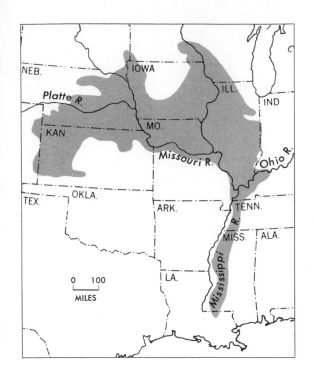

Fig. 6–7. *Loess accumulation in the central United States. Deriving chiefly from the dry regions to the west, wind-carried soils accumulate along the Mississippi. Lesser amounts were brought into this region by gravity winds off ancient continental ice sheets that swept up fine rock powder from glacial deposits.*

Fig. 6–8. *Fine-grained loessal soils compact readily and can maintain vertical faces when they are cut, but when exposed to humid conditions, they erode rapidly unless protected by a cover of continuous vegetation. This view is in the Red River Valley, Louisiana. (Courtesy of U.S. Soil Conservation Service.)*

been transported twice from its place of origin, first by wind and then by stream.

THE INFLUENCE OF PARENT ROCK

Another variant affecting soil fertility is the chemical composition of the parent rock. The previous generalizations have been based on the fairly valid assumption that most rocks have a normal complement of minerals, but occasionally a soil will be formed from parent material that is definitely lacking in several important minerals. Such a rock is quartzite, almost pure silica, that when it breaks down becomes a sterile sand. Climate, whether dry or humid, will have little effect on a soil of this type. The so-called *rendzina* soils are also examples of the dominating effects of certain parent rocks—Kentucky's Blue Grass region may serve as an example. Here, in a humid area where one would expect to find leached acid soils and a forest cover, was an original island of grass amid the trees. The soil is derived from strata of soluble limestone, and despite heavy precipitation it maintains its alkalinity. The grasses, with their affinity for alkaline soils, were visual evidence of this inherent fertility. No wonder the Blue Grass was a magnet for early trans-Appalachian farmers, notwithstanding its reputation as the "Dark and Bloody Ground."

So it becomes apparent that the relationship between climate and mature soils is intimate. Exceptions are found to be sure, but the exceptions are most easily understood and explained in the light of the climatic relationship. Once again, the thumbnail rule to keep in mind is *dry climate equals fertile alkaline soils,* and *wet climate equals infertile acid soils.* This is expressed in the accepted pedological nomenclature of the two basic groups. Dry-land soils are called *pedocals* (*ped* from pedology, *cal* from calcium). Humid-region soils are called *pedalfers* (*ped* from pedology, *al* from aluminum, and *fer* from iron). Pedocals then are high in alkalies, especially the most common one calcium, and pedalfers are leached of their soluble plant foods, leaving behind concentrations of aluminum and iron. (Fig. 6–9.)

SOIL CLASSIFICATION

The classification of soils on a world basis, as represented on Map III, pp. 410–11, must of necessity be limited to zonal soils. This system has its weaknesses, for locally azonal and interzonal soils often are of considerable significance and the broad zonal picture of lesser importance. However, the processes involved in the formation of

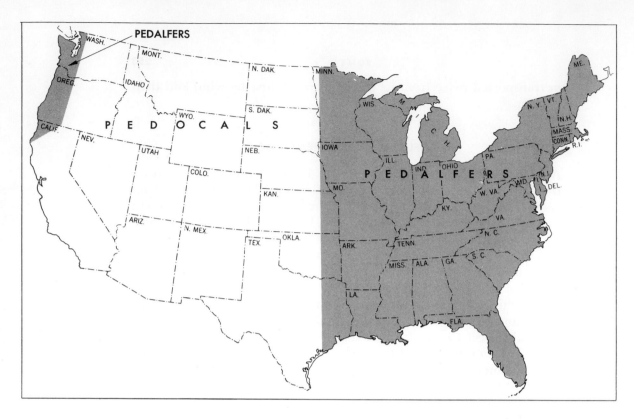

Fig. 6–9. *Pedalfers vs. pedocals in the United States. The United States breaks down rather neatly into a dry half and a wet half. Only in the mountains and the Pacific Northwest are acid pedalfers encountered in the west.*

zonal soils and their widespread occurrence make it mandatory that we stress them to foster an understanding of the worldwide patterns that develop. At this scale, the great variety of immature soils simply cannot be shown.

Laterite and Lateritic Soils

These are soils where the laterization process is dominant, and they are characterized by great depth, efficient leaching of the soluble minerals including silica, a minimum of organic material, indistinct horizons in the profile, and a reddish to yellowish color. Warm humid climatic conditions are necessary for this type of soil formation, and it naturally follows then that the laterites reach their greatest development in the Tropical Rain Forests. Here, the heavy daily rain tends to wash the solubles completely out of the soil, and they are removed by groundwater drainage so that no real B horizon exists. And the chemical disintegration of the parent rock is so accelerated that the C horizon is very deep and difficult to recognize. Neither is there an A_1 horizon for, despite the continuous falling of large amounts of forest debris to the ground, its decomposition is much too rapid for it to accumulate.

The removal of virtually all the minerals from the soil except iron, aluminum, and magnesium sometimes causes these non-solubles to be concentrated into workable ore bodies called *residual* ores. But this tremendous leaching also means that Tropical Rain Forest soils are largely deficient in plant nutrients and have proved to be infertile in the extreme for agricultural purposes. It seems anomalous that the Tropical Rain Forest, one of the heaviest naturally occurring vegetative associations anywhere in the world, should flourish on soils that are so lacking in basic fertility. But trees have different requirements than cultivated crops, and once established, they appear capable of maintaining a fertility cycle that is broken only when the land is cleared. Rapid and continuous weathering of rock materials partially offsets the loss of solubles through leaching. And, although not as deeply rooted as most forests, the tree roots of the tropics do probe greater depths than the root systems of cultivated plants, thus tapping more remote strata for nutrients. As these are drawn up through the roots, they nourish heavy foliage which supplies a constant rain of leaves and forest debris to decompose with great rapidity and further feed the forest. As a result, the soil water is only moderately acid despite torrential rains and heavy leaching. But once the forest is removed for cultivation, the cycle is broken and it can no longer maintain this minimal topsoil fertility. Large amounts of fertilizer are required for any sort of successful agriculture. Even these added plant foods leach away at a rapid rate and must be applied frequently if fertility is to be maintained.

Beyond the margins of the Tropical Rain Forest, a dry season breaks the daily rainfall pattern, and evaporation begins to offset leaching to some degree. The soil profile reflects this in exhibiting a sharper definition of the B horizon. But as long as the rainfall remains heavy for a large part of the year and organic material fails to accumulate at the surface, the lateritic trend continues. These soils develop under tropical scrub forest and even tall savanna grass, becoming gradually more alkaline as the tropical deserts are approached. Curiously, the term "laterite" was first applied to soils occurring in the monsoon region of Southeast Asia where there is a distinct dry season each year. In certain widely scattered localities, an iron-rich hardpan is found at the top of the groundwater table. When dug up, it is soft and malleable, but quickly hardens when exposed to the air into hard bricks that can be used for construction. Hence, laterite derived from the Latin, meaning brick. In today's usage, laterite has come to mean the heavily leached soils of the Tropical Rain Forest, and the old bricklike laterite soil is merely a variant of this and not even especially typical.[2]

These lateritic soils developing under climatic conditions featuring a dry season are somewhat more fertile than the true laterite. They still require careful management and fertilization to allow cropping, but in many places, particularly the Orient, intensive agriculture has supported large populations for centuries on such soils.

Within the lateritic soil grouping should be included the Humid Subtropic climatic regions with the exception of Uruguay and the Argentine Pampas. Here again are warm humid conditions and a forest vegetation. There are those who claim that the short cool winter slows microbiotic activity sufficiently to allow some minor accumulation of litter on the forest floor and thus the beginnings of podzolization. Admittedly, this is a transitional region between the lateritics and the podzolics, but the red to yellow soils coloring strongly points to laterization being dominant. The yellow of the sandy coastal plain in southeastern United States indicates greater leaching and smaller amounts of iron in the parent material than elsewhere. Among the laterites and lateritics, this soil of the Humid Subtropics is probably the most fertile, displaying the same shortcomings of its tropical relatives but to a lesser degree.

Podzol and Podzolic Soils

Cool to cold winters, fairly heavy precipitation the year round, and forest vegetation are the requisites for podzolization, and these conditions are met over broad areas in the Northern Hemisphere middle and high latitudes. The soils of the Taiga appear to represent the ultimate in podzol development. Here the relatively small numbers of decay-producing microorganisms, active only during the short summer, fail to remove the thick carpet of needles on the forest floor. Rainfall, percolating through this soil cover, inevitably becomes an oxygen-poor acid and, as has been described previously, attacks the mineral elements in quite a different fashion than the clear water of the tropics. Leaching of the A horizon is complete, the only mineral remaining relatively insoluble being silica, and its concentration here for a few inches below the surface gives podzol soils their typical white to gray color. At the top, the A_1 horizon may be quite dark, but at most is only a thin veneer. In the zone of illuviation, which receives

[2] Because of continuing arguments as to the proper use of the word "laterite," some authorities have introduced such terms as "latosol" and "ferrallite," reserving laterite for the infrequently occurring construction material.

the material washed down from above, fine clays and iron complexes produce a considerably darker and heavier soil, often a dense hardpan.

Its topsoil leached of alkaline plant nutrients, the unimproved podzol appears to be acceptable only to acid-loving conifers that in turn drop their highly acid needles to the ground to perpetuate the cycle. Obviously, this soil does not have a great agricultural potential, yet it can be utilized if properly managed. Deep plowing to turn up the more fertile B horizon, alkaline fertilizers, and the addition of organic matter have made podzol soils fairly productive in parts of northern Europe. One reason for their poor reputation is shortness of growing season at these latitudes, which rules out the maturation of many crops. But concentration on rapidly maturing truck and grains such as rye and buckwheat, combined with reasonable accessibility to market, can lead to a greater use of podzols for agriculture.

Outside the Taiga, the middle latitude forest soils are called podzolic rather than podzol, indicating that the podzolization process is dominant, but not to the degree that it is in the Taiga. The lower latitudes of the forested Humid Continental and Marine West Coast climate regions ameliorate the severe temperatures of the Taiga— longer hotter summers in the former, milder winters in the latter. In both cases, this means more rapid decay of forest litter and somewhat less acid groundwater. The type of forest reflects the degree of podzolization. Broadleafs prefer a more alkaline condition and in turn drop less acid debris than do conifers, so that in the broadleaf forest regions, the A horizon, although high in silica content, displays a brownish to dark gray color. In the mixed forest districts, stands of conifers usually occupy areas where the parent material is more acid than normal, such as the pine barrens of New Jersey which have developed on sandy soils.

Basic fertility is greater, obviously, in the podzolics than the podzols, especially those of the broadleaf forests, and the combination of an adequate growing season plus reasonable fertility has resulted in the rapid removal of the forest and in large-scale cultivation of crops.

Chernozem Soils

The chernozem soils could rather easily be grouped along with their near relatives the prairie soils and the brown and chestnut soils into a single category, because all three normally develop under a middle latitude grass cover and are, generally speaking, mere variants of one another as far as the soil-forming processes are concerned. However, the chernozems figure so prominently in the pedological literature because of pioneer Russian soil research that they are regarded as a classic-type example, and every physical geography student should be able to identify them explicitly. Therefore, they are treated separately here.

These are the black soils (introduced previously) where essentially the A_1 horizon makes up the whole of the deep A horizon. (Fig. 6–10.) The B horizon is brownish and breaks off sharply to a light colored C.

Fig. 6–10. The dominance of the black A_1 horizon in chernozem soils is clearly illustrated in this profile from South Dakota. (Courtesy of U.S. Soil Conservation Service.)

Characteristic of the chernozem is the zone of lime concentration well within reach of the plow, and this tendency to accumulation rather than leaching, combined with a high humus content, makes this soil as fine an agricultural soil as can be found anywhere. The humus imparts to the topsoil a friable crumblike texture that will not clod and promotes soil aeration and water availability to plant roots. The only drawback to the chernozem as a cultivatable soil is the somewhat low precipitation necessary for its formation and the tendency toward extended periods of drought.

On the subtropical margins of the chernozem zones, as in east-central Texas, soils of a reddish-chestnut color are found developing under conditions of slightly more heat and moisture. They are very similar to the typical chernozem but lack some of the lime concentration near the surface, display slightly less humus, and have greater amounts of oxidized iron. Sometimes referred to as degraded chernozems, these soils are very close to the chernozem both in location and character, and it is both convenient and logical to classify them as one.

Black Tropical Soils

There has long been a temptation to call these soils chernozem on the basis of color alone. They are certainly black like the chernozem, but the color does not arise from their humus content for it is quite low. They appear to be a result of the breakdown of black alkaline basaltic rock under the influence of tropical weathering, possibly in combination with inadequate drainage. Northern peninsular India and east-central Africa where a Tropical Wet and Dry climate supports a scrub forest are the chief regions of occurrence of this rather specialized soil. If the parent material is the dominating factor in soil formation, then these black tropical soils are intrazonal; but we are not sure and they are noted here because, although their fertility is not equal to that of the chernozem, among tropical soils they stand out as extremely fertile and have long been utilized for agriculture with minimal fertilization.

Prairie Soils

Very similar to the chernozem, the prairie soil marks the transition between the humid forest podzolics and lateritics of the middle latitudes and the semiarid grasslands of the chernozem. These are the soils of the tall grass prairie, and although having a high content of humus in the A horizon, they are dark brown rather than black. Somewhat greater leaching takes place with an average of 30 inches of precipitation, so that there is less lime accumulation and it is distributed more widely through the B horizon. These are almost as fertile soils as the chernozem, and the greater amount and increased reliability of rainfall make them tremendously productive for crops.

Chestnut and Brown Soils

On the dry side of the chernozems and merging into the middle latitude desert are the short grass prairies or steppes under which develop highly alkaline brownish soils. Here again are strong similarities to the chernozem except that more limited vegetation supplies less humus, and the salt accumulation is more exaggerated because of high evaporation. (Except for increased decay of organic matter resulting in less humus and also a reddish cast to the soil, the short grass tropical desert margins are also usually included in this same category.) Fertility is generally quite high, but low and sporadic rainfall makes agriculture precarious, although special dry-farming techniques have met with some success despite a strong tendency to wind erosion. There are many who maintain, following the unhappy experiences of the U.S. "Dust Bowl," that these soils should never be plowed and the grasslands subject to controlled grazing only.

One other region, the Mediterranean climate zone, exhibits a similar soil that might well be classified here also. Frequently, these soils, which are formed under conditions of subtropical temperatures and a scrub woodland vegetation, are called lateritic. But despite a tendency to reddish color and only moderate humus, the long dry season is not conducive to laterization. Perhaps the question is academic in that the Mediterranean climate regions are limited in area and hilly in character so that zonal soils are scarce, but we will include them here with the chestnut and brown soils on the basis of low precipitation resulting in alkaline accumulation.

Here too is basically a fertile soil requiring chiefly nitrogen fertilizers to offset its shortage of organic matter. From an agricultural viewpoint, the chief drawback is the Mediterranean climate with its rainfall at the wrong time of the year. Given sufficient moisture during the growing season through irrigation, these soils are very productive.

Desert Soils

Theoretically, the desert soils should have a great deal of inherent fertility in that leaching is non-existent, but there are some considerable prohibitions to agriculture even assuming that irrigation water can be obtained. One of these is soil texture which tends to coarse-

Fig. 6–11. *Coarse rocky soils are widespread in desert regions. This view is from the northern Kaokoveldt in southwestern Africa. (Courtesy of Information Service of South Africa.)*

ness. (Fig. 6–11.) Since mechanical weathering is dominant, its end products tend to be rough and angular, and these are strongly represented through the desert soil profile. Also, wind erosion at the surface removes much of the finer material, leaving behind, to make up the topsoil, the pebbles and larger rocks. These may even be cemented together by the saline remains of evaporating moisture into a desert pavement, or these same salts often accumulate through the capillary movement of groundwater into a rocklike hardpan at a shallow depth.

The general grayish (middle latitude deserts) or reddish (tropical deserts) color of desert soils indicates the deficiency of humus where sparse vegetation predominates, and this in turn means that desert soils lack nitrogen. Without humus or even rudimentary leaching, soil profiles fail to develop. All of this does not mean that desert soils do not have an agricultural potential, but often in the past, irrigation has been unsuccessful because the character of desert soil was not understood. Finely textured soils that can be easily worked are not entirely lacking in the desert, and if sufficient water and adequate drainage are supplied, surplus salts can be flushed out. There are many examples in all parts of the world where the desert "blossoms like the rose," an indication that their soils are fertile. (Fig. 6–12.)

Fig. 6–12. Sufficient water applied in the right places can make the desert a different world. These basically fertile desert soils in eastern Oregon have realized their productive potential with irrigation, but beyond the limits of the canals (right), even sparse sagebrush is hard put to survive. (Courtesy of U.S. Department of Agriculture.)

Tundra Soils

Because it is so widespread, the tundra soil is always classified as a zonal soil, yet it is definitely immature in most of its characteristics. In many ways, it closely resembles a typical bog soil of lower latitudes. Normal drainage is impeded by generally flat terrain and particularly by permafrost, so that no real profile develops. It must be remembered that the entire soil is frozen during 10 months of each year and that the soil-forming processes are operative only during the short summer season and only in that shallow layer above the permafrost. Leaching is entirely lacking and decomposition of the thick vegetative mat at the surface, although giving the soil a dark grayish color, is extremely slow. There is some vertical movement of soil elements in the late summer when the surface first freezes, and hydraulic pressures build up between this ice layer and the permafrost. Surface heaving and occasional ruptures of the ice allow outpourings of mud forced up from below.

CLASSIFICATION OF ZONAL SOILS

Pedocals (In order of decreasing precipitation)		*Pedalfers* (In order of decreasing temperature)
1. Chernozems (and related) }	Prairie Soils {	1. Laterites and lateritics
2. Chestnut and brown		2. Podzols and podzolics
3. Desert soils		3. Tundra

THE HUMAN ELEMENT

Once man evolves beyond a simple hunting-gathering culture, he begins to disrupt nature's delicately balanced soil ecology. Perhaps he learns to domesticate grazing animals and, forming them in herds, runs them in large numbers on the natural grasslands. If the price of wives is measured in cows, he may react to such an incentive by attempting to overgraze the carrying power of a given range and burn the rank growth to encourage new green shoots and temporary better feed. But now he has altered the natural vegetation, burned away some humus, and encouraged erosion; the soil-forming processes, closely linked to their covering vegetation, will change also. Or maybe the need for more substantial housing will lead to a lumbering operation and the removal of forest trees. Certainly, agricultural endeavors of even the smallest magnitude require a clearing of the land as the first preliminary step, and immediate corollary soil changes are inevitable.

With the introduction of the plow, he turns up the B horizon, forms ready-made channels for surface runoff with his furrows, and

Fig. 6–13. *Gullying on a clean-tilled Alabama cornfield. (Courtesy of U.S. Soil Conservation Service.)*

loosens the soil so that it can be carried away by such runoff. (Fig. 6–13.) The original vegetation, although removing nutrition from the soil as it grew, returned those same nutrients when it died and decomposed. But man replaces this vegetation with his own in the form of crops, and then, each year, takes those crops off the land to be consumed elsewhere. Even if he runs his product through a cow and returns the farm manures to the soil, he has not put back all the initial fertility that was removed, for there stands a healthy animal, evidence that some of the nutrition has been used up. In most parts of the world, agricultural soil fertility is declining, often at an accelerated rate, simply because the farmer cannot afford the chemical fertilizers that are necessary to maintain it after he has removed the crop.

It is possible, of course, to improve soils from the standpoint of fertility as well as to exploit them. Crushed lime to counteract acidity, cover crops plowed back in regularly to offset lack of humus, and tiled fields to facilitate drainage are all methods for making the soil more productive. And chemical fertilizers are being applied today to not only maintain fertility balance, and even increase the fertility each year, but to improve texture and structure as well. In every case, however, man becomes an element in soil formation and the original soil is changed.

Soil erosion, the actual physical removal of soil, is probably the most striking and best publicized of the deleterious effects of man on soil. But it should be remembered that wind and water are constantly moving sediments from one place to another, and it is only when man implements and encourages this activity so that large quantities of soil are involved that he can be called to account. Fundamentally, it is the removal of the natural vegetation that is at fault. It may be logging, mining, or agriculture that requires this, but once the bare soil is free of the anchoring effects of plant roots, it can be very effectively attacked by the elements. Great gullies form rapidly on steep slopes—miniature canyons biting down to bedrock. More insidious, and therefore in some ways more dangerous, is sheet erosion which occurs on clean-tilled gentle slopes following a heavy shower; and the surface runoff, carrying topsoil with it, is in a sheet rather than following a well-defined channel. (Fig. 6–14.) Wind too can carry large

Fig. 6–14. *The accumulated topsoil at the base of the slope has been removed from the field by severe sheet erosion. (Courtesy of U.S. Soil Conservation Service.)*

quantities of fine soil following overgrazing or the unwise plowing of the turf in semiarid regions. (Fig. 6–15.)

But erosion can be countered, to a degree at least, once it is recognized and considered to be urgent, and if the resources and techniques are known and available. (Fig. 6–16.) Strip miners are now required

Fig. 6–15. *Overgrazing, the scourge of the semiarid rangeland, allows both water and wind to erode the soil. Here, in Union County, New Mexico, it is the wind at work. Note the rippled drifts in the middle foreground. (Courtesy of U.S. Soil Conservation Service.)*

Fig. 6–16. *Man can, of course, make effective attempts to control erosion. The rubble left by a Kentucky strip-mining operation (above) is being fixed by planted pines. And contour plowing followed by strip cropping (right), on gently rolling Iowa farmland, discourages soil from moving downslope. (Courtesy of U.S. Soil Conservation Service.)*

to fill their cuts and plant trees in the more enlightened societies, and hydraulic mining has been declared illegal. Lumbermen replant as they cut, and reforestation of barren slopes, whose timber was removed even centuries ago, is more widespread than ever. On the farm, contour plowing, terracing, strip cropping, and cover crops are all helping to cut down erosion. Yet even here in the United States, where we regard ourselves as efficient technicians, one can still stand beside the tawny Mississippi and watch somebody's farm go by every few minutes.

7

Landforms

Landforms is a general rather all-inclusive term referring here to the seemingly endless manifestations of terrain that occur on the earth's surface, the emphasis being on the word "surface," for this is the habitat of man, our prime concern. In the study and classification of landforms (geomorphology), whether we consider merely the gross features of continents vs. ocean basins or the details of a local valley, stream bottoms, or coastline character, the conformation and configuration of the earth's surface play an important role in determining where and how man will adapt himself to his environment. But we cannot content ourselves with simply cataloging and locating all the world's mountains and valleys. To fully understand the potential human utility of each landform as well as to aid us in classification, we must delve into something of their genesis. There are those who would argue that only the geologist is legitimately concerned with cause since, of necessity, this leads us into subsurface matters, but if this were true, the geographer would be placed in the position of merely describing. As scientists, we must understand cause to properly interpret result.

THE EARTH'S CRUST—COMPOSITION

Although it is considered old fashioned today to say that the earth is in the process of cooling from an original molten state, and that only a thin crust has cooled and solidified, the fact is that no single alternative proposal has been universally accepted. And, whatever the cause, there does exist a thin rigid crust (10–30 miles thick) and a heated interior. But because of our inadequate tools, even this crust is not entirely known and its full depth has never been plumbed. Beneath

the crust to the center of the earth, our knowledge is limited to educated speculation based on gravity, high-pressure laboratory experi-
ments, and seismic studies. Undoubtedly, the core of the earth is
very hot, in the neighborhood of 5,000° F., and very dense, with probably high concentrations of nickel and iron. Both heat and density
decrease with distance away from the center. But despite the generally high temperatures of the earth's interior, it is probably not wholly
molten because of the great pressures that the surrounding materials
exert through gravity. Surrounding the core is a zone of solid material
called the *mantle*. About 1,800 miles thick, it is thought to be com-
posed chiefly of the mineral olivine (magnesium iron silicate). (Fig.
7–1.)

The crust itself is made up of the lightest minerals on the earth
and might be conceived of as "floating" on the hot, less-brittle, and
denser interior. This crust in turn has been subdivided into two
layers: the *sial* (*si*–silica and *al*–aluminum dominated) which makes up
the continents and is the lightest rock of all, and the *sima* (*si*–silica
and *ma*–magnesium dominated), somewhat heavier, underlying the
sial of the continents and flooring the ocean basins. The contact line

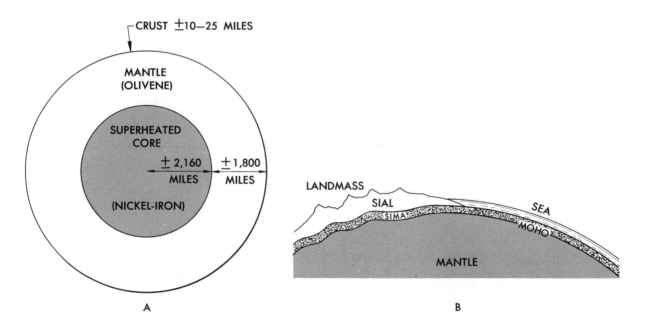

Fig. 7–1. *Composition of the earth and its crust. (A) is a generalized
cross-section of the layered earth; (B) the several elements that go to make
up the crust proper.*

or discontinuity between the sima and the heavier mantle, i.e., the bottom of the crust, has been called the *Moho* (a shortened version of the name of the Yugoslavian Mohorovic who first described this phenomenon). A major effort to penetrate the Moho and sample the mantle is currently under way. Drilling will begin shortly at a site off Hawaii from a platform at sea, for it is believed that the mantle most closely approaches the surface in the ocean basins. Sea depth here is about 14,000 feet, and the crustal rock and overlying sea sediments are estimated to be some 17,000 feet thick. If the Moho project is successful, man will have drilled 2 miles deeper than ever before, but the scientists are confident that modern turbo drills are capable of the job.

Elements

The earth, the water on it, and the atmosphere are made up of ninety-two elements (or atoms). In addition, ten elements have been produced in the laboratory, so that all known matter has an atomic or elemental base. Each of these is a distinctive combination of protons, neutrons, and electrons and has been assigned a specific name and letter abbreviation as a label, i.e., Fe (iron) and O (oxygen). The two most common elements in the crust, by far, are oxygen, 46.59 per cent, and silicon, 27.72 per cent (by weight).

Minerals

Minerals are ordinarily combinations of elements in the solid state, and their composition may be expressed in a chemical formula, for example, NaCl (sodium chloride or common table salt) or SiO_2 (silica dioxide or quartz). In addition, most minerals exhibit a distinctive crystalline form that aids in its identification. Occasionally, a mineral may be a single element such as graphite and diamonds, which are pure carbon (C) in two different forms—or so-called native gold (Au) or native copper (Cu) may occur in nature in the pure form rather than in ores. But these are relatively rare and most minerals are combinations of elements.

Rocks

Rocks are combinations of minerals. But if 102 elements may be merged in a virtual endless number of combinations to produce minerals, then combining these in turn to form rocks gives us an infinity of possibilities as far as the chemical composition of rocks is concerned.

To inject some order into this multiplicity, the classification of rocks according to their chemical composition has been rejected in favor of a *genetic classification*. In other words, we break down all the rocks existent in the earth's crust on the basis of *how they were formed*. Now we find that all rocks fall into one of the three following categories: *igneous, sedimentary,* and *metamorphic*.

Igneous rocks. *Any rock that has cooled and solidified from the molten state is an igneous rock.* Therefore, if the earth's history is that of a molten sphere in space, all the rocks making up its crust must have originally been igneous and thus the ancestors of all other rocks. Even today, approximately 95 per cent of the entire crust, all of the sima and most of the sial, is igneous.

As molten material periodically wells out of the earth's interior to invade the surface layers or to flow onto the surface itself, it cools into a wide variety of igneous rocks. In the molten state, this liquid is called *magma* as it pushes out into the crust, but the name *lava* is applied when it ejects itself onto the surface.

Although all magma is made up basically of a variety of silicate minerals, the chemical composition of any given flow may differ radically from that of any other, and thus the resulting rocks will reflect these differences. But in addition to these sharp chemical differences, igneous rocks also exhibit considerable variation in texture. *Granite,* for instance, is a coarse-grained igneous rock whose individual mineral crystals have formed to a size where they are easily visible to the naked eye. A slow rate of cooling has allowed the growth of the crystals to this size. Normally, slow cooling results from the invasion of the crust by a magmatic body that remains buried well below the surface. We may encounter granite as a surface rock in the contemporary landscape, but we know from its coarse texture that it must have formed cooling slowly at a considerable depth and then been laid bare by subsequent erosion. On the other hand, if this identical magma flows onto the surface and is subject to the rapid cooling effects of the atmosphere, the resulting rock will be fine grained and quite different in appearance from granite and is called *rhyolite*. These two rocks have identical chemical compositions, as do *diorite* and *andesite, gabbro* and *basalt,* and *pyroxenite* and *augite*. There are many other couplets of this type differing only in texture. Certainly, the extreme in fine-grained rocks is volcanic glass or *obsidian* where no crystals have had a chance to form because of virtually instantaneous cooling. (Fig. 7–2.)

Once again, irrespective of color, texture, or chemical composition, if a rock has formed from the solidification of magma or lava, it falls into the igneous category.

Fig. 7–2. Igenous rock. This photo shows dark, relatively fine-grained basalt poured out onto the surface as lava, and on cooling and solidifying, cracking (or jointing) through contraction. (Courtesy of U.S. Bureau of Reclamation.)

Sedimentary rocks. *All sedimentary rocks have in common a history of once having been simply an accumulation of loose unconsolidated rock materials that have become compressed or cemented into solid rocks.* It does not matter whether the individual particles are of organic or inorganic origin, what the circumstances of the accumulation were, or what the chemical composition might be; if they have gone through this transformation, they are classified as sedimentary. This word "sedimentary" implies the settling of the basic rock materials to the bottom of a body of water. Loose sands and silts may be accumulated by wind, stream, or ice action on the land and eventually become sedimentary rocks, evaporating seas may form massive salt deposits, or organic matter may be solidified into rock (such as coal), but by far the largest part of the earth's sedimentary rocks were formed (and are being formed today) by sedimentation in the sea, so the choice of *sedimentary* as a descriptive term is an apt one. This constant deposition of material on the relatively flat floors of continental shelves has resulted in the *layered* or *stratified* appearance of the rocks developed from them that is so characteristic of sedimentary rocks.

A typical example will serve to illustrate four basic types of sedimentary rocks. Let us assume a stream discharging into the sea whose bottom is of a gentle shelving character. As the stream strikes the sea, its velocity is checked rather abruptly, and since a stream's velocity is the chief control of its ability to carry rock material in suspension, it is forced to drop the heaviest portion of its load, pebbles and larger rocks, near the shore. Beyond this, as the stream's impetus continues to slow, will be deposited progressively coarse sands, fine sands, and finally minute mud particles. This sorting by size is typical of stream deposition. But beyond the influence of the stream, further sedimentation is occurring. Tiny microscopic plants and animals with a life span of a few days or weeks (called plankton) are constantly raining down on the ocean floor to mingle with the organic remains of bottom dwellers. Commonly, the shells and skeletons of this sea life are made up of calcium carbonate or lime, so that the resulting product is a black ooze high in content of both carbon, from the decomposing organic matter, and lime. Lime may also be precipitated directly from the sea by changes in water temperature. (Fig. 7–3.)

We have, then, on the ocean floor a succession of loose unconsolidated sediments ranging from coarse pebbles to fine muds and lime-rich organic remains. This is not yet rock, but if compression and cementation follow, these sedimentary raw materials will become sedimentary rock.

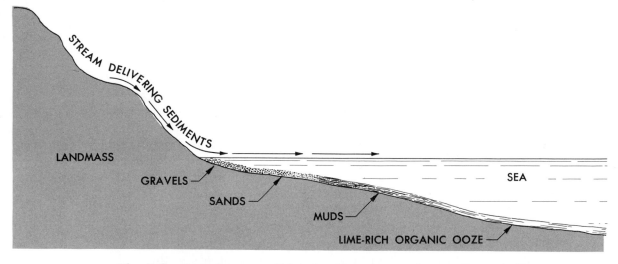

Fig. 7–3. *Sorted unconsolidated sediments on the sea floor. Sedimentary rock in the making. If the proper sequence of events follows this simple deposition, each of these categories will develop into a distinctive rock.*

Fig. 7–4. *Thick beds of limestone laid down on some ancient sea bottom, but subsequently uplifted and eroded to form these spectacular cliffs in Canyon de Chelly, Arizona. (Courtesy of U.S. National Park Service.)*

Pressure alone is sufficient to transform the fine-grained and somewhat colloidal limey ooze and muds into rocks. A handful of mud, if squeezed firmly to wring out the moisture, can become a compact mud ball. If this simple pressure is multiplied many times, by the piling of layers of sediments on top of the original or the folding and flexing of the ocean bottom, the muds and lime will be compacted into solid rock. In the limey ooze, the liquid carbon material (embryonic petroleum) is squeezed out, and the resultant solid calcium carbonate rock is called *limestone.* (Fig. 7–4.) The muds lose their water content and become a rock called *shale,* a chief characteristic of which is to develop foliation at right angles to the pressure that formed it; that is, shale, when struck with a hammer, tends to break into thin planes or foliations parallel to each other.

Simple pressure, however, unless it is of unusual force, normally is not adequate to consolidate sands and pebbles into rock. Sand is not only larger in size than the mud particles, but is harder and more angular. The great bulk of the world's sand is silica, one of nature's hardest widely occurring minerals. Most minerals when worn down to this size through weathering and abrasion disintegrate into silt, but silica can maintain its identity at sand size and even resist smoothing and rounding. Thus, through natural selection, most particles of this size are light colored, angular silica. The individual grains of sand do not fit tightly one to the other, and the many pores and interstices make it highly porous and allow ready movement of water through it. Gradually, various minerals in solution or materials in suspension in the water build up in the intergrain openings and set as a cement. The resulting *sandstone* takes a great deal of its character from the cementing agent. For instance, reddish sandstones probably have iron as a cement or dark sandstones may have mud. These are relatively weak stones as the cement is less resistant than the sand grains. On the other hand if silica is deposited as the cement, the sandstone will be light colored and very hard. Seldom are all the interstices filled completely with cementing material, and sandstone very frequently is porous and capable of holding liquid: ancient sea brines, groundwater, or oil. (Fig. 7–5.)

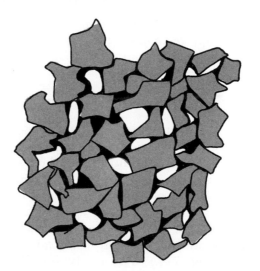

Fig. 7–5. *Sandstone. The cement (black) fails to completely occupy the large intergrain spaces formed by the angular sand particles. The hardness of the cement largely determines the hardness of the sandstone, and its degree of filling the interstices determines the ability of the rock to hold and transfer liquids.*

Pebbles and larger stones also commonly are cemented together as are sand grains. Each pebble is a sizable piece of rock with its own characteristics of color and hardness, and it is usually worn down to a rounded form through stream abrasion before deposition. The large number of possibilities of rock character resulting from the many different cementing agents and variety of pebbles makes it difficult to generalize, but any coarse-grained rock with this history of pebbles cemented together is called a *conglomerate*.

These then are four basic types of sedimentary rocks: (1) limestone, (2) shale, (3) sandstone, and (4) conglomerate. Numerous subdivisions exist and remember that sedimentary rocks do not have to be formed from sedimentation on ocean floors nor do they absolutely have to show stratification, but most do and the foregoing explanation of their formation is highly typical.

In the surface rocks of the continents, the sedimentaries are strongly represented. Although they make up only about 5 per cent of the total earth's crust, they form a widespread thin covering over much of the continental regions. In a few places where deposition has been continuing for long periods of time, as in the Ganges Valley, sedimentaries are estimated to be at least 50,000 feet thick.

Metamorphic rocks. The word "metamorphism" means change of form. *Thus, metamorphic rocks are already existing rocks that exhibit a change of form.* Sedimentary, igneous, and even previously formed metamorphic rocks may be changed in appearance, mineral distribution, size, and complete molecular structure if they have been affected by certain forces in sufficient quantity. These forces are pressure and heat, operating in unison. The end results are new rocks that did not exist before.

There are many ways in nature in which intense heat and pressure may be generated, thereby causing changes in the rocks involved. Sediments may pile up in a sinking trough to great depths thereby applying tremendous pressures on the bottom layers—and pressure produces heat. Or deep low-angle fractures (or faults) may occur in rock layers, allowing skidding along the fault plane. Heat from friction combined with the pressure of overlying strata may alter the character of the rocks in the immediate vicinity. Igneous intrusions into existing rock masses will frequently furnish adequate heat and pressure at the zone of contact (and often some chemical activity as well), and the folding and deformation of original flat-lying beds into involved uplands will be equally effective. Most major mountain systems have experienced all of the above effects and many more in the general process of mountain building, so metamorphism is not rare and metamorphic rocks of many kinds abound in the earth's crust.

Given sufficient heat and pressure, fine-grained limestone will be changed into coarse-grained *marble,* a completely different rock. Usually, the metamorphic rock will be harder than the rock from which it was formed, as in coal where anthracite is the metamorphosed variety. Shale will become *slate,* harder and more emphatically foliated, and the metamorphism of sandstone fuses the individual sand grains into an extremely hard silica rock, *quartzite.* Distinctive coloring often results from the various cementing materials and impurities, such as carbon or iron particles in limestone causing the typical dark or reddish streaks in marble, or iron-rich cements in sandstone giving quartzite a pinkish hue.

Igneous rocks too may be metamorphosed, for despite their having been under considerable pressure in their original molten state, subsequent pressure and heat applied to the solid igneous rocks will cause them to change their form. A wide variety of rocks called *schists* and *gneisses* [1] are commonly a result of this metamorphism. The schist is characterized by the formation of mica or similar crystals which are aligned at right angles to the pressure. This lineation is visible to the naked eye and gives the rock a rough foliation, as well as a shiny, almost metallic appearance as the light reflects off the many crystal faces. Gneisses too exhibit a lineation of minerals, but typically are banded, that is wide sharply defined bands of alternating dark and light minerals.

Theoretically, remetamorphism of metamorphic rocks is also possible but is often difficult to recognize without radioactive dating in the laboratory; so any rock is susceptible to metamorphism if given sufficient heat and pressure.

The crust of the earth as we know it today then is a scrambled combination of these three types of rocks. The original crust was probably igneous as the molten earth cooled at the surface (if we are willing to accept such a theory). But immediately, weathering and erosion began to break this crust up into small particles and individual minerals that were carried off, sorted, and deposited as unconsolidated sediments, while at the same time, organic remains were accumulating in certain favored locations. As these became cemented and compressed into rock, they were frequently uplifted into mountains and continental masses. The forces exerted by such constant crustal deformation caused many of these igneous and sedimentary rocks to be metamorphosed. This cycle repeated over and over, supplemented by fresh magmatic intrusions and continuing at this moment, accounts for the great variety of rocks that are encountered in the earth's crust,

---

[1] Schists and gneisses may also be formed on occasion by the metamorphism of sedimentary rocks.

and especially the continental regions. But notwithstanding this great variety, each of these rocks can be placed in one of the three basic rock categories: (1) igneous, (2) sedimentary, or (3) metamorphic.

THE EARTH'S CRUST—DEFORMATION AND SCULPTURING

In attempting to classify the virtual infinity of features that make up the totality of our landscape, it has been common to break them down into the familiar terms of plains and plateaus, mountains and hills. Although these appear at first glance to be logical and well understood categories, before long it becomes apparent that there are high plains and low plains, plateaus of many variations, and that one man's hills are another man's mountains. For instance, the commonly referred to Appalachian Plateau has been so cut up and dissected that its appearance is that of myriad steep-sided hills—some call them mountains. To the resident of featureless Australia, the 1,500-foot Mt. Lofty Range near Adelaide is a sizable mountain mass as the name would indicate, but to the New Zealander brought up in the shadow of snow-covered 12,000-foot Mt. Cook or 8,000-foot Mt. Egmont, the Australian mountains are mere hills. We can place arbitrary definitive limits to these features but this does not change the common everyday nomenclature of the local people, and within such a classification are inherent misunderstandings. In the light of this, the map of the world's topography (Map IV, pp. 412–13) is merely one of relative elevations, separating by color the low places from the high ones. Such a map does bring out the distribution of upland vs. lowland, but does not attempt classification of landforms on the basis of elevation.

Therefore, a completely different approach to the classification of landforms will be used here—one that recognizes something of the means of formation, that is to say, again a genetic system. Such a treatment is by no means original, but appears to be the most logical way to approach the problem.

First, we must recognize two basic forces constantly at work on the surface of and within the earth's crust. We call these the *tectonic forces* and the *gradational forces,* and they work in opposition, each attempting to cancel out the other. The tectonic forces are the great forces that distort, buckle, and break the surface of the earth, causing mountains and ocean basins. It may be that a cooling, shrinking earth forces its outer shell to deform as it adjusts to a smaller core. Or, if we have outgrown old simplifications, we may be tempted to accept new attempts at explaining crustal movement, such as the so-called "phase change" theory wherein it is postulated that certain dense rocks increase their volume when they are heated (probably by pressure or radioactivity), thus causing vertical rupture of the surrounding rocks. However it is explained, there are evidences all about us of the tectonic forces at work—earthquakes, volcanic explosions, and high rugged mountain ranges that must have been formed just a short while ago.[2] The gradational forces attack these features and attempt to destroy them. They wear down the high places and fill in the low ones. Left to themselves, without the tectonic forces to offset them, the gradational forces would smooth the surface of the earth until theoretically it would be completely covered with water. There are certain parts of the earth where the tectonic forces have not been active for an extended period, and here, as in the Amazon lowland or western Australia, the land is low and featureless. Elsewhere, the tectonic forces have, temporarily at least, achieved major ascendancy over the gradational forces, and high mountains or great ocean deeps are the present-day features.

The tectonic forces may be broken·down·into three basic processes: (1) *folding,* (2) *faulting,* and (3) *vulcanism.* The gradational forces are four in number: (1) *running water,* (2) *moving ice (glaciation),* (3) *wind,* and (4) *waves.* These gradational agents have in common not only the ability to abrade and erode, but to transport the end products of this erosion and deposit it elsewhere.

In the following discussion, we will take up first the tectonic forces and then the gradational forces one at a time, analyzing the character of the resulting landforms and seeing something of their distribution in the world today.

Shields

However, before we consider the individual tectonic forces we should be aware that the continents as we know them today were blocked out roughly very early in geologic time. Each continent has a stable hard rock core made up of ancient granitic and metamorphosed rocks that, although subjected to eons of stresses and pressures, have maintained themselves as relatively stable masses. Erosion has worn them down to low featureless plains or plateaus, where they can be observed on the surface, but their margins are often masked by more recent sedimentary mantles. Along the edges of these *shields,* as they are called, a great deal of frequent activity has occurred. Extensive regions have been alternately above and below the sea, and it

---

[2] In dealing with geologic matters, we must reorient our entire concept of time. Remember that the earth is probably 5,000,000,000 years old. Man has been present for perhaps 1,000,000 years, so when we think in terms of human lifetimes or even historical time, this is but a minute instant in geologic time. We must learn to regard a period of 500,000 to 1,000,000 years as a relatively short time, and thus what appear to us from day to day as painfully slow processes may be in reality extremely rapid. (See Appendix B)

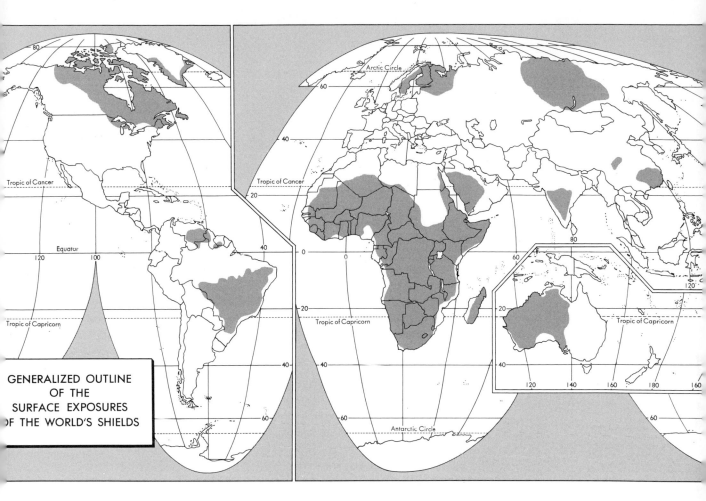

Fig. 7–6. *Generalized outline of the surface exposures of the world's shields. Every continent has its stable hard-rock core or shield.*

is here that most of the world's mountain systems are found, a result of the tectonic forces at work. (Fig. 7–6.)

In North America, the hard rock core is called the *Canadian* or *Laurentian Shield,* and its surface exposures are evident over a large part of eastern Canada and the Great Lakes and New England area in the United States. Undoubtedly, it extends beyond these limits below the surface. The *Fennoscandian Shield,* exposed in Scandinavia and northwestern Russia, is the European equivalent. Asia exhibits a shield in central Siberia, southern China, India, and Arabia; South America in the southern two-thirds of Brazil; Australia in the western two-thirds of the continent; and virtually the entire continent of Africa is a single shield. (Fig. 7–7.)

Fig. 7–7. *The Drakensburg Mountains, paralleling the coast for many miles in southeastern Africa, appear to be a range. Actually, they are the hard-rock edge of the extensive African continental shield. (Courtesy of Information Service of South Africa.)*

So when we deal with the tectonic forces, at least as they have been operative since very ancient time, we will find that the shields have been relatively immune to their effects and that the margins of the shields show the greatest activity.

Tectonic Forces

Folding. It scarcely seems possible that strong brittle rocks may be bent into sharp folds without first reducing them to a molten mass. Certainly if we placed a slab of rock in a powerful vise, it would become cracked and broken. But there are many evidences all around us of what must have been originally flat-lying beds with, for instance, marine fossils as evidence of their formation on the sea bottom which we can observe now folded into a variety of flexures. *It appears that if strong lateral pressures are exerted over a very long period of time, while simultaneously the strata involved is buried at some depth beneath the confining pressures of overlying layers, folding may be accomplished in all of its many forms.* In other words, both vertical and horizontal pressures are required, and a great deal of time in the formation of even modest folds.

Folds, as we find them existent today, may vary all the way from mild arches and domes scarcely visible to the eye, to involuted and recumbent folds where the rock strata have been squeezed into tight folds that have overturned and even curled about themselves. The general terminology applied to folds is *anticline* vs. *syncline*. (Fig. 7–8.) An upbowed stratum on a relatively small scale is called an *anti-*

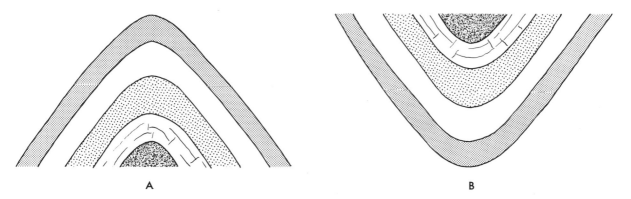

A   B

Fig. 7–8. *(A) Anticline.* *(B) Syncline.*

cline, while one that is bent downward is a *syncline.* If this same sort of folding occurs on a larger scale involving perhaps hundreds of miles, then they are called *geanticlines* and *geosynclines* (the prefix from the Greek word *geos*-earth emphasizing the size of such structures). (Figs. 7–9 and 7–10.)

It does not necessarily follow that anticlines are evidenced as hills on the earth's surface, for their formation is so slow that erosion may easily wear away the top of the fold as rapidly as it is uplifted. It is not uncommon to find a syncline at the top of a hill in present-day topography and an eroded anticline in a valley. For instance, the Appalachian ridges and valleys are the end result of tremendous folding, but the original folds made up of sedimentary beds from an earlier sea in this location have been largely removed by erosion. The rather subdued Appalachian ridges and valleys are merely the roots of the old folds, the steeply tilted harder layers standing up as ridges with the softer ones etched out as valleys.

Extending in an east-west direction across southern Europe and Asia are a series of high mountains exhibiting some of the most spectacular and severe folding to be found anywhere in the world. The Pyrenees, Alps, Caucasus, and Himalayas are all basically folded mountains. At one time just south of these mountains, in the general area

Fig. 7–9. *The upturned beds of Umtanum anticline are clearly visible along the wall of the Columbia River Gorge at Priest Rapids, Washington. (Courtesy of Wanapum Development, P.U.D. of Grant County, Wash.)*

Fig. 7–10. *A synclinal valley in the northern Cascades. Note the protruding stubs of the downfolded strata at the upper right. (Courtesy of Washington State Department of Commerce & Economic Development.)*

of today's Mediterranean and Indo-Gangetic Plain, there existed a great sea-filled geosyncline called *Tethys Basin*. For millions of years, sediments from the adjacent continents filled this basin and formed many thousands of feet of sedimentary rocks. Then, quite recently, pressures from the south squeezed these layers against the resistant margins of the European and Asiatic shields causing intricate folding and the formation of the east-west mountain ranges. Subsequent erosion, especially intense glaciation, has carved and hewn them to their present form, but in reconstruction, the original folds are clearly evident.

Occasionally in a road cut or on a cliff side, a perfect fold may be easily visible. Formed beneath the surface, erosion has not yet laid it bare, and its undisturbed outline is evidence of the manner in which folding occurs. Presumably, folding is going on in a great many places around the world today, but its progress is so slow that it is virtually impossible to measure. We know, however, from observing folds of all kinds in many places that folding has been a major force in the deformation of the earth's crust.

Faulting. *Faults are nothing more than breaks or fractures in the earth's crust along which there is or has been movement.* Nearly all rocks display cracks or joints resulting from their method of formation, such as the contraction of cooling lava or the alternating cooling and heating of surface rocks with the seasons. But if the fracturing is on a larger scale and there is readjustment along the plane of breakage, it is called a *fault*.

The compressional forces at work in the earth's crust that cause folding also are responsible for faulting. But if the rock is too brittle or massive to relieve these pressures by folding, or if the forces are exerted abruptly rather than slowly over a long period, then faulting will occur. Much of this crustal faulting takes place beneath the surface of the earth or beneath the sea and is traceable only through earthquake studies, but surface faulting causes certain characteristic landforms. Vertical displacement may be on a minor scale, forming escarpments or cliffs and making the fault line easily visible, or massive blocks may be tilted up along the fault, resulting in high asymmetrical mountain ranges. The Sierra Nevada in California, although slightly modified in places, is essentially a single tilted fault block. The sheer eastern scarp marks the fault line, and when viewed from Nevada or the Owens Valley is a spectacular sight in sharp contrast to the long gentle slope of the inclined western side of the block.

If two relatively vertical faults develop parallel to each other, then the block between may drop, causing a sheer-sided, flat-bottomed valley called a *graben* (German meaning literally grave or ditch). The

Fig. 7–11. *The Dead Sea occupies the bottom of the flat-floored Jordan graben, a part of the Rift Valley complex of East Africa and the Middle East. The Rosh Zohar Mountains in the distance mark a marginal fault line. (Courtesy of Israel Information Office.)*

Jordan River and the Dead Sea occupy the northern end of an extensive series of related grabens (Fig. 7–11) that include the Red Sea and the so-called Rift Valleys of East Africa (Fig. 7–12). Lake Tanganyika marks its southern terminus. It is often difficult to determine whether a graben has been formed by the middle block dropping or the blocks on either side being lifted, but the name graben still applies. In the upper Rhine Valley where the river is the boundary between Germany and France, it appears that, although the Rhine flows northward in a graben, the Vosges on the west and the Black Forest on the east have been raised while at the same time the central block was slightly depressed.

Now, if the central block is thrown up, resulting in an angular fault block upland, it is called a *horst*. (Fig. 7–13.) The Sierra Nevada is not a horst since it is merely tilted along a single fault plane, but the Great Basin, especially Nevada, displays many horsts. Here is a remarkable assemblage of faulted features extending for hundreds of

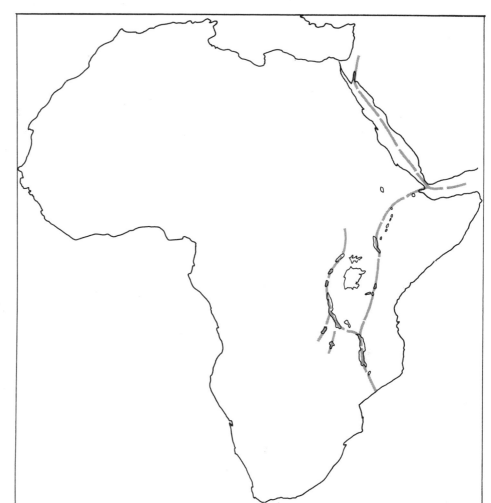

Fig. 7–12. *The Rift Valleys of eastern Africa. The Red Sea and the many linear lakes render visible on the map the great east African fault system.*

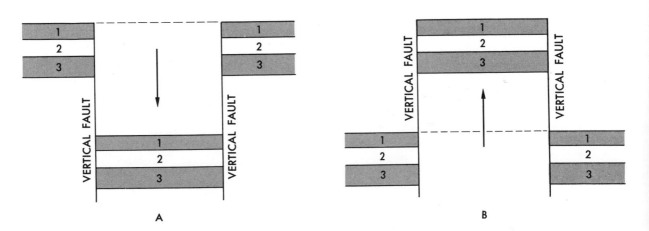

Fig. 7–13. *Formation of a graben and a horst. In (A), a central block has slipped down along two vertical faults, as evidenced by strata 1, 2, and 3, which were previously contiguous along the dotted line. This is called a* graben. *A* horst *is the reverse (B), an upraised central block.*

miles over a wide area and all oriented in a roughly north-south lineation. Apparently, tensional and compressional forces were applied in
an east-west direction, and the resulting clusters of faults were formed
at right angles to them. Movement along these fault planes over many
years has caused literally thousands of horsts, grabens, tilted blocks,
and enclosed basins at various levels. Continuing erosion has subdued the stark outlines of some of the uplands and partially filled the
basins, but in this arid region where erosion is somewhat retarded, the
more recently formed features still retain much of their original character and are easily recognizable. (Fig. 7–14.)

Often cut off one from the other and at different levels, each basin
becomes a separate receptacle to collect the runoff from infrequent
rains in its surrounding uplands. Periodically, broad sheets of water
called *playa lakes* cover the basin floor, but they may attain only a foot
or two maximum depth and evaporate away almost overnight. Hence,
the name "playa," literally beach; these lakes feature more beach than
water. The normal aspect of the basin, except immediately following
a rain, is a blinding white residual alkaline flat.

*Fig. 7–14. The sharp fault escarpment at the western side of the
Funeral Mountain horst, viewed from Death Valley. (Courtesy of U.S.
National Park Service.)*

EARTHQUAKES. There has been a popular image from as far back as the early Greeks, relating earthquakes and volcanoes. It has been observed that volcanic zones and seismic zones frequently show a good deal of coincidence, and there is no gainsaying that people in the immediate vicinity of a violently erupting volcano experience a shaking and rumbling of the earth. However, except for these relatively mild local tremors, *volcanoes do not cause earthquakes*. Faulting is the cause of seismic activity and to a large extent also is responsible for the occurrence of volcanoes. So very frequently, faulting, earthquakes, and volcanoes are found together, but faulting is the basic cause.

The margin of the Pacific Ocean in its present outline is a very unstable region marked by widespread faulting and continuing slippage and readjustment. From the Andes and the Sierra Nevada to Alaska, and from Kamchatka, Japan, and Indonesia to New Zealand and Antarctica, continuing seismic shocks must be accepted as an unalterable environmental stringency even as tornadoes are in other parts of the world. As further evidence of faulting, this area displays some of the great ocean deeps that very possibly are grabens or related forms.

Crustal movement along existing faults or the formation of new faults is not a gradual thing. Pressures may build up slowly over many years, but when the rocks can no longer sustain that pressure, the break or the slippage comes with explosive suddenness. A part of the shock comes from this skidding and realignment along the fault plane, but a part comes from what is called *elastic rebound* as rocks which have been somewhat deformed as they have attempted to sustain the increasing pressure suddenly snap back to their original shape. The result of this is an earthquake with the shock waves rolling out in all directions from the epicenter.

Displacement of mass may occur vertically or horizontally or both. If the fault is at the surface, vertical displacement is sometimes visible in the sudden formation of low cliffs, or if it is horizontal, fences and roads crossing the fault will be forced out of line. The famous San Francisco earthquake of 1906 involved horizontal movement along the San Andreas fault that runs over one-half the length of California and well out to sea north of San Francisco. (Fig. 7–15.)

Coastal areas, even those well outside of seismic zones, are subject to the effects of earthquakes at the sea bottom. Their shock waves are not only transmitted through the earth, but through the overlying water as well. Such ocean waves, emanating from the sea depths, travel outward in all directions from the earthquake epicenter at speeds of hundreds of miles per hour and may devastate coastlines 1,000 miles away with only a little warning. The great Chilean earthquake of

Fig. 7–15. *This old photo, taken along the San Andreas fault immediately following the San Francisco earthquake of 1906, clearly illustrates in the radically offset road the great horizontal slippage along the fault. (Courtesy of California Division of Mines & Geology.)*

1960 was complicated by *tidal waves*,[3] as they are called, and within 24–36 hours, coastal areas as far distant as New Zealand and Japan had experienced destructive high seas. The Anchorage quake in March, 1964, similarly caused damage along the Oregon and California coasts.

Buildings of reinforced concrete, of moderate height, and constructed on bedrock withstand the whipping, rolling action of earthquakes fairly well. But brick and masonry, especially if built on a loose fill base, are likely to be totally destroyed. Frame construction

[3] "Tidal waves" is something of a misnomer, and the Japanese term "tsunami" is coming into more frequent use. These may also be caused by volcanic explosions beneath the sea.

stands up well because it is flexible, although chimneys, plaster, and plumbing are usually damaged. Also, landslides are often a destructive result of earthquakes. In the Hebgen Lake, Montana, quake of August, 1959, landslides blocked a sizable river to form a lake, and in the process, a number of people were killed. So, living in a seismic region is an adventure, for earthquakes occur suddenly with no advance warning; and although many are harmless, it is likely, even inevitable, that sooner or later a killer will come.

No part of the world is immune to earthquakes, but there are two great zones of almost constant activity. One is the aforementioned Pacific littoral including the West Indies and the largely submarine Atlantic ridge, and the second extends east-west through the high mountains of the northern Mediterranean, Asia Minor, the Caucasus, and the Himalayas.

Vulcanism. The term "vulcanism" implies volcanoes—and they are, to be sure, a spectacular product of it. But vulcanism involves much more than mere volcanoes. *Any invasion of the earth's crustal zone by magma from below is properly called vulcanism.* If the magma pushes its way well up into the crustal strata but does not reach the surface, it is termed *intrusive* vulcanism, but if it wells out onto the surface via volcanic or other vents, it is called *extrusive* vulcanism. (Fig. 7–16.)

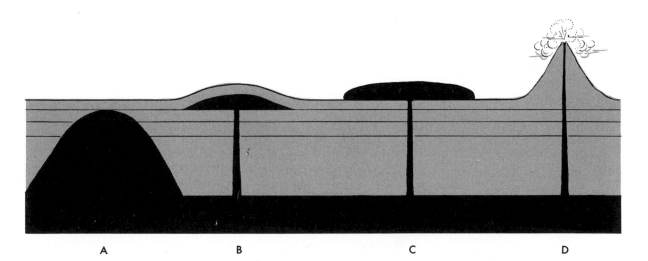

A   B   C   D

Fig. 7–16. Types of vulcanism. Molten rock may merely invade the crustal layers, or it may flow out onto the surface. In (A) and (B), two types of intrusive vulcanism are illustrated: (A) a batholith and (B) a lacolith. In extrusive vulcanism, the lava may issue via a fissure to cover large areas (C), or it may discharge in explosive fashion via a volcanic vent (D).

The question may well be asked, "Why does molten material from the earth's interior force its way into and through the hard rock of the crust?" This is one of the questions that has vexed geologists for many years—not only "Why does magma invade the crust?" but "Where precisely does the magma originate?" It seems reasonably certain that release of pressure on the interior of the earth by deformation and fracturing of the crust triggers the outward movement of magma, but whether it originates initially at the earth's core, the mantle, or even the crust itself is difficult to determine. Several studies have suggested that most volcanoes tap only relatively shallow source regions; however, this does not obviate the possibility of deep-seated sources for certain types of volcanic activity. (Fig. 7–17.)

Fig. 7–17. A lava stream newly hardened into igneous rock still exhibits the flow lines of the liquid lava. (Courtesy of Hawaii Visitors Bureau.)

Fig. 7–18. *Devil's Tower, Wyoming, is a volcanic plug. Magma solidified in the vent of a former volcano that has been removed by subsequent erosion. (Courtesy of U.S. National Park Service.)*

Thus, nearly all major mountain masses are underlain by intrusive masses, and frequently there is some sort of extrusive vulcanism in evidence as well. Mountain-building mechanisms such as folding and faulting cause vulcanism, but vulcanism, once set in motion, can be a potent mountain-building mechanism in its own right. Massive intrusions may lift and warp the surface layers,[4] and extrusive magma, finding its way to the surface through faults, can build huge piles of volcanic rock. Also, intrusions may be exposed by the wearing away of the softer overlying strata by erosion, and the hard igneous mass will stand up as highlands. The Adirondacks and mountains of New England are of this type. (Fig. 7–18.) Volcanoes are, of course, of

---

[4] The various types of intrusive forms have been given descriptive names. The largest of these (over 40 square miles in size) is called a *batholith,* while a smaller intrusion wedging its way between flat-lying sedimentary layers and warping the surface is termed a *lacolith.* There are others such as *sills* and *dikes.* It is recommended that a text on physical geology or geomorphology (such as W. D. Thornbury, *Principles of Geomorphology* [New York: John Wiley & Sons, Inc., 1954]) be consulted by those who are interested in the details of these forms.

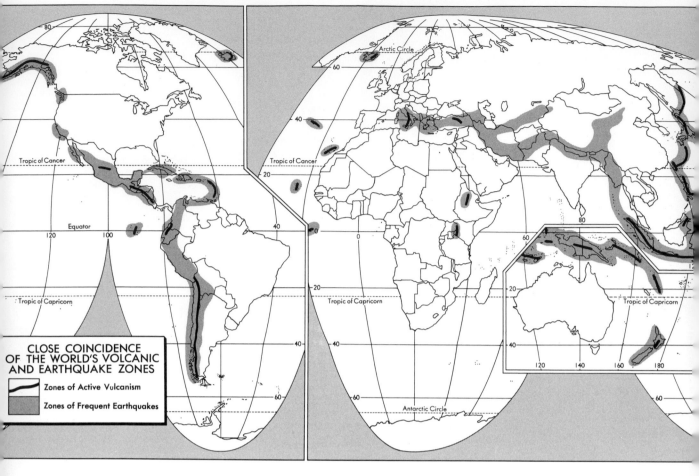

Fig. 7–19. *The close coincidence of the world's volcanic and earthquake zones.*

particular interest not only because of their unpredictable explosive habits, but because of their imposing structure. They tend to follow fault lines, and thus the world's great volcanic zones are coincident with the world's great seismic zones—these three go together (faulting, earthquakes, and volcanoes), and faulting is the basic cause for the other two. The Pacific's unstable margin is often popularly referred to as the "Pacific Ring of Fire" because of its great volcanic activity. Everywhere cones of all sizes, both active and dormant, are evidence of continuing vulcanism. (Fig. 7–19.)

The simplest classification of volcanoes is on the basis of the shape of the cone, for most of them fall generally into one of three types that are easily recognizable, and the cone shape also gives some indication of the type of ejecta and the eruptive habits of the volcano.

First, there is the *cinder cone*. This is the product of a violently explosive volcano where the lava has solidified in the vent, forming a plug. (Fig. 7–18.) The accumulation of steam and magmatic gases gradually develops sufficient pressure to blow the plug with such force as to shatter it into tiny fragments (called *cinders*), and these are deposited in a symmetrical pile around the vent, the larger particles nearest the vent and the finer ones farther away. The resulting cinder cone is steep sided (about 37°, the maximum angle of repose of loose unconsolidated material) and usually symmetrical. (Fig. 7–20.) Although evident in many parts of the world, the cinder cone seldom achieves any great size, as erosion rapidly wears away what is essentially merely a pile of loose rocks. The disappearing islands of the Pacific are of this type, where an eruption may throw up a cinder pile above the ocean level to be visible for a few days or months until wave action removes it.

Fig. 7–20. *Imaginatively named, Cinder Cone in Mt. Lassen National Park illustrates in its steep slope the maximum angle of repose of unconsolidated material. (Courtesy of California Division of Mines & Geology.)*

Fig. 7–21. *Mauna Kea, viewed from Hilo Harbor, displays the typical low-angle slope of a dome volcano. (Courtesy of Hawaii Visitors Bureau.)*

The second type of volcanic cone is called *shield* or *dome*. Here a quiet flow of fairly viscous lava issues from the vent, forming a vast low-angle cone as it cools. Mauna Loa–Mauna Kea whose 13,000-foot tips form the island of Hawaii is an excellent example of this type of cone, and if the low angle of the island's slope is traced to the sea bottom some 5 miles deep, the true size of this twin cone becomes apparent. (Fig. 7–21.)

As often as not, however, a volcano passes through several stages in its history, alternating between explosive eruptions and lava flows. The resulting cone develops a combination of the low-angle shield and the high-angle cinder cone. These are *composite cones* and display concave slopes with a sharp peak. (Fig. 7–22.) Imagine first a cinder cone, but before it can erode away, it is overlain by lava flows. Then built on top of this another cinder cone, followed again by lava. The end product looks like Fujiyama, Shasta, Rainier, or Egmont, the world famous volcanoes that inspire poets and legends. These four are now all dormant, but El Misti in Peru is equally as spectacular

Fig. 7–22. *The classic cone of Mt. Fuji is a perfect example of composite development. (Courtesy of Pan American Airways.)*

and still active as is Mayon in the Philippines. Mayon, despite its generally low elevation and lack of picturesque snowcap, is the most perfectly shaped of the world's composite volcanoes.

There are, of course, exceptions to these standard forms, such as *calderas* whose entire tops have either subsided or blown to bits. Crater Lake, Oregon, and the center of Ambrim Island in the New Hebrides are of this type. (Fig. 7–23.) Another type is the unlikely volcano that erupts gases, cinders, or lava from its sides rather than the top, such as Pelée in Martinique. But variations and exceptions are rare, and most volcanic cones, if not highly typical, still can be roughly categorized as cinder, shield, or composite. (Fig. 7–24.)

Lava, in pouring out onto the earth's surface, does not always issue from volcanic vents; it may well out of faults or fissures many miles in length. If the lava is highly liquid and the terrain fairly subdued,

Fig. 7–23. *Despite its name, Crater Lake is not a crater, but a* caldera. *The small cinder cone forming Wizard Island indicates that volcanic activity did not wholly cease after the top of the original volcano disappeared. (Courtesy of U.S. National Park Service.)*

Fig. 7–24. *Inside Haleakala crater on the island of Maui, Hawaii. This is a true crater and not a caldera, although nearly 30 miles in circumference. Note the many little cinder cones. (Courtesy of U.S. National Park Service.)*

such *fissure flows* have been known to cover thousands of square miles and build up extensive plateaus as in eastern Washington, eastern Oregon, southern Idaho, and northern California. The bulk of peninsular India is also of this origin. In Washington, the Columbia River Gorge and the Grand Coulee reveal along their sides a banded layering of differing colors and textures, each of which represents a separate flow. (Fig. 7–25.) On occasion, the hot lava will be heavily charged with gases, and as the lava cools, the escaping gases leave holes in the rock, making it extremely porous. In southern Idaho, the Snake River Canyon has cut across such a layer imprisoned between two impervious flows, and thousands of springs issue from the side of the canyon; water flows from the melting snows of the Rockies through the permeable (scoriaceous) rock as though it were a pipe.

Fig. 7–25. *The rim of Washington's Grand Coulee. The various flat-lying beds of repeated fissure flows* (left) *are readily identifiable by color and texture differences. The upswept basaltic sheets in the center foreground* (above) *indicate a vent through which highly liquid lava welled out onto the surface. (Courtesy of U.S. Bureau of Reclamation.)*

So we have seen the tectonic forces folding, faulting, and vulcanism working alone or in conjunction to deform and change the surface of the earth—sometimes scarcely evident to the human eye, at other times violent and destructive. No part of the world is free from their effects, and if we but look about us, we can see innumerable evidences of their past performances, and we are frequently made aware of their continuing activity.

Gradational Forces

Now we must consider the effects of the gradational forces as they operate to offset the tectonic forces. The great rock masses thrown up by faulting, folding, and vulcanism are a formidable challenge to the erosive capacity of running water, moving ice, wind, and waves, but they can and do wear away the world's great mountains as has been repeatedly demonstrated, given the tools with which to work and especially given unlimited time. A means of organizing and classifying the various stages of this erosional cycle has been worked out by the renowned geographer William Morris Davis and is a useful tool for the student in the field in recognizing and describing the various landforms that he may observe. It is called the *Geomorphic Cycle*.

The geomorphic cycle. We must first assume a new landform, perhaps a flat-topped plateau just raised out of the sea by faulting. But no sooner is it exposed to the atmosphere than the gradational forces begin to attack it and to alter its outline as they attempt to lower it back to sea level. Newly established streams flow across its face, cutting as they go and carrying away their cuttings to the sea. But for a while at least, depending on the hardness of the rock to be worn away, the basic tabular outline of the plateau remains intact, scarred to be sure, but easily recognizable as a flat-topped block. Between the narrow stream valleys, there still remain extensive areas of the original surface. At this stage, the erosion cycle is called *youthful,* i.e., relatively little progress has been made in altering the landform. (Fig. 7–26.)

But erosion is inexorable, and eventually, as the streams cut deeper and multiply their tributaries, the flat top of the plateau will become so mutilated that it loses completely its earlier appearance. Interstream divides have now been reduced to sharp ridges or peaks, and the only indication that the surface was once at a constant level is the accordance (same height) of these ridges. Now the entire landform exhibits a maximum of relief—slope is everywhere and no flat land exists. Such a highly dissected landform has reached a *mature* erosional stage, and a significant part of it has been cut away and removed, leaving its form greatly altered. (Fig. 7–27.)

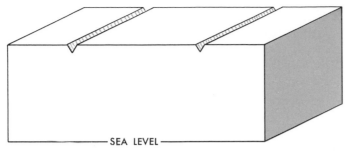

SEA LEVEL

YOUTHFUL LANDFORM

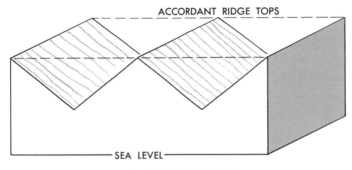

ACCORDANT RIDGE TOPS

SEA LEVEL

MATURE LANDFORM

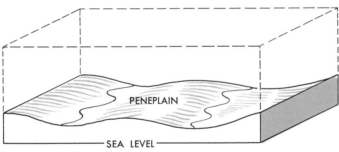

PENEPLAIN

SEA LEVEL

OLD-AGE LANDFORM

Fig. 7–26. The geomorphic cycle (highly diagrammatic). A youthful landform is only slightly modified, a mature landform is carved dramatically, and an old-age landform is an erosional plain reduced to near sea level.

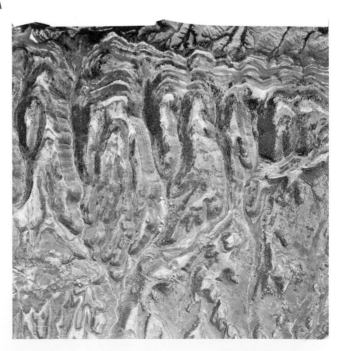

Fig. 7–27. This unusual vertical aerial photo of a mature landscape near Cheyenne, Wyoming, illustrates clearly the almost complete lack of level terrain. (Courtesy of U.S. Coast & Geodetic Survey.)

Fig. 7–28. *In the distance, the flat surface of an uplifted* peneplain *in Angola. (Courtesy of Casa de Portugal.)*

Finally, as the rivers approach the completion of their work, they have cut their valleys down to a point not far above sea level, and in so doing lost much of their velocity and vigorous downward cutting ability. Now they flow languidly across broad plains, and the rolling interstream divides are far below the level of the original plateau. This is an *old-age* stage of erosion and the landform has been planed away. A nearly flat surface once again appears, but this time at a level very near that of the sea. It is called a *peneplain* or an erosional plain —not quite at sea level and not quite flat because the streams require gravity to erode and at this stage have lost that ability. (Fig. 7–28.) Often, standing above this rolling surface, there will be a hard-rock remnant that did not erode away as rapidly as the rest. This is called a *monadnock,* but it too will disappear given time. (Fig. 7–29.)

Fig. 7–29. *The more resistant rock of this volcanic plug at Le Puy en Velay, France, stands as a* monadnock *above the general level of the surrounding erosional surface. (Courtesy of French Cultural Services.)*

This geomorphic cycle is a theoretical cycle in that the tectonic forces do not always wait for the gradational forces to complete their work before beginning anew. Any erosional cycle may be interrupted at midpoint by a new uplift, outpouring of lava, or the like. And the landform does not have to be a plateau as was used as an example or the erosive agent a stream. A volcanic cone may pass through the various cycles of erosion, leading to its complete removal, and glaciers on its flanks may contribute to its destruction quite as effectively as running water. The basic concept merely assumes that, *all other things being equal and given sufficient time, every landform will pass through the sequence of erosion, resulting in peneplanation.*

Weathering. Aiding and abetting the efforts of the gradational forces to smooth the earth's surface is a complementary process called *weathering.* It is a gradational force in itself to a certain extent, but unlike streams, ice, wind, and waves, weathering does not transport materials. Instead, it functions to disintegrate massive rock formations into a size and form so that they can be moved and deposited elsewhere by other agents. Thus, weathering complements and aids gradation.

Two distinct methods of weathering are generally recognized: *chemical* and *mechanical.* They operate in conjunction and most rocks are broken up by both means. However, since chemical weathering requires water and is most effective under conditions of high temperature, it is strongly dominant in warm, moist regions, while the rocks of the deserts, high altitudes, and high latitudes exhibit most strongly the effects of mechanical processes.

CHEMICAL WEATHERING. The most familiar example of the chemical decomposition of a seemingly indestructible material is the rusting of steel. In a relatively short time, a piece of shiny steel, virtually immune to abrasion or other mechanical wear, may be reduced to a reddish powder in the presence of water. This is an example of *oxidation* (chemical union with oxygen) and *hydration* (chemical union with water). Copper turns green and soft on the surface through *carbonation* as it reacts with the carbon dioxide in water or the air. So, since rocks are made up of combinations of minerals, each mineral may be attacked and broken down by a different chemical process. Those minerals that do not react directly to water or the atmosphere may be highly susceptible to acid groundwater resulting from these previous chemical changes or the passage of water through an overlying layer of decaying vegetation. Limestone, for instance, is only moderately soluble in clear water but dissolves readily when carbonic acid is present and may be carried away, leaving cavities which weaken the rock. Feldspar too, a very common mineral in many rocks, breaks down into clay when attacked by acids. Quartz on the other hand, also widely distributed, resists chemical weathering, and upon being released by the decomposition of its neighboring minerals is carried off and shows up in unaltered form in beach sands.

Chemical weathering, then, is essentially the *rotting* of hard rock and thus changing its form so that it can be easily attacked and removed by the agents of gradation. Landforms in areas where chemical weather is dominant exhibit a characteristic rounded or subdued outline and lack the jagged sharp-edged appearance of the typical mechanically weathered landform.

MECHANICAL WEATHERING. All rocks have cracks and crevices even if only of microscopic dimensions, and if water is introduced into them and freezes, they are rapidly expanded and eventually big chunks will be broken off. This is a powerful mechanical force, especially if, as in high elevations, alternate freezing and thawing are almost a daily occurrence. The greater volume of ice over water and its destructive capacity are readily observable on your own back porch when the milk freezes in its bottle on winter mornings. If the cap does not rupture readily allowing the frozen cream to extrude itself, the heavy bottle will shatter. Even in the desert, dew may supply sufficient moisture to cause a certain amount of *frost wedging* if temperatures fall below freezing. This is mechanical weathering rather than chemical, operating to break rock into small pieces. Inasmuch as water is involved, chemical change is inevitable too, but the ice action is a mechanical force.

Radical temperature changes too will weaken rock, at least in theory. Every mineral in the rock has a different coefficient of expansion, and so temperature change will cause the surface to crumble and peel as it tears itself apart. It is difficult to separate the mechanical from the chemical effects in general surface crumbling, but this is analogous roughly to the difficulties that plagued the aluminum siding industry when they initially installed the siding with steel nails. Until aluminum nails were used, the differing expansion of aluminum vs. steel caused the siding to rip itself off the walls in one year.

Roots of growing plants and trees and burrowing animals inserting themselves in rock crevices likewise must be classified as means of mechanical weathering. And also in this category should be included simple gravity and impact as large rock fragments tumble down steep slopes to smash into smaller pieces. (Fig. 7–30.)

So, weathering of all types prepares rock for easy removal by the gradational agents. Without it, gradation would continue but at a much slower rate and with considerably less effectiveness.

Fig. 7–30. *Mechanical weathering. Angular fragments derived from the cliff (above)* form a steep apron at its base called a *talus slope. This is in an arid region. Columnar jointing in igneous rock (right) has allowed ice wedging to pry off huge blocks, which are further broken by impact as they tumble down the steep cliff face. (Courtesy of Wanapum Development, P.U.D. of Grant County, Wash., and U.S. National Park Service.)*

Running water. By all odds, the most important of the gradational agents is running water. Without question, wave erosion of shorelines is very effective and widespread, but waves merely nibble at the periphery of continents, while running water operates over their entire surface. Even in the desert where surface streams carry water only spasmodically after infrequent storms, they may move an enormous amount of material in a very short time. The hard baked earth and the violence of the typical desert downpour mean maximum surface runoff, leaving the land scarred and eroded into numerous deeply cut channels and arroyos. Elsewhere, every little rivulet and creek is a gradational agent delivering its load of material to the master stream to carry away, and gullying as it goes.

Slope, of course, is a major factor in stream erosion because without slope the stream ceases to flow. But remember, all gradational agents must accomplish three functions: they (1) *pick up materials,* (2) *transport them,* and (3) *ultimately deposit them.* So when streams encounter a low gradient, which is frequent in their lower courses when they debouch into the sea, they deposit their load and thus fulfill the last part of their gradational function. It is sometimes useful to break *gradation* down into its components of *degradation* or cutting and eroding, and *aggradation* or depositing and building up. *Transportation* comes in between these two, and the final result is to carve away the high spots and fill up the low ones.

All streams carry sediments. There is no such thing as absolutely clear running water on the surface of the earth. Obviously, a big muddy-appearing river such as the Hwang Ho or the Missouri is moving a great deal of soil in suspension, but even sparkling mountain cascades are transporting surprisingly large amounts of material. It is simply that their capacity is so great relative to their load that they appear clear. *The chief control of a stream's ability to transport material is its velocity.* Volume too affects this but the importance of velocity is overwhelming; thus, high-velocity mountain streams exhibit a huge load-carrying capacity, while sluggish streams barely moving across a gentle gradient are very ineffective transporters of sediment. On this basis, we attempt to classify running water into general types.

Try to visualize streams as living entities attempting to reach an equilibrium between actual sediment load and their capacity. Such a balanced stream where the load is exactly equal to the amount it is equipped to carry is called a *graded stream*. Although this perfect equilibrium is virtually impossible to achieve in nature, many streams come fairly close and all strive toward this graded ideal. This means that a high-velocity stream with tremendous energy but underloaded will work hard to find more materials to carry. This type of water course is called *youthful*. On the other hand, a placid low-velocity stream may find itself heavily overloaded, especially if it is fed by vigorous tributaries. Its increased volume fails to offset its low velocity, and such a stream attempts to rid itself of its surplus load. Such a stream is classed as *old age*. In between these two extremes are many streams with median velocity and median load that approach the ideal of a graded stream. On occasion from season to season, such streams may exhibit youthful or old-age tendencies, but since they normally show a reasonable balance between load and velocity, they are called *mature*. The vigor of youth, senility of old age, and balance of maturity are all represented here, and the simile aids in understanding stream behavior.

Although this same classification system and terminology of youth, maturity, and old age was used earlier to characterize the various stages of the geomorphic cycle, it does not necessarily follow that youthful streams must flow on youthfully eroded landforms, mature streams on maturely eroded landforms, etc.

YOUTHFUL STREAMS.   The high-velocity stream with its tremendous energy is attempting to avail itself of a sediment load commensurate with its velocity.   It has only one arena of operation and that is its channel, so it works with great vigor on that channel.   But the friction of running water over rocks is scarcely capable of eroding those rocks at all effectively.   Certainly, water is able to take into solution some of the minerals, thereby weakening the rock and allowing pieces to tear away and be carried off, but it is these rock fragments and others delivered from the valley slopes, varying in size from boulders to sands and silts, that become the "teeth" of the stream and give it great cutting ability.   Especially effective are the hard, sharp-edged quartz fragments in sands that allow a youthful stream to abrade and corrade its channel downward at a very rapid rate.   In doing so, it begins to appease its appetite for sediments by cutting them out of the channel while at the same time gradually lowering its gradient (and velocity), thus requiring an increasingly smaller amount of load to balance velocity.

Typically, the youthful stream forms a V-shaped valley and occupies the entire narrow valley bottom. (Fig. 7–31.) The slope of the V is determined by the steepest angle of repose of loose soil.   But as the stream works its way rapidly downward, that angle is increased, and great volumes of soil and rock slide into the valley and supply the

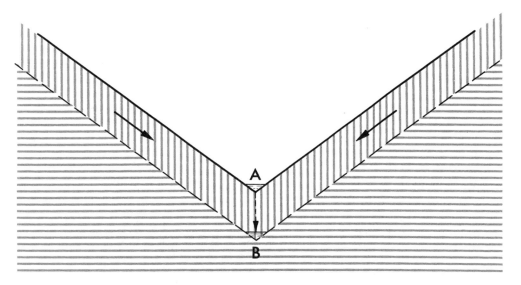

Fig. 7–31. *V-shaped valley and youthful stream erosion. As the stream works its channel down from (A) to (B), the material on the valley sides, their slopes steepened now, is delivered to the stream via gravity.*

Fig. 7–32. *The steep slopes and narrow valley bottom, here at the Middle Fork of the Kings River in the Sierra Nevadas, point to a youthful development. Falls and rapids too are frequent features of early youth. Note the polished surface of the rock in the left foreground, abraded by stream sediments (up to boulder size) during high water. (Courtesy of U.S. National Park Service.)*

stream with added material. Also, any tributary creeks and rivulets find their gradients becoming steeper as they attempt to maintain their mouths at the level of the constantly lower master stream, and thus they become more effective eroders and deliver increased quantities of sediment. (Fig. 7–32.)

Where the youthful stream flows across hard-rock strata, it cuts a vertical-sided gorge or slot rather than a V, since the rock is capable of maintaining sheer cliffs without sliding. However, as soft layers which have been protected previously from the atmosphere by overlying hard rock are exposed along the sides of the gorge, weathering begins its work immediately and further weakens them, so that eventually the harder stratum is undercut to the point where it collapses, and all this debris is delivered to the stream via gravity. (Fig. 7–33.) Many of

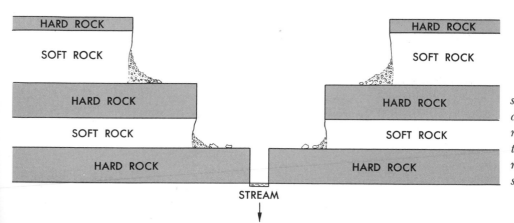

Fig. 7–33. *Youthful stream erosion—canyon. In cutting its way across alternating hard and soft strata, the stream exposed the soft rock to weathering and erosion.*

the spectacular gorges in the Colorado Plateau have been developed in this manner. They are commonly ½ mile or more in width across the top, narrowing via terraces toward the bottom. Each terrace surface represents a hard-rock layer overlying softer strata, while far below in the bottom of the canyon, the stream occupies a narrow slot as it busily cuts its way downward. This type of canyon development, of course, depends on the exposure of beds with differing resistances to weathering as in the Grand Canyon and many others. (Fig. 7–34.) The Snake and Columbia rivers, on the other hand, have worked their way down through hard rocks of similar resistance, and their gorges tend to be narrow and sheer-sided.

As youthful streams charge across the countryside, they have a marked tendency to maintain relatively straight courses, as it is characteristic of them to overrun and cut away obstacles rather than detour around them. Slides may choke its channel for short periods, but the energetic stream will rapidly chew its way through. Lakes,

Fig. 7–34. *Despite its dimensions (10 miles from lip to lip and over 1 mile deep), the Grand Canyon of the Colorado is a youthful stream valley, and all of that missing material has been carried off to be deposited in the Gulf of California. (Courtesy of U.S. National Park Service.)*

falls, and rapids are common features in early youth as a drainage pattern establishes itself over newly uplifted terrain, but these are transitory. The upper end of a lake will silt up rapidly, while at the same time, the downward erosion at its outlet will cut away the lip that maintains the water level and the lake will drain away. Similarly, falls and rapids will be erased within a short time. Close to home, we have the example of the St. Lawrence with many rapids, Niagara Falls, and the Great Lakes in its drainage system. The rapids are being smoothed out, Niagara Falls is retreating rapidly and left to itself (which is unlikely in the light of its economic benefits), and the river will drain the lakes within a very short geologic span.

A word of caution here—do not equate the length of time that a stream has been in existence with its category of youth, maturity, or old age. *It is its behavior that determines its classification.* Like people, streams are only as old as they act. Obviously, a stream attempting to erode a hard-rock channel will maintain its youthful characteristics much longer than one cutting through soft strata. But given sufficient time with no tectonic interruptions, in the normal course of events, all youthful streams will lower their gradient to the point where they can achieve maturity.

MATURE STREAMS.   Mature streams come closest to the graded ideal. Remember that there is actually no such thing as a perfectly graded stream. Even one where velocity matches load most of the year may find itself with increased volume during springtime's melting snows or a sustained rainy season, and will sweep its channel clean and cut into its bed in an attempt to find a larger load to match its somewhat large capacity. In this case, increased volume rather than velocity will allow it to carry somewhat more. Conversely, during a dry season, its volume may be somewhat reduced so that it must drop some of its load, thereby choking its channel with sand bars which render it difficult for the main current to find its way directly, and it may break up into many lesser courses flowing tortuous routes around the barriers (*braided stream*). But nonetheless, any stream that normally exhibits a reasonable balance between load and carrying capacity is called *mature.*

Typically, the mature stream, having lost some of the ability of the youthful stream to overrun obstacles in its path, has developed moderate bends or meanders in its course. For instance, if a slide were to block the course of a stream in early maturity, it would detour around it. In doing so, the current that attempts to run in straight lines would be diverted against the bank. (Fig. 7–35.) Here it would cut horizontally on the outside of the bend, expanding that bend farther to the side. Then bouncing off of this side, it would be diverted

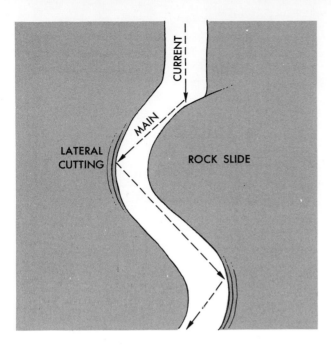

Fig. 7–35. Early meander develop-ment. Once a youthful stream loses its ability to cut through impediments in its path, it is forced to work lat-erally as well as vertically. The ero-sion on the outside bends of the chan-nel leads to meanders, an indication of incipient maturity.

In the figure: CURRENT, MAIN, LATERAL CUTTING, ROCK SLIDE

again to the other side and cut again laterally to form another bend, and so on downstream. Thus, once these bends or meanders are es-tablished, the main current, moving alternately back and forth across the river, cuts at the outside of bends and enlarges the meanders. Here we have something quite different from the youthful stream where all of its great erosional energy is expended downward; the mature stream which cuts moderately downward during high water normally erodes laterally, forming meanders and widening its valley floor. To illuminate the full picture, we should divide the flowing water of the mature stream into two segments: first, the main current which has the greatest velocity and some youthful characteristics as it cuts away at the bank of the outside bends and keeps its channel clean and deep; and second, the more slowly moving bulk of the stream which flows along the inside bends. It displays some old-age charac-teristics as it cannot carry the entire load supplied it and drops it along the inside bend, thus building up these areas to become a por-tion of the valley bottom. Inside bends then display gently shelving bottoms built up by deposition, while outside bends will be deep with a cliffed bank. (Fig. 7–36.)

This lateral cutting combined with matching deposition across the river means that a mature stream occupies a broad valley floor as op-posed to the youthful stream where the channel was the only valley floor. (Fig. 7–37.) The outside bends touch and cut away the sides of the valley on both sides, continually expanding the width of the flat bottom. The proper way to express this is to say that the meander belt (the width from outside bend to outside bend) is the exact width of the valley floor. (Fig. 7–38.) Any road attempting to take advan-

Fig. 7–36. *Cutting laterally on the outside of the bend while depositing on the inside to form a shelving bottom, this small mature stream not only balances its sedimentary load, but widens its valley. (Courtesy of U.S. Army Corps of Engineers, St. Louis, Mo.)*

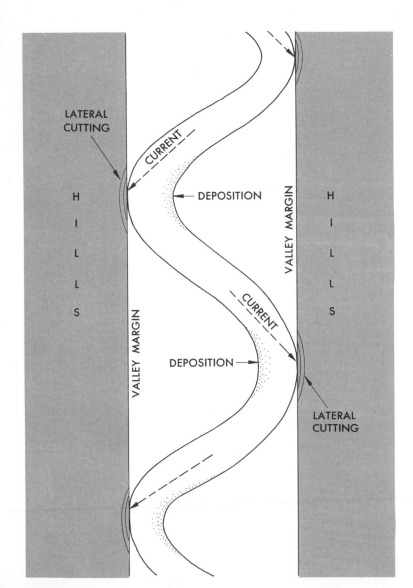

Fig. 7–37. *Mature stream behavior.*

Fig. 7–38. *This stream, in the Meramec River Basin, Mo., is mature as indicated by its moderate meander belt exactly matching the width of the valley. (Courtesy of U.S. Army Corps of Engineers, St. Louis, Mo.)*

tage of such a valley through rough country must bridge the same stream repeatedly. Also, because of the flat valley floor, flooding may occur during high-water periods.

OLD-AGE STREAMS. Any stream flowing across a low-gradient plain and attempting to transport a load of sediment beyond its capacity is properly called an *old-age stream,* irrespective of how long that stream has been in existence. For under these circumstances, it rapidly acquires a fundamental set of senile characteristics. Basically, it is an overloaded stream and therefore an active depositor as it attempts, like all other streams, to balance load and velocity. The place of obvious deposition is the stream channel itself, and typically it is choked with islands and bars and is very shallow. However, since most old-age streams have developed from the mature stage, the already formed moderate meanders are becoming enlarged, and again we must divide the stream flow up into two parts: the swifter-flowing main current attacking the outer bends vs. the slow-moving portion of the inside bends. Despite the fact that an old-age stream is overloaded, sufficient deposition occurs at the inner bends to allow active lateral erosion on the outside bends, and thus the meander pattern becomes extremely sinuous and involved. When this looping course has reached its ultimate development, it becomes increasingly frequent for two outside bends to work their way laterally toward each other until they coalesce and the stream flow cuts across, establishing a new channel and leaving an abandoned meander called an *oxbow lake.* (Figs. 7–39

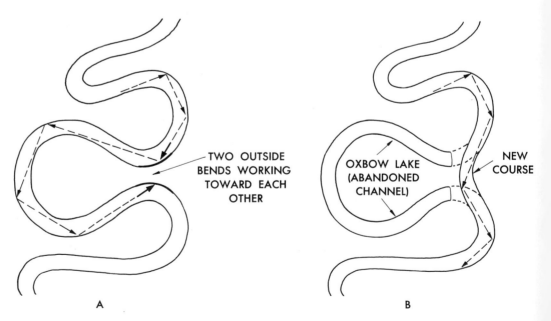

TWO OUTSIDE BENDS WORKING TOWARD EACH OTHER

OXBOW LAKE (ABANDONED CHANNEL)

NEW COURSE

A

B

Fig. 7–39. *The formation of an oxbow lake. The lateral cutting on outside bends is carried to its extreme when two involved bends coalesce to form a new channel, leaving the old abandoned loop as an* oxbow lake.

Fig. 7–40. *Oxbow lakes in the valley of the lower Arkansas River. (Courtesy of U.S. Army Corps of Engineers, Vicksburg, Miss.)*

and 7–40.) Unlike the mature stream, the meander belt occupies only a small part of the wide old-age stream valley. Scars on the bluffs on both sides of the valley (*cusps*) indicate that the stream has been at work, widening its valley and giving evidence that the meander belt shifts back and forth across the valley from time to time.

Although the old-age stream carries all the sediment that it can to the sea and deposits it in the form of a delta, and loses a part of its excess load through channel deposition, this is far from adequate for complete relief. Normal behavior is for the stream to overflow its banks during even relatively minor high-water periods. Several days

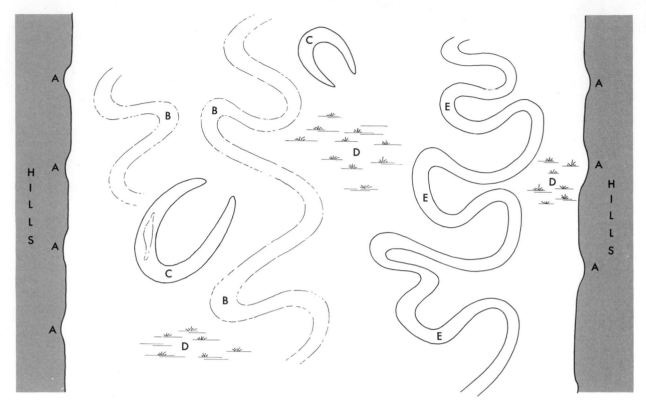

Fig. 7–41. *Old-age stream valley. Meander scars (cusps) on the bounding bluffs (A), abandoned channels (B), oxbow lakes (C), swamps (D), and a serpentine river course occupying only a part of a broad floodplain (E) are all distinctive features of the old-age stream valley.*

of heavy rain in its drainage area are usually enough to cause some overflow, and during the spring, snow melt in the uplands drained by its tributaries often results in extensive flooding. The low banks that suffice to keep the stream in its channel during normal times are easily overrun during high water. These banks, called *natural levees,* exist because as the stream leaves its channel, its velocity is suddenly checked, and heavy deposition occurs here along the channel margin. Then the water spreads out for miles across the entire valley floor as a still lake and drops its entire load of sediments. In this way, the old-age stream gets rid of its overload and at the same time builds up its valley higher above the sea in an attempt to increase the gradient and the stream velocity to enable it to carry its load.[5]

[5] In lower courses of rivers debouching into the sea, this is seldom successful, as delta building at the stream mouth offsets the added height of the valley floor.

Fig. 7–42. The shifting course, wide valley, and sinuous meanders of the Mississippi River below Memphis. (Courtesy of U.S. Army Corps of Engineers, Vicksburg, Miss.)

Once the old-age stream has flooded, the former channel may be abandoned, for usually it is slightly higher than the general level of the valley because of constant channel deposition. So an entire new drainage system may establish itself, or more than one, only to repeat the overflow and abandoning again and again. Thus, the broad, flat valley of an old-age stream presents an amphibious appearance with permanent swamps, oxbow lakes, and constantly changing channels. (Figs. 7–41 and 7–42.)

The valley of the lower Mississippi was like this before it was occupied. De Soto found it to be a 300-mile wide malarial swamp. But such valleys have a certain attractiveness to an agricultural civilization if only the river can be tamed. The deep and constantly rejuvenated soils and dead-flat terrain make exceptionally productive farmland. So, clear the tangled vegetation and drain the swamps and then above all make the river stay in its channel where all self-respecting rivers are supposed to flow. The obvious and most simple way to do this is to build up the natural levees so that at next year's high water, they will be just high enough to contain it. This works nicely except that all the sediments that used to be deposited on the floodplain must now be dropped in the channel bottom. A few years of this and the channel has built itself up to the point where high water comes dangerously close to the levee top, and it must be extended a little higher. (Fig. 7–43.) The people of the North China Plain have had long ex-

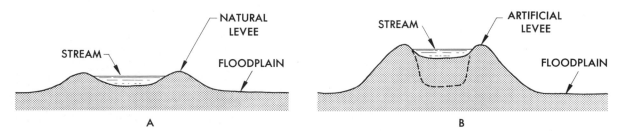

Fig. 7–43. Levees. The natural levee (A) serves to contain the stream during normal water periods, but the man-made artificial levees (B), which hold the river in its channel even during high water, must be built constantly higher to offset increased channel deposition.

perience with building the levees a "little higher." In forcing the Hwang Ho to flow along a sinuous ridge of its own making by building levees, they have magnified the enormity of flooding in the event of a single break in the thousands of miles of levees. They call their stream "China's Sorrow" because levees do break, and periodically the entire river flows down the steep levee side to inundate for months millions of acres of crops. Perhaps people should not attempt to farm old-age stream valleys, for they are trying to have their cake and eat it too. The deep soils are there because old-age streams are supposed to flood as a mechanism to get rid of surplus load. In making the river stay in its channel, man is creating an artificiality, and a stream flowing along a ridgetop 30–50–100 feet above the roof of his house is a dangerous neighbor. (Fig. 7–44.) There may be other ways to control the river and many have been tried, but none with complete success as yet.

DELTAS AND ALLUVIAL FANS. In order to be classified as full-fledged gradational agents, streams must pick up, transport, and deposit materials. Youthful streams, aided and abetted by weathering, are espe-

Fig. 7–44. *The low natural levees have been overrun during high water here at Mayersville, Miss. So far, the second line of higher artificial levees are holding, but the water level is many feet above the town. (Courtesy of U.S. Army Corps of Engineers, Vicksburg, Miss.)*

cially effective in picking up sediments of all sizes, but even mature and old-age streams can erode if often only laterally. And then these sediments must be deposited elsewhere. Here the old-age stream is most efficient both in its channel and its floodplain, with the mature stream accomplishing the same objective to a lesser degree. But any river can be made to deposit simply by lowering its velocity. For instance, when a stream discharges into the sea or a lake, no matter whether it is youthful, mature, or old-age, its velocity is suddenly checked, and it begins to deposit its load. First, the larger and heavier materials are dropped near the shore, and then, as its forward impetus declines, the progressively smaller sediments precipitate. This sorting action of stream deposits is typical. Such a depositional feature is called a *delta,* and it eventually builds up to sea level or slightly above, thus extending the shoreline. (Fig. 7–45.) Often it is much wider than the stream itself, as the offshore currents distribute the

Fig. 7–45. *The fan-shaped delta develops as the stream fouls its own channel and constantly seeks a less impeded course to the sea. Vegetation rapidly establishes itself on the newly made land. This photo was taken along the shore of Cook Inlet, Alaska. (Courtesy of U.S. Coast & Geodetic Survey.)*

loose deposits extensively, or the stream chokes its own channel as the delta reaches sea level and constantly switches to alternate lower channels.

A very similar situation occurs when a high-velocity stream suddenly runs out of the uplands onto a plain. Here again an abrupt checking of velocity results in deposition along the mountain front, and the dry-land equivalent of a delta is formed. Coarse materials are piled up into a steep slope at the valley mouth, succeeded by finer sediments and lesser slope. Finally the stream flows on across the

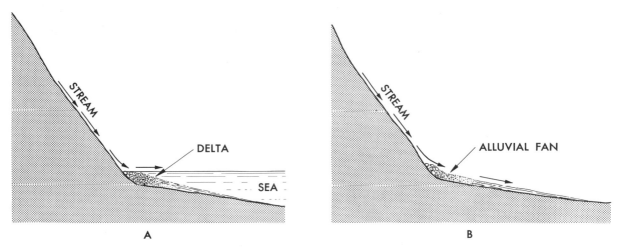

Fig. 7–46. *Deltas and alluvial fans. Both display the sorting of sedi-ments by size that is so typical of stream deposition.*

plain carrying what it can. This type of deposit is called an *alluvial fan* (alluvial, meaning water-deposited) and is fan-shaped because all deposits must be in the stream channel. (Fig. 7–46.) As this becomes rapidly choked, the stream establishes a new channel to one side that in turn is fouled with deposits. The net result is that the stream oscillates from side to side, spreading its deposits in a triangle or fan, with its apex at the mouth of the mountain valley. (Fig. 7–47.) During

Fig. 7–47. *An alluvial fan in Death Valley. The symmetrical markings in the left foreground are abandoned borax workings. (Courtesy of California Division of Mines & Geology.)*

drier periods, much of the water soaks into the coarse gravel at the head of the fan to percolate downslope underground and reappear as springs on the lower fan. Along the western front of the California Sierra Nevadas are a series of overlapping alluvial fans (*alluvial piedmont*) extending for hundreds of miles with their lower gentle slopes utilized for orchard plantings.

Glaciation.   Brittle ice like solid rock can be made plastic through pressure; however, ice requires a great deal less pressure. Usually, the simple accumulation of deep deposits of snow in a region where snow receipt is in excess of the rate of melt, and where the terrain is subdued enough to retain the snow depth without loss via avalanche or slide, is sufficient to start the process. The weight of the total snow mass plus alternating seasonal freezing and thawing will change the lower elements from snow crystals into ice crystals which eventually compact into an ice sheet. Further weight from above will be translated into slow outward flow along the ground. Normally, ice, like water, will find it easiest to move down whatever slope exists, but unlike water, if sufficient pressure is exerted from behind, it can run up over moderate elevations in its path. Such a moving mass of ice can obviously accomplish a good deal of gradation.

Essentially, we recognize two types of glaciers: (1) *valley or alpine glaciers,* which are relatively small and restricted to a single valley or series of valleys in the mountains; and (2) *continental glaciers,* which move across whole continents or large parts of them. Valley glaciers are widespread today in nearly all high-mountain ranges, and many of them are fairly easy of access. (Fig. 7–48.) But there are only two continental glaciers in existence today: the great ice sheet covering Antarctica and the smaller Greenland icecap. (Fig. 7–49.) Both are remote, and it becomes difficult if not impossible for the average researcher to observe continental ice sheets in action. Luckily, moving ice operates very similarly regardless of scale so that the accessible valley glaciers are very effective little laboratory examples of the principles of glacial behavior.

VALLEY GLACIERS.   By observing the behavior of moving ice in all types of valley situations, i.e., valleys filled with ice clear to the sea, receding glaciers that are no longer as far advanced as they have previously been, and abandoned valleys with the evidence of ice erosion exposed to full view, we have a very clear picture of how moving ice functions and what kind of work it can accomplish.

First, ice has a very considerable ability to erode and pick up material from the valley floor and sides. Let us begin with a basin of snow accumulation high in the mountains. Here the vertical pres-

Fig. 7–48. *Several "live" glaciers gnaw at the flanks of Mt. Rainier. (Courtesy of Washington State Department of Commerce & Economic Development.)*

Fig. 7–49. *Greenland's continental ice sheet. From the air, it is not difficult to believe that ice moves, as the waves and flow lines on its surface make it appear as a sea. The glacial scouring of the exposed rocky areas is essentially identical to that which occurred in the past in Scandinavia and Canada. (Courtesy of Danish Information Office.)*

sure of deep snow is causing the bottom layers of ice to move horizontally. Now, obviously such a basin will have been drained of its annual melt water by streams flowing out of the downslope margins, and such streams will have cut valleys. When the ice attempts to move outward, it will tend to divide into lobes and follow these already existing easy avenues of egress. In the bottom of the basin where the ice is thickest and the pressure greatest, a good deal of gouging and scraping will take place, thus deepening the basin floor. Also, large blocks of rock will be frozen into the underside of the ice, and as it begins to move, these will be carried away, acting at the same time as tools or teeth to further cut and polish the floor. While the bottom of the basin of accumulation is being eroded in this manner, the edges of the ice around the perimeter of the basin will similarly take hold of rocks and soil by freezing them into the ice mass and pulling them away from the sides. This process is called *plucking* and acts to steepen the sides of the basin into cliffs. The action is continuous, as new ice is immediately formed in contact with the cliffs as the plucked materials are carried off with the general flow. Gradually, constant plucking will enlarge the basin and cut it farther and farther back toward the mountain peak. The resulting roughly circular amphitheatre with steep cliffs on all sides except the downslope side where the ice is spilling out is called a *cirque*. (Fig. 7–50.) In order for ice

Fig. 7–50. *Le Cirque de Garvarne in the Pyrenees, now abandoned, clearly illustrates the plucking power of ice and its ability to work its way headward at the same time that the glacier is moving downslope. (Courtesy of French Embassy Press & Information Division.)*

to develop cirque cliffs hundreds of feet in height, it need not fill the cirque to the top, but by simply being in contact with all cirque margins and continuously plucking at their base, the cliffs are undercut to the point where great masses of rock slide and tumble onto the ice surface from above and are carried off. If enough of these cirques are gnawing at a mountain's flanks, each working its way headward, they are capable of eroding away an entire mountain peak.

So right here at the headwaters, so to speak, of a valley glacier, the ice is capable of removing large quantities of material (1) by freezing rocks into its underside, which in turn produce further debris as they cut and grind, (2) by plucking and freezing material into its sides wherever it is in contact, which again supplies it with tools for additional cutting, and (3) by carrying on its surface rocks and soil that have fallen from above.

As the tongues of ice push out of the cirque and down the original stream valleys, they continue to erode and modify the shape of the valleys. Normal youthful stream valleys in mountainous regions are V-shaped, you will recall, but as the blunt-nosed ice lobe pushes down them, it deepens and widens them into U-shaped valleys. (Fig. 7–51.)

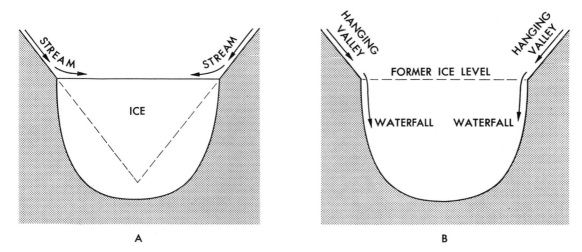

Fig. 7–51. Ice-modified youthful stream valley. The dashed line in (A) traces the outline of the former stream valley now occupied by ice, the glacier changing the original V to a deepened U. Tributaries of the previous master stream fall freely as waterfalls (B) from the mouths of hanging valleys after the ice has retreated.

The plowing action of the inexorable ice advance is not to be ignored, but the same types of freezing at the bottom and plucking at the sides as occurred in the cirque, continued for as long as the ice occupies the valley, are immeasurably more effective.

The surface of a typical valley glacier is scarred with deep crevasses, usually crescentic in shape with their concavities presented upslope. Such ice chasms are a result of the frictional drag of the glacier along its sides and bottom, thus allowing the top central portion to move more rapidly. Frequently, tributaries of the original stream which occupied the valley floor flow down the overhanging mountain slopes and across the surface of the ice, only to plunge down the crevasses and eventually find their way out via under-ice tunnels. Such streams usually deposit part of their sedimentary load on the ice as their velocity is suddenly lessened, and it is mingled here with piles of loose material that slide down the continually undercut valley sides. Many glaciers eventually become so mantled with rock debris that they appear as massive mud slides rather than ice.

Once the ice has melted away, the real effects of ice erosion become apparent in the abandoned valley. Outstanding is Yosemite Valley in the California Sierras where many thousands of years ago, temperatures must have been sufficiently cooler than they are today to support a sizable glacier. (Fig. 7–52.) Now it is gone, but the ice-modified

Fig. 7–52. *These two photos, Yosemite Valley* (left) *and Glacier Park* (right), *demonstrate the ability of a valley glacier to modify the shape of a typical* V-*shaped mountain valley into a broad* U. *The waterfall in Yosemite marks the mouth of a* hanging *valley. Upper St. Mary's Lake in Glacier Park is a* finger lake, *dammed by morainal deposits at its lower end. (Courtesy of U.S. National Park Service.)*

valley remains with its evidences of former ice occupation visible to even the casual tourist. The Merced River flows peacefully along the broad valley floor that is somewhat flattened today by post-ice alluvial deposits. The sheer valley sides are polished and scarred with *striations,* deep grooves cut by the rocks frozen into the side of the ice as it advanced. Near the top of these cliffs, above the level of the ice surface, are seen the sloping remnants of the old V-shaped stream valley; and the original tributaries to the pre-ice Merced River which at one time flowed down these slopes and onto the glacier top, now occupy what are called *hanging valleys* and drop off the cliff top in scenic waterfalls. And far up at the head of the valley is a cirque with its deepened bottom occupied by a *tarn lake.*

At higher latitudes than California where temperatures were cool enough to support ice clear to sea level, glaciers ran down valleys to the sea. Many of these are abandoned now, and the sea has pushed up the valleys in long fingers for many miles. These are called *fiords,* the Norwegian term being applied because of their wide occurrence along the Norwegian coast, but they are also found in large numbers in southeastern Alaska, British Columbia, southern Chile, and New Zealand. (Fig. 7–53.) Aside from the fact that they are now arms of

Fig. 7–53. The U-shaped valley demonstrated again at Milford Sound in southern New Zealand. This time it opens to the sea and the long channel, reaching far inland, and is called a fiord. (Courtesy of New Zealand Government Travel Commissioner.)

Fig. 7–54. *A fiord in the making. This valley glacier, carrying a load of debris on its surface, flows into the head of Glacier Bay in Alaska. Notice the stream-deposited sediments in the left foreground. (Courtesy of U.S. National Park Service.)*

the sea, fiords exhibit identical features to those of Yosemite and other similar ice-carved valleys well above sea level. (Fig. 7–54.) The sea has been able to invade fiords for great distances for two reasons. First, ice deepens the original stream valley, and since the stream reached the sea at sea level, the ice cutting has deepened the lower valley below sea level. Second, during the period when major ice sheets covered extensive land areas, the normal runoff of continental precipitation was held up. Thus, the sea, from which all precipitation ultimately derives via evaporation from its surface, must have been considerably lower. As the water level rose with general ice melting, the invasion of deepened valleys was inevitable. However, seldom does the sea push inland as far as the cirque, so that streams normally now flow down the old ice-glaciated valley into the head of the fiord. In many cases at these relatively high latitudes, the cirques and upper valleys still support small glaciers.

Moving ice with its great erosional and transportational capacity must eventually deposit all of its accumulated load at a lower level. This is done in several ways, but first we must recognize that *as long as a glacier exists, it continues to move forward.* The so-called receding glacier is flowing forward and carrying its load of debris downslope despite the fact that the tip of the glacier is measurably retreating. This simply means that the rate of melt at its lowest extremity is more rapid than its rate of advance. Once the glacier has melted back to a high enough elevation for melt to decrease so that it equals advance, the nose of the ice becomes static. This is the normal situation when melt and advance reach an equilibrium, but once again, whether the nose is advancing or retreating, the ice mass is moving forward. This is important to remember because this forward flow allows the glacier to function like an endless belt and constantly deliver its load of debris to the ice margin and deposit it there.

As the chunks of rock, varying in size from many tons to finely ground powder, that are frozen into the glacier and carried on its surface come to the end of the line, the ice melts out from under them, and they are dumped helter-skelter into an unsorted heap at the ice margin. When the glacier nose is static (neither advancing nor retreating), this heap of loose material builds up to a considerable height and is called a *terminal moraine.*[6] Its upslope side next to the ice is typically quite steep, but the downslope gradient is modified by rocks sliding and tumbling as they are released by the ice. Occasionally, a terminal moraine ranging from valley wall to valley wall will act as a dam to impound the glacial melt water, and as the glacier eventually melts away, long *finger lakes* will appear, as in the Italian Alps. More commonly, however, the streams issuing from under the melting ice will break through the moraine here and there and flow off down the valley. This melt water characteristically appears muddy or milky, as it carries a heavy load of sediment prepared for it by the abrasive grinding action of the glacial mill, and it deposits the surplus as soon as possible upon leaving the glacier. The usual point of deposition is at the downslope margin of the moraine. Here glacio-fluvial deposits take the form of alluvial fans as the streams constantly choke their channels and seek new ones, eventually forming convex aprons of sorted alluvium in advance of the moraine stretching far down the valley. This feature is called a *valley train* and may be separated from

---

[6] There are other types of moraines that will not be discussed here, for the terminal moraine is the most important as a major element in ice deposition.

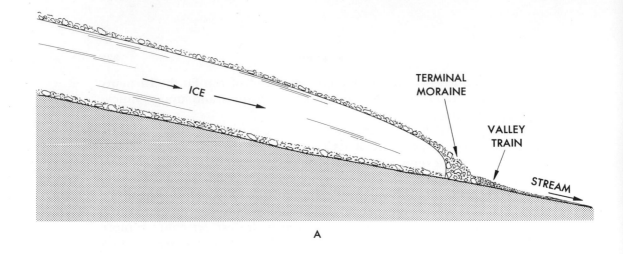

A

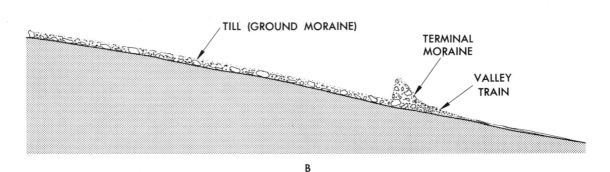

B

Fig. 7–55. *Glacial deposition. In (A), a valley glacier brings material downslope to build up depositional forms at its terminus, while in (B), these features are shown following their abandonment by the ice.*

the moraine to which it is attached by noting the absence of sorting of materials in the ice-deposited moraine as opposed to the careful sorting according to size of the alluvium. (Fig. 7–55.)

There is one other area of deposition in conjunction with the lower end of the glacier and that is under the ice itself. Near the nose of the glacier, not only is the underside of the ice heavily charged with the debris that it has picked up in its journey, but the holding capacity of the ice is becoming less as the rate of melt increases. So, like an over-loaded old-age stream, the glacier must drop some of its load. This deposition of every sized materials is under the ice, the weight of which compacts it into what is usually described as boulder studded clay. It is called *till* (or *ground moraine*).

So there are three types of glacial deposition near the nose of the ice: first, till deposited as a compacted flat mass under the ice; second, the terminal moraine as an asymmetrical crescent-shaped ridge deposited at the ice margin; and third, the valley train as a convex-shaped, sorted alluvial apron deposited by melt water at the outer edge of the moraine.

One word of caution relative to the speed of these operations: the entire concept of moving ice as an agent of gradation is dependent on an understanding of the time involved. Even running water, which requires considerable time to accomplish significant gradation, is more obvious than ice, for water moves rapidly, can be observed carrying and depositing materials, and on a small scale as in the formation of gullies, can demonstrate its cutting power before your very eyes. But ice does not appear to flow and must be measured carefully over a period of years to ascertain even slight movement. The best way to appreciate what it is capable of doing is through a before-and-after comparison of mountain valleys. Here we can find ice in all its phases and fully appreciate its capabilities.

CONTINENTAL GLACIERS. It is one thing to point to the continental glaciers of Greenland and Antarctica (Fig. 7–56) and classify them as

Fig. 7–56. The margin of the Antarctic ice sheet pushes out into the frozen sea. View is near Marble Point, North Victoria Land. (Courtesy of New Zealand National Publicity Studios.)

the only ones in the world, but it is quite another to convince oneself
of the radical theory that much more extensive ice sheets covered large
parts of North America and Europe in the none too distant past. This
is a difficult propostion to swallow and a good deal of very convincing
evidence had to be presented before the unbelievers came around.
Today, we not only have conclusive proof that such continental glaciers
did indeed exist, but we know all the details of multiple advances and
retreats. The history of the ice is written on the land for all to see,
but the observers were blind until they could imagine that such a
thing was possible. It remained for Louis Agassiz, a Swiss naturalist,
to first suggest in 1834 that ice-abandoned valleys in the Alps must
have at one time supported glaciers.[7] He based his reasoning on a
comparison of the similarities of deposits between the empty valley
and one in which an active glacier was present. In other words, ice
left evidences of its former existence. Some of these evidences had
been puzzling geologists in both Europe and the United States for
many years. Why were large boulders present in Iowa that had no
relationship to the local bedrock but did resemble that of Canada?
Some researchers had suggested such far-fetched answers as Noah's
flood. And what about those deep grooves in solid rock, as on Kelley's
Island, Ohio? Probably made by dinosaurs in the rutting season?
Agassiz's theories answered these questions and many more very logically, and further investigation gradually built up a body of irrefutable
proof that continental glaciers must have existed. It is entirely fitting
that Louis Agassiz, the champion of continental glaciers that no one
ever witnessed, should have his memory perpetuated in the name of a
lake that must have existed once but vanished thousands of years ago
(Lake Agassiz at one time covered a large part of North Dakota and
adjacent Manitoba).

About a million years ago ice began to form in Canada and northern
Europe in much the same manner as has been described in mountain
basins, that is, a continuing accumulation of snow gradually changing
its lower elements into ice over a very extensive area. As the depth
and pressure increased, the ice was forced outward in all directions.
In some cases, this was downslope or, as in much of North America,
across generally subdued terrain, but in Europe the pressure was sufficient to cause ice, centered in the Karelia-Finnish region, to surmount
and overrun such major obstructions as the Scandinavian mountains
and Scottish highlands. Even in North America, the Adirondacks,

---

[7] Others preceded Agassiz in the novel notion that continental glaciers may have covered
northern Europe, notably Venetz, 1821, and Charpentier, 1830, but Agassiz introduced the
idea to the world, expanded the scope of the ice to include North America, and generally
was responsible for bringing the whole theory to public attention.

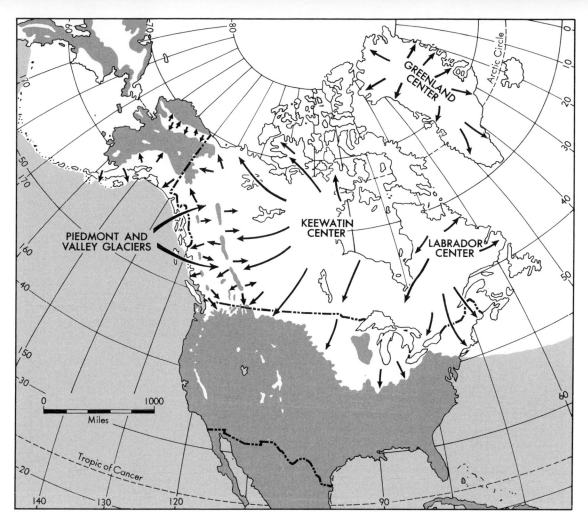

Fig. 7–57. *Extent of continental glaciation in North America.*

New England mountains, and northern Appalachians were overwhelmed by an extensive sheet of continental ice. Four or five major advances and retreats have been traced, extending roughly as far south as the Ohio and Missouri rivers in the United States (Fig. 7–57) and southern England to central Germany and the Ukraine in Europe, a result of fluctuating temperatures over the centuries. But on the whole, the behavior of these continental glaciers and the gradational work they accomplished were almost identical to those of ice in Alpine glaciers except that not being confined to limited valleys, the scope of their influence was very much larger.

By carefully examining the countryside over which the continental glaciers must have swept again and again, two somewhat differing zones may be established. First, an inner zone extending a few hundred miles out in all directions from the center or centers of ice origin.

Here the ice was thickest as it passed over the land and therefore exerted a great deal of vertical pressure. And also the underside was fresh, clean, and relatively unclogged with soils and rocks, so that like a youthful stream, it had a great capacity for freezing materials into it. This might be called the *zone of active erosion,* for as we observe the surface today, it is obvious that the glacial effect was not only to remove all soil right down to bedrock, but to gouge and abrade the rock itself, cutting out in many places deep cavities which have subsequently become lakes (the Great Lakes included here). There is a great deal of similarity in the general aspect of landscape in northern Minnesota, Michigan, Wisconsin, and eastern Canada and that of Finland and northern Russia. The thousands of lakes at varying levels, scrambled drainage, and great exposure of bedrock are typical everywhere. And the uplands overrun by such ice sheets are rounded, striated, and polished. (Fig. 7–58.)

The second zone is beyond the first, far out from the center of activation, and, especially, near the southern edge of the glacier. Here the ice was thinner, melting much more rapidly, and heavily choked with the waste it had accumulated in passing over the erosional zone. This is the *zone of active deposition,* where like the old-age stream, the ice was not only overloaded but demonstrated increasingly less capacity for picking up and carrying material. Here too the leading edge of the glacier had reached a point of equilibrium between melt and advance, and even minor temperature changes could cause violent fluctuations in the position of the ice front. Extensive moraine belts,

Fig. 7–58. The passage of continental ice across Kelly's Island on Lake Erie left these marks on the bedrock. Gougings of this magnitude are not mere striations, but are properly called glacial grooves. *(Courtesy of Ohio Historical Society.)*

Fig. 7–59. *This lush rolling farm country in North Jutland is a portion of a moraine built by the European continental ice 500,000 years ago. In Denmark, where much of the land is excessively sandy, the mixed soils of the many moraines are considered the nation's best. (Courtesy of Danish Information Office.)*

great loops extending for hundreds of miles, occur throughout this zone and indicate temporary pauses and readjustments of the glacial margin. (Fig. 7–59.) In front of each moraine is the alluvial apron laid down by melt water, here called *outwash plain* (identical to the valley train except that it is much more extensive), and throughout the region are great depths of ice compacted till effectively masking the original terrain details. This is the history of the North German Plain and much of the Middle West.

The question is often asked, "From the standpoint of man's utilization of the land, has continental glaciation been advantageous?" To those who occupy the zone of deposition, the answer is probably "Yes." Deep new soils and generally subdued landscape have helped to make this region one of productive farms. It is possible that the soils are too sandy or gravelly in places and clayey in others, and disrupted drainage has caused considerable swamp development, but on the whole, such soils can be made productive with proper management. An excellent comparison with "what might have been" is provided by the *driftless area* of southwestern Wisconsin where for unknown reasons the glaciers completely surrounded but did not move over several thousand square miles.[8] Here is a sample of what the Middle West might have been like without glaciation—rough hill country with thin soil, except in the river bottoms, and generally an unproductive region.

In the zone of erosion, glacial action, in removing the soil, has ruled out agriculture, but at these northerly latitudes, agriculture could only be marginal at best. So in laying bare the bedrock, a good many mineral deposits have been exposed at the surface, the disorganized drainage has produced hydroelectric sites, and the many lakes make a fisherman's paradise. Even here glaciation might be interpreted as a blessing.

Continental glaciation also has some secondary effects beyond the direct effects of the passage of ice over land. The general lowering of the world's sea level has already been mentioned, and it is obvious that coastlines everywhere have felt the repercussions of such an effect. For instance, the movements of animals and humans across land bridges that must have existed in Southeast Asia and the Bering Strait are indirectly related to glaciation through the lowering of the sea.

And then there is the great volume of melt water released upon the land. Existing rivers must have carried more water than they do today and were more effective eroders. In many places, enclosed basins such as the one occupied by the Great Salt Lake were filled to the brim with huge lakes. Old beach lines of ancient Lake Bonneville are easily visible along the Wasatch slopes near Salt Lake City, and the salt deposits of the now evaporated lake form the well known Bonneville salt flats. Lake Agassiz was formed when normal drainage to the north was blocked by the ice, and until the glacier disappeared the lake maintained itself. Today, only Lake Winnipeg remains as a tiny remnant of the original. Ice also blocked the northeast drainage of the Great Lakes via the St. Lawrence River and caused them first to drain southward via the Chicago River to the Mississippi and later to drain eastward through the Mohawk gap and the Hudson River. The only good break through the Appalachians occurs here, formed by a tremendous stream of melt water. The Erie Canal, so influential in our history, was virtually foreordained by this great channel. Equally important in the Pacific Northwest is the Grand Coulee, a drainage channel dug out by the ice-diverted Columbia River carrying many times the volume of water it does today. After the ice melted back,

---

[8] Drift is a general term referring to all types of glacial deposition; therefore, "driftless area" is a negative terminology denoting no drift and thus no glaciation.

Fig. 7–60. *The huge Grand Coulee Dam is dwarfed by the immensity of this eastern Washington landscape. The present (and pre-ice) course of the Columbia River is at the lower right. The dam is situated to divert irrigation water down the Coulee (upper center). Some idea of the size of the ice-age Columbia can be gained by comparing the dimensions of the Grand Coulee, which it carved, with the present Columbia gorge. (Courtesy of U.S. Bureau of Reclamation.)*

the Columbia abandoned the Coulee and resumed its normal course, but the Grand Coulee Dam at the head of the Coulee now can divert Columbia water once again down this ready-made channel to irrigate the desert. (Fig. 7–60.)

So these are the gradational effects of moving ice. What caused the sporadic cooling and warming that allowed the continental glaciers to advance and retreat and caused the development of extensive valley glaciers in the high mountains all over the world? Nobody knows— speculation is rife and there are theories without end. We do know that the overall long-term climatic trend today is warming, and nearly all existing glaciers are in retreat. How long will this last? It is perhaps provocative to note that the time lapse between the last retreat of the continental glaciers and the present is not as long as some of the inter-ice periods between advance and retreat. Maybe we are merely in an inter-ice period and there are more advances to come.

Wind. In order for wind to be an effective gradational agent, loose, dry sands and soils must be present at the surface protected by a minimal vegetative cover. This means that to a large extent, wind erosion is relegated to the arid regions of the world where vegetation is scarce to non-existent and the lack of moisture in the soil keeps the particles from clodding and adhering one to the other. However, it is possible for beach sands, even in humid areas, to dry out rapidly above the high-tide line and thus be subject to wind attack. And also, it has been demonstrated in several parts of the world that glacial debris or alluvial deposits may be removed by wind if its velocity and the vegetation and moisture conditions are permissive. But all things considered, of the several gradational forces with which we are dealing, wind is probably the least widespread and effective.

The carrying capacity of wind and its ability to pick up materials is, like running water, determined by its velocity. Most any vagrant breeze can sweep up dust and fine particles, but it takes a steady wind of at least moderate velocity to move sand. And once these sharp-edged particles are in suspension, the moving air has armed itself with effective cutting tools to wear away whatever is in its path, thereby supplying itself with still more teeth. The original load may have derived from a mantle of mechanically weathered rock or the loosely deposited alluvium of an infrequent stream. Their removal lowers the surface, often to bedrock which is polished and abraded as the wind-blown materials scour it. If bedrock is hard and massive, it resists abrasion and will acquire a high polish, but if it is of softer material, it will be progressively cut away. Frequently, sandstone is exposed on the desert floor or cliff faces, the hard sand grains cemented by softer muds that can be rapidly eroded, freeing the sharp-edged quartz to aid in further cutting. On the other hand, when sizable stones and pebbles are mixed with finer material, the erosive action of the wind is selective and only particles up to sand size are removed, the desert floor eventually becoming paved with smoothed cobbles called *gibbers* or *desert pavement* that protect the underlying strata.

Any surface exposed to the constant sand-blast effect of wind-carried debris, especially sand, will inevitably be cut, chewed, and polished. Even automobiles caught in sandstorms have their paint removed, metal surfaces pitted, and glass frosted in a remarkably short time. Rocky cliffs facing prevailing winds in the desert display tremendous honeycombing, as the softer elements are etched away leaving the hard materials in high relief. (Fig. 7–61.) One of the peculiar features of some desert landscapes often attributed to wind erosion is top-heavy balanced pinnacles. Whether wind is responsible for the original pinnacle is questionable, but the more rapid cutting at the bottom is typical of wind action, for sand, the most effective cutting tool, is relatively

Fig. 7–61. *The sandblast effect of wind erosion has played a major role in forming the striking double arch at Arches National Monument, Utah. Pitting of the cliff face and the polished rock surface atop the arch are typical. (Courtesy of U.S. National Park Service.)*

heavy and seldom is suspended more than a foot off the ground. Notice the telephone poles when you drive through dry country. They will either have metal shields attached at ground level or a pile of rocks to protect them from being cut down by the wind—and the wood of the lower portion of the pole will display an etched and polished surface.

Wind does not always move over the surface of these arid regions from a single direction or at a constant rate. Often it is gusty and capricious, and the something less than flat surface terrain sets in motion channeled air streams and eddy currents. For instance, a swirling eddy current in the lee of a minor ridge may cut downward and dig out a sizable basin. Tiny depressions called *blow outs* are frequent occurrences in soft sand. And narrow defiles will act as funnels to not only channel the moving air in a constant direction, but to increase its velocity within the limited confines, thereby scouring the walls and floor much more effectively than in open country.

As a transporting agent, wind may carry tiny dust particles high into the atmosphere and transport them great distances. Colored sunsets and muddy rainfalls are often experienced thousands of miles from major dust storms or explosive volcanic eruptions. The plowing of the buffalo grass along the eastern Rocky Mountain front followed by an extended drought in the thirties gave rise to an extensive "dust bowl" when the prevailing westerly winds carried the fine-grained topsoil eastward in great clouds. When these wind-carried soils are deposited, they are called *loess* and on occasion pile up to considerable depths. In northern China, the strong winter monsoons blowing out of the Gobi and adjacent deserts have, over the centuries, deposited loess to a depth of 1,000 feet or more, completely masking the original terrain. Some of the world's loess deposits, as in northern Europe and the Mississippi Basin, probably derived from finely ground "rock flour" resulting from glacial action and deposited by melt water in temporary lakes or outwash plains. The gravity winds, that is, cold air flowing via gravity off the cold ice, have picked up this newly formed and fertile soil and carried it away from the ice to be deposited elsewhere.

Larger particles than those that go to make up loess, particularly sand, require higher velocity winds than are normal to be taken into suspension. These are commonly carried short distances just above the surface and pushed along the ground, piling up and drifting against all sorts of minor obstacles. The result is the formation of dunes along beaches and in those portions of the desert where sand is plentiful. If the wind is rather constant from one direction, the dunes are likely to take on a crescentic shape with the convex exposure upwind and of rather gentle slope, while the concave inner slope is almost sheer (*barchans*). As long as the sand on the windward slope is not anchored by vegetation growing on it and is free to move, the entire dune will migrate slowly forward as the wind erodes the front of the dune and dumps it forward grain by grain over the crest. As each grain falls into the lee of the dune and out of the wind, it drops down the steep backside, maintaining this almost vertical slope. If the wind displays somewhat less constancy of direction, dunes will take on less classic, merely ridgelike forms. However, even these normally show a gentle windward slope vs. a steeper lee. And on the surfaces of most dunes, close examination will reveal tiny rows of ripple marks at right angles to the wind that are miniature dunes in themselves, moving forward and exhibiting the typical asymmetrical outline. (Fig. 7–62.)

Fig. 7–62. Barchans *near Moses Lake, Wash. The prevailing wind direction is from the left, and each surface ripple faithfully aligns itself at right angles to it, as do the large dunes, with their gentle slopes upwind. (Courtesy of U.S. Bureau of Reclamation.)*

Along many beaches and desert margins, these moving dunes have been known to march inexorably across virtually anything in their path. (Fig. 7–63.) Roads, oases, even woods and buildings have been overrun. They can be stopped if some kind of vegetation can be made to grow on their surfaces, but sterile sand is not an ideal bedding ground for plants, and new dunes are constantly being formed. In the Landes district of southern France, dunes from the Bay of Biscay shore have eventually been fixed after overrunning hundreds of square

Fig. 7–63. *Rank marram grass partially checks the landward migration of these German North Sea beach dunes, but at present they are still advancing at a rate of almost 10 feet per year. (Courtesy of German Information Center.)*

miles of territory and even a sizable village. Today, planted pine trees in the old dune region produce valuable timber and turpentine. (Fig. 7–64.)

There seems to be a commonly held misconception that most of the world's deserts are made up of endless miles of billowing sand. Such deserts are to be found and admittedly they are spectacular, but they are not so common as to be typical. In order for sand dunes to form, the supply of sand must develop more rapidly than it can blow away, that is, a seashore or a soft sandstone that erodes readily. This occurs only now and then so that rocky deserts of one kind or another are more common than the sand dune.

Fig. 7–64. *A pine forest, here being tapped for turpentine, has permanently anchored an extensive area of beach sand in southern France that at one time marched many miles inland. (Courtesy of French Embassy Press & Information Division.)*

Waves. Unlike clear running water that has little erosive capacity unless it carries sharp-edged tools, waves can throw themselves against an unprotected shoreline in such massive assaults that the sheer weight of the water is a powerful erosive agent. No one who has not seen at first hand storm waves battering a cliff front or beach can fully appreciate the violence attained. Tons of water repeatedly dashed at high velocity against even solid rock can accomplish a tremendous amount of erosive work in only a few days or hours, and loose sand offers virtually no resistance. Not only the weight of the water itself, but its effect of compressing air in cracks, vents, or caves in a cliff helps to tear loose great chunks of rock. (Fig. 7–65.) And like running water,

Fig. 7–65. Thunder Hole in Acadia National Park, where air compressed by the surge of the sea explodes with a great roar. Such air compression is an effective erosional force. (Courtesy of U.S. National Park Service.)

Fig. 7–66. *The stark outlines of Pointe du Raz, Brittany, reflect the powerful erosive force of constantly battering seas. (Courtesy of French Cultural Services.)*

seawater can take into solution certain minerals, thereby removing them from the rocks and weakening the entire structure. We must not forget the buoyancy of water which allows the waves to lift massive rocks up to several tons in weight, once they have been loosened, and if not carry them away, immediately jostle them until they gradually work free. All of this is accomplished without the aid of sands, gravels, and boulders as grinding and cutting agents. But waves do have cutting teeth of this kind, some very large, derived from the wearing away of shorelines, and their effect is to multiply many times the erosive effectiveness of waves. (Fig. 7–66.)

Although every day is not a stormy day and waves do the bulk of their work during storms, they are continuously active nonetheless, attempting to lower any land that stands above sea level, and even on a calm day this work is visible although at a much subdued rate. Island inhabitants know all about wave action, as it threatens them from all sides and they are frequently forced into a variety of attempts to

Fig. 7–67. Most of the German North Sea island of Heligoland has been protected from storm waves by breakwaters and rock and concrete sheathing, but this tortured sea cliff is still being cut back. (Courtesy of German Information Center.)

thwart the encroachment of the sea. The island of Helgoland in the stormy North Sea off the German coast is a classic example of rapid wave gradation. We have a long record of the accelerated decreasing size of this island through the centuries, and although it has been reduced to a tiny fraction of its former self today, it would have long since disappeared except for the reinforcement of its margins by cement breakwaters and sea walls. (Fig. 7–67.)

Waves (except tidal waves) are formed by the movement of wind across the surface of the sea, which causes undulations. These are pushed forward by the sea, giving the appearance of the water moving forward. Actually, it is only the wave form that progresses, not the water. This is not unlike the rippling of the wind through tall grass; the grass remains in place but the waves move forward rapidly. There is a movement of water set in motion by waves, but it is a vertical circular motion so that any given particle of water follows this circle (its size determined by the height and spacing of the waves) and returns to its place of origin. But when the waves approach the shore and the bottom begins to shoal, this vertical circulation is impeded and friction causes drag. This throws the surface water forward, the wave builds up higher and eventually breaks, and the mass of water rushes up the beach. The line of breakers then is some indication as to the shallowness of water. Generally speaking, a swimmer can wade out to the breakers even if they are far off shore, but if the breakers are in close to the beach, it means a rapid dropoff instead of a gently shelving bottom. (Fig. 7–68.)

Fig. 7–68. The line of breakers makes visible the outer margin of the gently shelving bottom. View is of German North Sea island of Norderney. (Courtesy of German Information Center.)

At this point, somewhat offshore where the drag begins, the first bit of shoreline erosion is accomplished as the water, attempting to complete its vertical circulation, bites into the bottom. So that just beyond the breaker line, the bottom is lowered sufficiently to allow the water to achieve its oscillatory cycle. Once this is accomplished, friction ceases and the line of breakers moves closer to the shore with the bottom erosion continuing just behind it. Thus, a flat bench (*wave-cut bench*) is formed at a specific depth, sometimes cut into solid rock, at other times excavated easily from loose sands and gravels. (Fig. 7–69.) The materials derived from this operation are carried forward by the breaking wave, cutting and scouring as they go, to aid in the formation of the beach. If the bottom is not too shelving and the line of breakers fairly close to shore, then the forward rushing water will attack the shore and break away quantities of debris, especially if a high cliff is being undercut and slides from above deliver added material periodically. All of this is worked over, broken, smoothed, and reduced in size by continued wave action, and then most of it is removed so that the waves can get back to work on the cliff itself.

The removal is accomplished in two ways. First, there is the *undertow* or the water retreating down the beach after each wave. It carries with it much of the eroded debris. Some of this is moved back up the beach by the next wave, but the finer particles eventually drift out into deeper water and are deposited beyond the wave-cut bench, building up a depositional terrace (*wave-built terrace*) at the rear of the

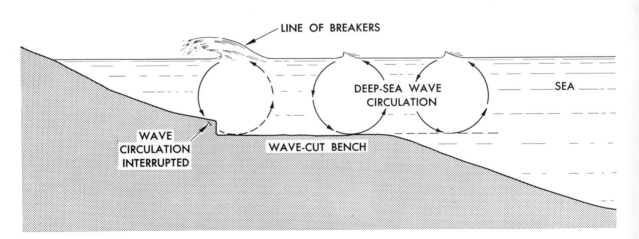

Fig. 7–69. *Wave-cut bench. When deep-sea wave circulation is interrupted by a shoaling bottom, the bottom is eroded to a depth sufficient to allow resumption of normal circulation.*

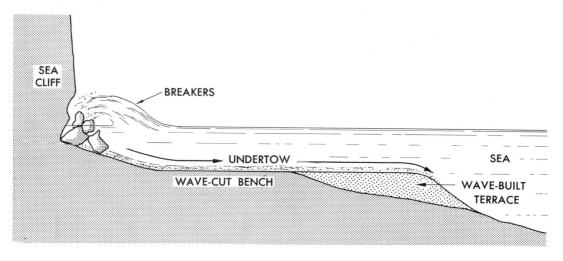

Fig. 7–70. *Wave-built terrace. Fine materials derived from the wearing away of bottom and cliff eventually find their way to the outer edge of the wave-cut bench to be deposited as a terrace.*

bench. (Fig. 7–70.) The rocks and sand that repeatedly advance and retreat with each wave aid in smoothing and abrading the beach, while at the same time they are being reduced in size so that gradually they too may be carried off by the undertow to be added to the wave-built terrace.

The second means by which material may be transported from its original site of erosion is via *longshore drift*. Very seldom does a wave strike the shore at right angles, so that if the winds that form the waves are prevailing from a particular direction for any considerable length of time, there will be a movement of sediments and debris along the shore in addition to onshore and offshore. (Fig. 7–71.) The under-

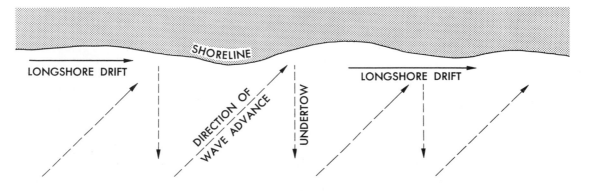

Fig. 7–71. *Longshore drift. Waves approaching the shore at an angle carry sediments forward, while the undertow returns them directly down-slope. The net movement of any given particle exposed repeatedly to these alternating forces is longshore.*

tow tends to move its load directly away from the shore downslope in answer to gravity, but the succeeding wave will carry the same material back up the beach at an angle, so that gradually beach-forming sands will be transported considerable distances longshore. Often they will come to rest in quiet coves, while cliffed headlands, which are producing much of the material as the waves beat against them, will have their bases swept clean. (Fig. 7–72.) *Spits* and *bars,* generally parallel to the shore, are also products of longshore drift. Of course, the winds may shift, often seasonally or even daily, and reverse the direction of drift. Locally, tidal currents set in motion by some peculiarity in shoreline configuration may complicate the pattern. And storms will periodically disrupt with great violence the formation of drift features.

Fig. 7–72.   *A bayhead beach in Brittany.*   *(Courtesy of French Cultural Services.)*

Fig. 7–73. *The breakwater protecting this small boat harbor at Half Moon Bay, Calif., also acts to trap sand moving longshore. Notice the white beach (upper right) that has built to this size in just 2 years. (Courtesy of U.S. Army Corps of Engineers, San Francisco, Calif.)*

During the construction of the breakwater enclosing the Los Angeles–Long Beach harbor, the famous beach for which Long Beach was named was almost entirely removed by new currents set in motion by the partially completed breakwater. For a number of years, the residents and city officials were greatly chagrined, living in a city named Long Beach with no beach at all. However, with the completion of the breakwater, the beach returned and all was well. This is not a rare occurrence, as longshore currents are fickle and subject to change as normal erosion alters the coastal outline. (Fig. 7–73.) Groins or

Fig. 7–74. *Wave action on a submerged coast, La Push, Wash. The most resistant rock is bypassed and left as stacks and islands to be worn away more slowly. Note the cliffed headlands and the accumulation of material derived from them as beaches in the more protected coves. (Courtesy of Washington State Department of Commercial & Economic Development.)*

jetties, man-made walls at right angles to the shore, are commonly seen as beach-front residents attempt to catch and hold the sand moving longshore. They are sometimes the subject of lawsuits by their neighbors downshore whose beaches would be the recipients of those sands if they were allowed to move normally.

SUBMERGED SHORELINE. Let us assume now a newly *drowned* or *submerged* shoreline where the river valleys become arms of the sea and the interstream ridges stand out as headlands. A large percentage of the world's sea frontage is of this type, to at least a degree. The effect of waves on such a ragged and indented coast is first to smooth it off and then to push it back. (Fig. 7–74.) The headlands are attacked with great vigor, especially if the sea is deep immediately off-shore and the full force of the waves can be concentrated directly on the land without the impediment of friction with the bottom. Under the effect of this attack, the point of land is cliffed and pushed back rapidly. If the rock is of varying resistance, islands may be formed or spires of harder rock (*stacks*) cut off from the mainland, but these are ephemeral and are shortly eroded away. The great mass of material resulting from this erosion is partially shifted longshore, the longshore currents depositing much of their load as *bayhead spits and bars* across the mouths of the adjacent coastal indentations and as beaches at their heads. Typically, these spits curve inland at their tips away from the waves which break on their seaward side, and except for minor breaks to accommodate tidal currents, they effectively cut off the bay from the ocean waves. Essentially, then, the bay becomes a quiet lagoon. Streams debouching into it from the land build undisturbed deltas which, with the tangled roots of their vegetative cover, gradually transform the lagoon into land—low-lying and swampy but land. So, as the waves continue to push back the headlands, the bays build out to meet the bars at their mouths, and the contour of the coastline changes from one of involved crenulations to a smooth straight line. (Fig. 7–75.)

Fig. 7–75. *The work of waves on a submerged shoreline.*

Now the sea can attack the shoreline impartially and does so, gradually eroding it back at a much retarded rate, for the wave-cut debris, some of which moved longshore to form spits and bars, has also formed beaches and a generally more shelving approach to the land so that

Fig. 7–76. *A former wave-cut bench has been exposed through uplift here in the Palos Verdes Mountains of southern California and appears as a level terrace at the right. In the distance, several are visible at successive elevations. Wave planation is active once again, but at a lower level. (Courtesy of California Division of Mines & Geology.)*

much of the energy of the waves is expended in running up the beach and erosion is slowed. During storms, however, the sea revives much of its old vigor and pushes the coastline back rapidly again.

EMERGED SHORELINE. *Emerged* coastlines are equally as common as those that are drowned. These involve the uplift of the land so that frequently wave-cut cliffs and benches are exposed to view well above sea level, and occasionally several terraces give evidences of repeated uplift in the past. (Fig. 7–76.) The newly formed coastline is a portion of the old sea bottom and is likely to be flat to shelving and generally featureless, reflecting its formation as wave-cut bench or wave-deposited terrace. This means that on a newly emerged coastline, the line of breakers is well offshore, and at this point the bottom is being eroded away to a depth sufficient for adequate vertical circulation of the water. The debris from this erosional work is thrown forward by the breakers and commonly piles up at this point into a sandy bar called an *offshore bar*. (Fig. 7–77.) These may extend for great distances, as off the Texas coast, as much as a mile offshore and broken only occasionally by tidal channels. (Fig. 7–78.) Once again

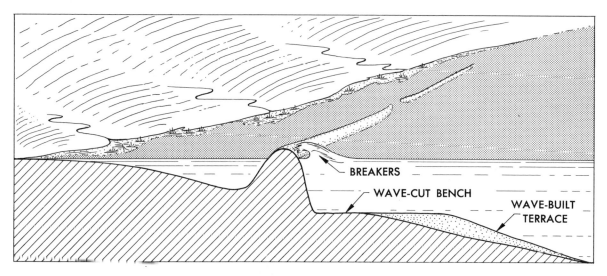

Fig. 7–77. *Offshore bar. The bar advances landward as rapidly as the waves can cut away the bottom to sufficient depth. At the same time, stream deposits build up the shore's margins so that it is advancing toward the bar.*

BREAKERS

WAVE-CUT BENCH

WAVE-BUILT TERRACE

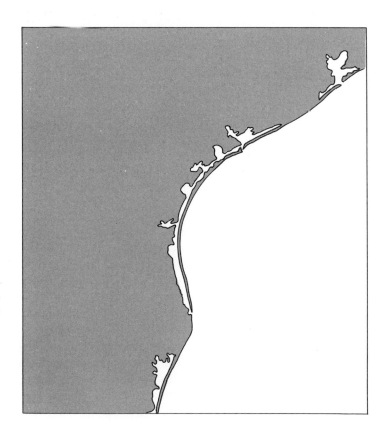

Fig. 7–78. *Offshore bar. Texas – northern Mexico emerged coast.*

Fig. 7–79. *Ocean waves work at the seaward side of Cape Hatteras, a very extensive offshore bar. Despite the coarse vegetation, this entire feature is made up of sand. (Courtesy of U.S. National Park Service.)*

as in the case of the bayhead bar, a quiet lagoon is established that rapidly fills with shore-derived sediments and becomes a marshy extension of the mainland. Meanwhile, the big ocean waves are lashing the seaward side of the bar and, as rapidly as the wave-cut bench can be expanded, are pushing the bar inland. (Fig. 7–79.) So here the bar is moving onshore and the land is moving offshore, and when they meet a new shoreline has been established. Wave action now continues to wear away the coast and move it back at a modest rate.

Left to itself, the sea could conceivably reduce all of the world's land masses to below sea level. There is more than sufficient water on the earth to completely cover a smooth globe. And the sea is not working alone; ice, streams, and wind are all aiding in this smoothing process. So it remains for the tectonic forces to constantly counteract this action. Landforms as we know them in their endless variations are resultants of this constant interaction, and an educated observation of any landscape in the world can be described, explained, and interpreted within this frame.

8

Groundwater

In some ways, moving subsurface water can be classified with streams, ice, wind, and waves as a gradational agent, for, given the proper set of circumstances, it has the ability to take rock materials into solution, transport these solutions, and redeposit them. Some of this has been mentioned previously relative to chemical weathering and the weakening of rocks by removal of minerals, thereby preparing them for further attacks by other gradational agents. But, although groundwater can and does pick up, transport, and deposit materials, it is not as efficient a gradational agent as the others, and the erosive ability is only a small part of its total activity. Of more importance to man is its function as a control of stream discharge, water level of rivers and swamps, and particularly as a source of irrigation and potable water for a large part of the world's population.

THE HYDROLOGIC CYCLE

What is groundwater and how does it get there? All of the world's water derives primarily from the sea, and most of it returns ultimately to this source (the *hydrologic cycle*). (Fig. 8–1.) Evaporation from the sea provides the water vapor for rain and snow. If it condenses and precipitates over the oceans, then its return is immediate, but if it is carried over the land, a number of things may happen to it before it finds its way back to the sea. Some of it may fall as snow and remain on the land until the spring melt before flowing back to the sea via rivers. Or it may become part of a semipermanent ice mass and be detained many hundreds or thousands of years. Much of the water vapor will fall as rain, some flowing off immediately on the surface,

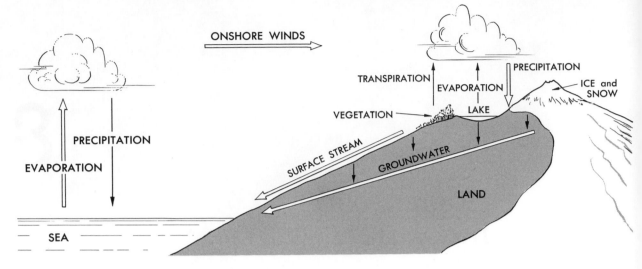

Fig. 8–1. *The hydrologic cycle. The basic cycle involves four elements: (1) evaporation of moisture from the sea, (2) movement of water vapor from over the sea to over the land, (3) precipitation of rain and snow onto the land, and (4) the return of this precipitation to the sea via gravity drainage.*

some evaporating directly or via plants to be precipitated again, and some soaking deep into the ground to percolate gradually downslope to the sea or to appear at a lower level at the surface as springs and seepages. This last is groundwater.

POROSITY VS. PERMEABILITY

How much groundwater occurs in any given place and its character and movement depend largely upon two variables: (1) climate, which controls precipitation, evaporation, and vegetation; and (2) the peculiarities of the soil and subsurface rock. The great bulk of groundwater has simply seeped down from above, but certain rocks and rock materials have a much greater water-holding capacity, *porosity*, than others. Loose sands and gravels, with their irregular particles allowing a maximum pore space, may contain up to 50 per cent water as can some clays. Sandstones too, although part of the intergrain areas are filled with cement, may be highly porous. On the other hand, dense shales and igneous rocks usually exhibit a very low porosity. But an igneous rock in cooling often develops fissures, joints, or cavities from escaping gases and then, even though the rock itself is dense, may be capable of containing large quantities of groundwater.

But we should make a distinction here between *porosity* and *per-*

meability. It does not always follow that a material capable of hold-ing large quantities of groundwater will allow that water to move through it, and it is this freedom of movement that is the essence of *permeability.* Clay, with its frequent spongelike ability to soak up water, is not generally permeable, for the tiny size of each clay particle holds the groundwater through molecular attraction. Fissures too, if formed in dense rock with an opening only at the top, may collect water and hold it, but horizontal percolation or flow will be impossible. On the other hand, coarse granular layers, whether unconsolidated or indurated, normally allow ready movement of water through them, as do rocks whose fissures, joints, or cracks are interconnected throughout an entire strata. Permeability, then, is obviously an important factor in the completion of the hydrologic cycle and in the feeding of wells, springs, and seepages. (Fig. 8–2.)

THE WATER TABLE

Assuming a considerable depth of homogeneous permeable mate-rial, *the groundwater table is the top of the saturated rock.* In a humid region, this may be quite near the surface or even coinciding with it after a particularly heavy rain. But normally, it is at least a few feet down, overlain by a layer of loose soil where water is rapidly lost through evaporation and transpiration. This zone of soil water or *vadose water* is generally within the reach of plant roots and reflects immediately day-to-day or even hour-to-hour weather fluctuations, so that characteristically it is saturated for only short periods and more often than not holds as much air as water in its pores.

Under usual conditions, a water table will roughly approximate the contours of the terrain that it underlies, higher under hills and declining under valleys. (Fig. 8–3.) The groundwater is percolating downslope and its upper margin thus assumes the gradient of a surface stream, and like a surface stream, discharges into the master drainage artery in the valley. The river at the valley bottom may receive the groundwater discharge directly via springs as it intersects the water table, or, if the river itself is slightly above the water table, the coarse sands and gravels of its bed will intercept the flow and direct it down the valley under the surface waters of the river. Swamps, rivers, or the sea, which occupy the lowest point of a given region, act as regu-lators of the slope of that region's water table. Loss of water supply, as during an extended dry period, will cause the water table to flatten out and be found at an increasingly greater depth beneath the hills, but it will continue to intersect the surface in the valleys; and as long as any gradient at all is maintained, groundwater will percolate down-slope.

Fig. 8–2. *Groundwater flows rather than percolates through a highly permeable aquifer of scoriaceous lava in the Snake River Canyon, western Idaho. These flows discharge at Thousand Springs where the course of the Snake cuts across the aquifer. (Courtesy of U.S. Bureau of Reclamation.)*

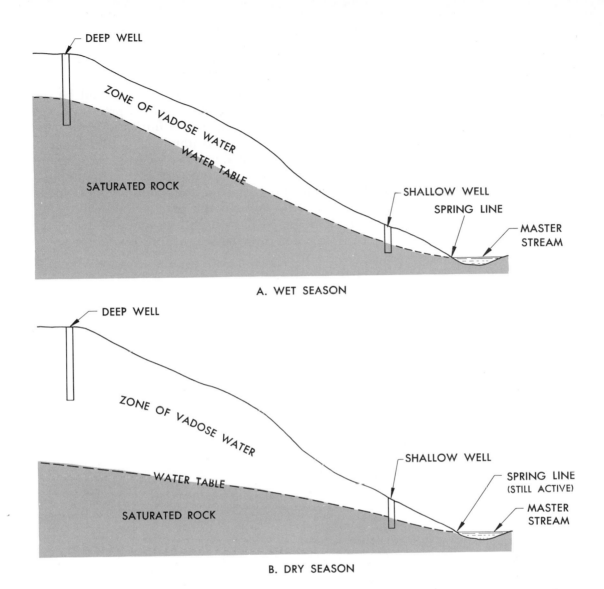

Fig. 8–3. *The groundwater table. The water table tends to approximate the surface contour (A), but during an extended dry period (B), it flattens out considerably, although still intersecting the surface at the spring line. Consequently, the well at the top of the hill, despite its greater depth, is in a less-advantageous position than the much more shallow one on the lower slope.*

Wells bored below the water table will produce water, but how rapidly they will refill themselves after emptying is determined by the permeability of the rock. But no matter how permeable the rock or how humid the climate, too many wells will lower the water table, and increasingly deeper bores will be required to tap groundwater.

Obviously, an inventory of the groundwater resources should be undertaken before uncontrolled well boring takes place, a procedure that has seldom been followed anywhere in the world until the water table has been lowered drastically and disaster is imminent.

The Santa Clara Valley in California, a region of irrigated orchards and, more recently, burgeoning urbanization, is a case in point illustrating the results of continued overdraft on the groundwater supplies. The increasing depths of wells through the years are shown in Fig. 8–4. Many coastal regions find that with decline in water table, the lessened pressure of fresh water moving seaward allows salt water to

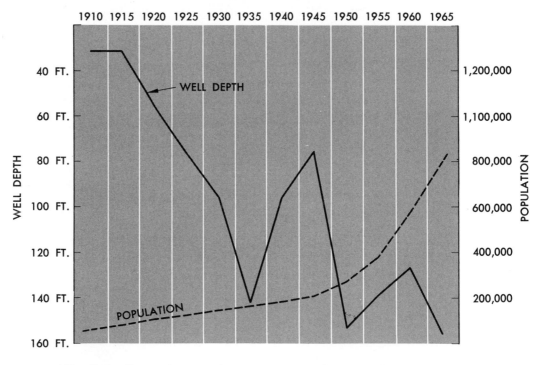

AVERAGE WELL DEPTH

SANTA CLARA VALLEY WATER CONSERVATION DISTRICT

Fig. 8–4. Increasing depths of wells in California's Santa Clara Valley. A general trend toward increased depth is apparent. The fluctuations are, to a degree, a result of periodic heavier rainfall, but of greater significance has been the construction of reservoirs to recharge the underground strata, as in the 1940's.

Fig. 8–5. *Anderson Reservoir in Santa Clara County traps and holds the runoff of winter rain. During the long dry season, water is gradually removed to percolation beds in the valley below to recharge the underground strata. This photo, taken in late summer, clearly shows the winter beach lines on the hills in the background. (Courtesy of Santa Clara Valley Water Conservation District.)*

invade the permeable strata and to "salt out" wells miles from the seashore. The Santa Clara Valley is fortunate in having a closed system that precludes this problem, but the situation is serious and will not be alleviated until expensive exotic water is brought in via pipeline from the Sacramento River.

It is possible to supplement the normal receipt of rainfall, which generally controls the height of the water table, by impounding surface waters in farm ponds or large reservoirs. A part of this water will soak downward through a porous bottom to become groundwater, and even more can be added by diverting some of the impounded water into extensive percolating beds. Again, in the Santa Clara Valley where summers are dry and warm, the winter runoff is held behind dams, not to be used directly for irrigation or city water supply, but primarily to recharge the wells all over the valley. (Fig. 8–5.) The more water that can be forced to percolate underground the better, for surface storage is subject to extreme loss via evaporation, while subsurface water is immune. Also, groundwater has been naturally purified by filtration and is often of better quality than that of polluted streams. In some areas, experimentation has been carried on with the reuse of sewage water after the sludge has been removed, the final purification being accomplished by natural filtration. However, depending upon the character of underground strata, groundwater may take salts into solution and become "hard water"—difficult to wash with and destructive of plumbing as the salts are deposited in the pipes. And occasionally, groundwater is so brackish as to be completely unusable without costly processing. (Fig. 8–6.)

Fig. 8–6. Well water at Roswell, New Mexico, is extremely brackish. In the U.S. government demonstration plant shown here, 1,000,000 gallons of saline water are treated each day to assure the community a potable supply. The recovered salts also have a potential commercial utility. (Courtesy of U.S. Office of Saline Water.)

AQUIFERS

So far, we have been discussing rock with a certain homogeneity of permeability, but this is not always the case, for many different strata may be present underlying a given region, each with its own characteristics. An important occurrence is a permeable layer, such as sandstone, confined between impervious strata and tilted so that it intersects the surface. Water entering the exposed sandstone outcrop percolates along it as if in a pipe. But normal groundwater will be limited to the zone above this confined *aquifer,* for the impervious layer immediately atop the sandstone stops its downward movement and also acts as a barrier between free association of the water in the aquifer and the groundwater. Shallow wells plumb only the local groundwater which is subject to the vagaries of seasonal rainfall and, if the region is arid, easily exhausted. But wells tapping the deeper aquifer assure themselves of a more continuous supply, especially if the intake is in a better watered area. Also, since the permeable surface outcrop is often the highest point in the aquifer, wells drilled to this lower level are usually *artesian* wells because of the hydrostatic pressure within the closed system. As long as the outlet is lower than the intake, water will rise in the well. Some will flow; others merely show a rise of level above that of the general water table. In either case, the term "artesian" is applied (taken from the first recognized well of this type in the French province of Artois).

One of the largest artesian systems in the world underlies much of interior Queensland and northern New South Wales in Australia. (Fig. 8–7.) Here a confined and highly permeable gravel bed receives water at its highest point in the humid Great Dividing Range and carries it for almost a thousand miles west beneath an arid to semiarid country where water is at a premium. (Fig. 8–8.) Many hundreds of bores tap this aquifer, supplying life to what would otherwise be desolate country. But inevitably, too much water has been withdrawn, and most wells that at one time flowed freely at the surface now must be pumped. And too, the quality of the water deteriorates with the distance it moves through the aquifer so that only in the eastern half of the basin is salinity low enough for reasonable utility, and even here it is too brackish for general irrigation and is used only for watering stock. (Fig. 8–9.)

In the Lake Eyre Basin, below sea level although in the heart of the continent, the lower end of the aquifer reaches the surface. The highly saline water flows out here as artesian springs, evaporating almost as rapidly as it appears and depositing salts around each outlet.

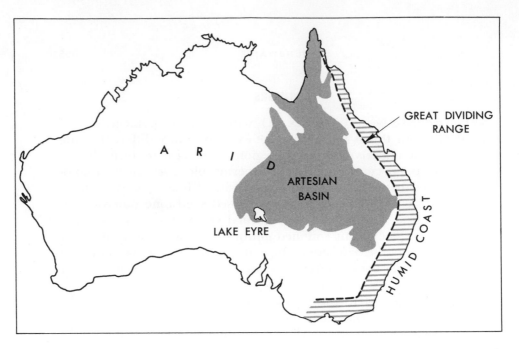

Fig. 8–7. *Australia's Great Artesian Basin. A part of the heavy rainfall along the Great Dividing Range finds its way into the exposed aquifer that carries it downslope under the semiarid interior to finally regain the surface in the below sea level greater Lake Eyre Basin.*

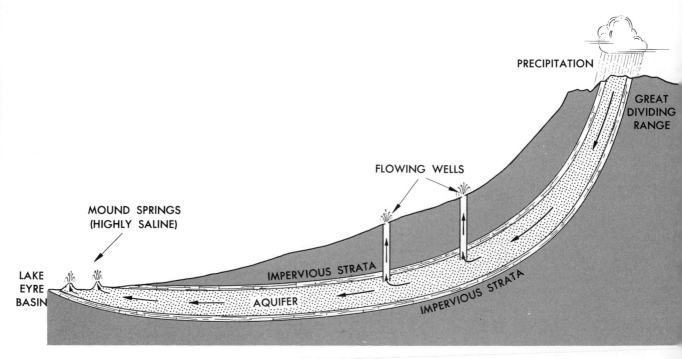

Fig. 8–8. *Generalized cross-section of Australia's Great Artesian Basin. Since the outlet of the wells and the mound springs are below the level of intake in the mountains, they are artesian in character. Salinity increases as the groundwater moves along the aquifer.*

Fig. 8–9. *The western Queensland outback country in Australia would be a wasteland were it not for artesian water. This bore at Bedouri delivers 1½ million gallons daily from a depth of 1,314 feet. Unhappily, the water is too brackish for irrigation, but it is used extensively for livestock. (Courtesy of Australian News & Information Bureau.)*

These are called *mound springs,* building up to a foot or two in height, and are a result of artesian water under great pressure, high salinity, and an extreme rate of evaporation.

Similar artesian systems are found in many other parts of the world, although none are as large as that in Australia. The Dakota sandstone, underlying the northern Great Plains, has its intake in the Rockies and is a major source of water for an extensive semiarid region. North of the Po River in Italy is a line of flowing springs, the *Fontanili.* Fed by melting snows in the Alps, the underground water moves down through an aquifer of coarse glacial and alluvial material. And many of the north Saharan oases exist because aquifers transport Atlas Mountain waters far out into the desert to reappear as artesian springs.

HOT GROUNDWATER

The *heat gradient* of the earth's crust, that is, the increase of heat with increase of depth, may affect groundwater moving along a deeply buried aquifer. Theoretically, there is a depth limit to rock that can contain water, for at several miles down, the pressures exerted by over-

Fig. 8–10. *The Lady Knox Geyser at Rotorua, New Zealand, is only one of many such features in the sizeable North Island thermal district. Note the silicate deposits at the vent, called geyserite. (Courtesy of New Zealand Government Travel Commissioner.)*

lying strata are such that rock pore space becomes inadequate to accommodate a liquid. Water may be present but it is chemically combined in the rocks. But above this limit, sufficient heat still exists to
raise the temperature of moving groundwater, and when it discharges
it is in the form of a thermal spring. This type of spring is not rare,
but much more common are the hot springs, geysers, and steam vents
associated with regions of recently active vulcanism. Here the heat of
the earth's interior has been brought well up into the crust where it
is easily encountered by even very shallow groundwater. Such well-
known tourist attractions as Yellowstone Park, the Rotorua district of
New Zealand, and Iceland are fantastic assemblages of every conceiv-
able type of thermal phenomena, and each is underlain by hot volcanic
rocks. (Fig. 8–10.) To be sure, cooling magma emits hot water,
steam, and other gases so that all of this activity is not wholly a result
of heated groundwater, but surface waters percolating downward to
contact the hot rocks below are without doubt an important element.

Hot springs originating in this manner may achieve very high temperatures indeed, many reaching the boiling point. (Fig. 8–11.) If the

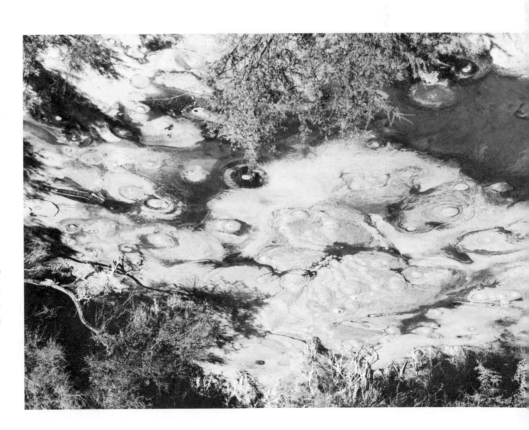

Fig. 8–11. A boiling mud pool in New Zealand. (Courtesy of New Zealand Government Travel Commissioner.)

heat is even greater, then the water becomes steam and issues through vents in the rock as jets. The term "fumerole" or "soltafera" is usually applied if the pure steam is contaminated with magmatic gases and emits an odor. Geysers, which are merely intermittently eruptive thermal springs, are of this same origin. They require a long tube reaching from the surface to the heated rocks below. As the tube fills, the superheated water at the bottom is under too much pressure from that above it to turn into steam, but when all of the water reaches the boiling point and some bubbles out at the top, pressure is released and the water at the bottom flashes into steam causing an eruption. The great volume thrown out by many geysers indicates that an underground reservoir must also be present, interconnected with the tube. (Fig. 8–12.)

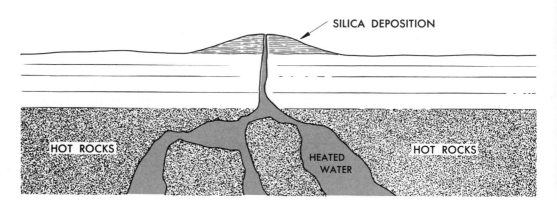

Fig. 8–12. Geysers. The various elements of the underground geyser tube are often quite involved. Vent deposition of silica compounds results from cooling at the surface and thus a loss of groundwater solvency.

Such violent forces are not merely so much spectacular scenery, but have in several parts of the world been put to productive use. A pioneer venture in generating electric power by harnessing the energy of underground steam to power generators (*geothermal* power) was begun in Tuscany, Italy, some years ago. Its success has led to a major project in New Zealand, involving the drilling of deep steam bores, and experimental operations in a number of other places, including a location near Santa Rosa, California. (Fig. 8–13.)

Fig. 8–13. *Wells have been put down, here in New Zealand, to tap the immense quantities of subterranean steam developed by cooling magma near the surface. The intricate plumbing in the foreground is designed to direct the steam jet through turbine blades for the generation of electric power. (Courtesy of New Zealand Government Travel Commissioner.)*

SOLUTION AND DEPOSITION

The very fact that a large proportion of our groundwater is hard or even brackish is an indication that in all of its movements groundwater is taking into solution and removing mineral matter from the rocks through which it passes. Even perfectly clear cold water has the ability to dissolve some minerals or to combine chemically with the rock to form new minerals. But groundwater is seldom clear, since it must pass through overlying material as it percolates downward to become groundwater. Decomposing vegetation on the surface and the soil below it all add elements which give the water certain solvent characteristics, and then, depending on the type of rock it encounters, it reacts chemically with those rocks. If the water is heated, it frequently becomes a much more efficient solvent, and in the process of being heated will often pick up various new elements from magmatic gases.

An excellent example of the sort of solution activity that groundwater can engage in is the removal of calcium carbonate by either hot or cold water with a high carbon dioxide content. Percolating through the cracks in a massive underground limestone stratum, such groundwater can etch out sizable cavities in a relatively short time. Given sufficient time, such huge caverns as Carlsbad and Mammoth Cave result. (Fig. 8–14.) Eventually, the terrain above these caves can be affected as the roof supports are removed and slumping and cave-ins manifest themselves at the surface in deep holes called *sinks or dolines*. Normal surface streams may disappear into such sinks only to reappear many miles away having flowed as an underground river through the cave. In central Florida where the groundwater level is high, these sinks become lakes. Further solution within the cave will

Fig. 8–14. *The Echo River flows through Mammoth Cave, Kentucky, a giant cavern formed by the solution activity of cold groundwater in massive limestone* (circa *1934). (Courtesy of U.S. National Park Service.)*

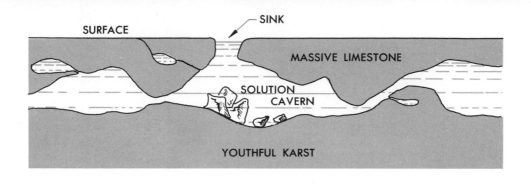

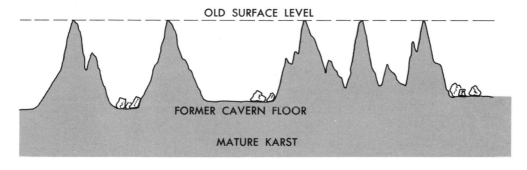

Fig. 8–15. *The development of karst landscapes.*

cause increased slumping until the original surface all but disappears and the landscape takes on a fantastic lunar aspect of sharp eroded spires. Eventually, even these become subdued through the activity of wind and rain, eroding, and weathering. Such a landscape, deriving its character from the continued expansion of solution caverns beneath it, is called *karst*, after the region in Yugoslavia where this type of landform was first described. Following our earlier discussion of the geomorphic cycle, karst landscapes display, like all others, the typical sequence of youth, maturity, and old age. Scattered sink holes only slightly deforming the original surface are youth; total collapse resulting in maximum local relief is maturity; and final virtual peneplanation at a lower level is old age. (Fig. 8–15.)

Fig. 8–16. *Stalactites and stalagmites, coalesced here, result from the evaporation of dripping lime-rich groundwater when air finds its way into caverns. (Courtesy of U.S. National Park Service.)*

All solution is admittedly not this scenic, but it is a constant process and, over the centuries, an effective one. And if there is solution
and removal of materials, then there must be deposition. Sometimes
it is long delayed as when the charged water finds its way to the sea
adding its bit to the salt content there, and it remains for the sea to
accomplish the deposition. Frequently, however, some deposition occurs along the route to the sea. Coarse aquifers become indurated,
mineral layers build up around spring outlets, and colorful crystals
develop in rock cavities. If a cave is open to the atmosphere, lime-
rich water dripping from the ceiling partially evaporates and deposits
hanging needles (*stalactites*) to be matched by counterneedles on the
floor (*stalagmites*) where each drop evaporates further. (Fig. 8–16.)

Even such elements as silica, normally strongly resistant to solution,
may be taken up by certain types of warm groundwater and re-
deposited. Where organic remains such as tree trunks gradually dissolve away, each molecule is faithfully replaced by silica to give us
petrified wood. (Fig. 8–17.) Other minerals too, many of them valu-

Fig. 8–17. *An ancient coniferous tree from Triassic times lay buried
for millennia in siliceous volcanic ash. Groundwater leached the silica from
the ash and substituted it for the vegetative material, so that the so-called
petrified wood is not petrified at all, but is solid rock formed by groundwater replacement. (Courtesy of U.S. National Park Service.)*

Fig. 8–18. *These terraces of the mineral travertine were formed at a Yellowstone hot spring as the waters lost their solution ability upon cooling. Minute plants give the terrace an aqua-blue coloration. (Courtesy of U.S. National Park Service.)*

able economic ones, are concentrated by replacement. What causes groundwater to give up its minerals? Cooling of hot water may account for some deposition; evaporation and chemical change, as new elements are taken into solution, are responsible elsewhere, or even the activity of specialized plants such as those that give color to some hot springs. (Fig. 8–18.) So, groundwater constantly dissolves, transports, and deposits and thus is deserving of recognition as at least a moderate gradational agent along with wind, waves, ice, and running water.

9

The Oceans

Well over two-thirds of the surface of the earth is covered by the sea at the present moment. This has not always been the case in the past nor will it be in the future, for although the great ocean basins have shown remarkable stability throughout the some 3–5 billion years of the earth's existence, the sea margins have fluctuated widely. On a great many occasions, large segments of the continents that are today high and dry have been invaded by shallow seas, while at other times, notably the Pleistocene period about 1,000,000 years ago, sea levels were greatly lowered as continental glaciers impounded an exorbitant fraction of the earth's total water supply, and this process of continually changing sea level is operating even now. Recent measurable uplift has occurred in the high middle latitudes merely because of the release of the great weight of continental ice, and frequent more dramatic volcanic eruptions and faulting are accomplishing rapid changes of level in many other parts of the earth. At the same time, erosion inexorably carries sediments into the sea and builds new land along its margins.

But despite the transitory nature of precise coastlines at any given moment, the ocean has dominated the earth's surface ever since primordial rains first filled the crustal cavities. Yet we know very little about it. Deep-water sailors, shore dwellers, and fishermen have had to amass a considerable body of practical knowledge to assure their livelihood, and this has been invaluable to those who would know the sea. But compared with our understanding of the land, or even the phenomena of the atmosphere, the total accumulation of oceanographic information from the earliest of times is relatively sparse and rudimentary. Only in very recent years has the science of oceanography been recognized and sophisticated instruments put to use to delve into the mysteries of the sea. Already, many long-held misconceptions have been corrected and old generalities hedged and qualified, and we may expect this process to continue for some time as is always the case during the pioneering stages of a science.

It behooves us to learn more about the oceans—and soon. For in a world rapidly depleting its mineral resources, increasing its population beyond the capacity of the land to feed it, constantly requiring larger quantities of fresh water than seem to be available for more than the near future, the sea offers some respite. Perhaps it is the ultimate resource if we but learn to use it, but the corollary of utility is knowledge.

MINERAL RESOURCES FROM THE SEA

Presumably, all the known elements of the earth's crust are represented in the salts of the sea, for it is the erosion of the land that is responsible for the ocean's salinity. No sooner is a land mass upraised above sea level than it is attacked by wind, rivers, ice, and waves, and the entire area with all of its mineral constituents is whittled away to be returned to the sea. But the problems of recovering selected salts for human use are manifold. Often it is the chemistry of the matter that defies solution, but even when the chemistry is possible, the economics of cost feasibility as often as not defeats such efforts. At present, only a relatively few salts are removed directly from seawater in commercial quantities. The age-old evaporation of seawater by the sun still furnishes sodium chloride to many coastal districts in the tropics, and more recently magnesium and bromine have been successfully isolated on a large scale at relatively low cost. (Fig. 9–1.)

On numerous occasions in the past, the oceans have cooperated in making salts available by intruding into shallow embayments far inland where they have been trapped and slowly evaporated away, depositing their salts in thick beds. These may be mined today, sometimes at great depth, by sinking shafts or forcing hot water into them to form brines that can be piped to the surface for processing and recovery. Some of the largest underground caverns ever made by man underlie the city of Detroit where thick salt strata have been mined for many years. (Fig. 9–2.) They date back to Silurian times when tropical temperatures evaporated a sea which overlay much of northeastern United States. Aiding further mining efforts was the fact that the salts precipitated selectively, thus concentrating various differing and reasonably pure layers.

On other occasions, portions of ancient seas have been trapped in underground cavities or porous rock, and there concentrated brines

Fig. 9–1. *A view of part of the largest solar evaporation salt recovery operation in the world on San Francisco Bay near Redwood City. In total, over 50,000 acres of tidal flat are involved. Here, a dredged channel leads to a deepwater terminal for loading from the stockpile. (Courtesy of Leslie Salt Co.)*

Fig. 9–2. *These thick salt strata, almost ¼ mile beneath Detroit, are also a result of solar evaporation as an ancient sea dried up. The salt is being extracted here by deep-mining methods. (Courtesy of International Salt Co.)*

are drawn off today by bores or wells for processing. The Dead Sea, so saline that its waters sustain no life, is the remnant of a former larger sea, and in this case at the surface, and therefore easy to "mine" for its minerals. (Fig. 4–9.)

Where man cannot cope with the chemical problems of isolating certain salts, plant and animal life in the sea may act as intermediaries. Many are equipped with the ability to select out and concentrate a particularly valuable mineral, and if large numbers of them are deposited along with the sediments of old evaporating seas, their remains may form a rich stratum susceptible to recovery by mining. Our familiar commercial petroleum is of organic origin too, and forms as a result of the precipitation of dead plants and animals to the bottom of shallow seas. The exact chemistry of decomposition and the effects of heat developed by subsequent rock deformation to form a liquid hydrocarbon are not fully understood; but without the sea and the life that inhabits it, we could have no oil, for it cannot be made economically in the laboratory.

Removal of salts from the sea has another practical aspect above and beyond the commercial use of those salts; that is, the recovery of fresh water—cheaply and in large quantities. This problem may be even more pressing than the need for minerals, for we live in a world of burgeoning population whose per capita water consumption is constantly increasing and whose available resources are limited and polluted. The sea is the obvious answer. The by-product of fresh water production is recovered salts, and their use may eventually pay for the high cost of clarifying the water. Old-fashioned distillation will do the job—so will ionic transfer and freezing. But all require high-cost fuel and intricate mechanisms difficult to operate on a really large scale. Perhaps solar furnaces or atomic energy will solve the fuel problem. The U.S. government and many other agencies the world around are working at it, and we may hope for a critical breakthrough in the not too distant future. (Fig. 9–3.)

THE FLOOR OF THE SEA

Except for shallow inshore fishing banks and well-frequented harbors, the sounding of the ocean bottom has been for centuries only a sometime thing. Even official pilot directions and hydrographic charts of coastal waters abound with notations such as "depth unknown" or "probably shoal." Out in the open ocean where the bottom is a long way from the top, only specially equipped oceanographic vessels have found it worthwhile to even attempt to measure depth, that is, until the development of sonic gear just prior to World War II, utilizing the

Fig. 9–3. *This joint state-federal financed seawater conversion plant at San Diego, operating on an experimental basis, supplied for several years a part of that city's fresh water requirements. In 1964, the entire plant was dismantled and shipped to the Guantánamo, Cuba, Naval Station to relieve its dependence on imported Cuban water. (Courtesy of U.S. Office of Saline Water.)*

principle of echo timing. Increasing numbers of ships are being equipped with these instruments, and sonar profiles are becoming more or less routine. Yet sonar has its limitations—2,000 fathoms (1 fathom = 6 feet) is the practical depth limit, underwater strata of differing densities and temperature make for an unfortunately high degree of error, and the sheer immensity of the oceans relative to the current number of sonar-equipped ships points to many years of work ahead. But we have evolved at least a general outline of the underwater topography of most of the world's seas, and although we are still a long way from being able to construct a detailed contour map of the sea floor, the present knowledge is a great advance from that of Magellan who, in 1521, hung a standard inshore sounding line over the gunwale as he crossed the South Pacific, and when it failed to touch bottom proclaimed that "Here was the deepest spot in the ocean."

The Continental Shelf

The major ocean basins are deep—there is no question about that. Average depths run in the neighborhood of 13,000 to 14,000 feet or almost 3 miles, but an important part of each ocean overlies the subdued margins of the continents. In some cases, this *continental shelf* extends for many miles offshore beneath its epicontinental sea; elsewhere it may be very narrow, but where it is existent, the continental shelf is regarded as a legitimate part of the continent, albeit temporarily flooded. (Fig. 9–4.) Only minor lowering in sea level would expose extensive tracts of this sea bottom, as it has undoubtedly in

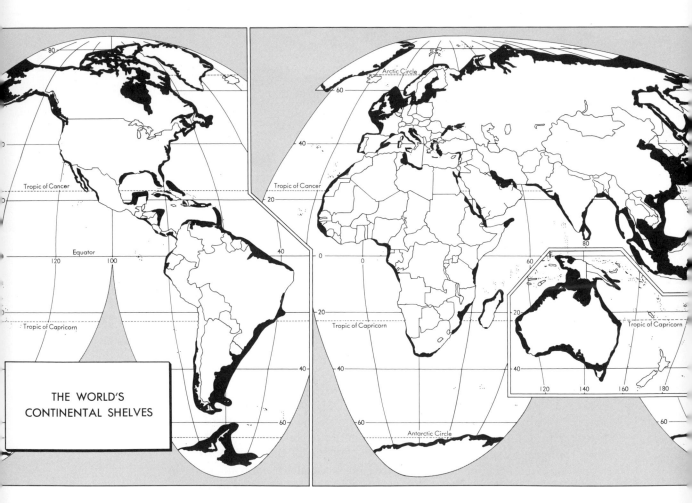

THE WORLD'S CONTINENTAL SHELVES

Fig. 9–4. *The world's continental shelves. The great ocean basins lie beyond the margins of these shelves.*

the past. Dogger Bank, a particularly shallow fishing grounds in the North Sea, is a part of the continental shelf today, yet trawlers have frequently brought up bits of wood and man-made artifacts indicating that this was recently a forested inhabited land.

The actual break-off point between the continent and the ocean depths is at the outer edge of the continental shelf, wherever that might be. The 100-fathom line was quite arbitrarily selected as this critical point for many years, but with increasing knowledge of the character of undersea topography, the International Committee on the Nomenclature of Ocean Bottom Features redefined, in 1953, the continental shelf as the "zone around the continents, extending from low-water line to the depth at which there is a marked increase of slope to greater depth"; in other words, no specific depth, for shelves vary in their shoalness, but rather where a sharp break in topography occurs.

The continental shelves are that part of the sea bottom most like the land. Light penetrates deeply, seaweed anchors itself to the rocks, the floor is veneered with sediments derived from the land, and sea life abounds, fed in large part by nutrients washed down by continental rivers, and most of the world's great fisheries are in these epicontinental seas.

It would appear at first glance that the continental shelves should be smooth surfaced because of the subduing effects of wave action and continuous sedimentation, but this is not necessarily the case. The floor is frequently irregular, especially where continental glaciers have run far out to sea and have not only scarred and gouged the surface, but also dumped huge quantities of debris that stand up today as *banks*. Much more dramatic than these relatively minor irregularities are the widespread canyons scoring the continental shelves to great depth. At their deepest points, the outer edge of the shelf, many of these canyons are over a mile below sea level and have frequently been compared with the Grand Canyon of the Colorado. (Fig. 9–5.) Their origin remains a mystery and a source of heated controversy among submarine geologists, but several of them have been studied rather carefully and their basic characteristics are known. They appear to be remarkably like stream-carved canyons on the land, having steep V-shaped contours with tributary valleys along the sides. Since most of the submarine canyons are off the mouths of present-day continental rivers, or where former rivers have flowed to the sea, it has been postulated that they were incised during a low-water period as normal stream valleys and subsequently drowned. The canyons of the Hudson and Congo rivers seem to be simple extensions of those river courses, and the Monterey canyon is immediately opposite the ancient mouth of the Salinas River. But this type of thinking assumes a low-

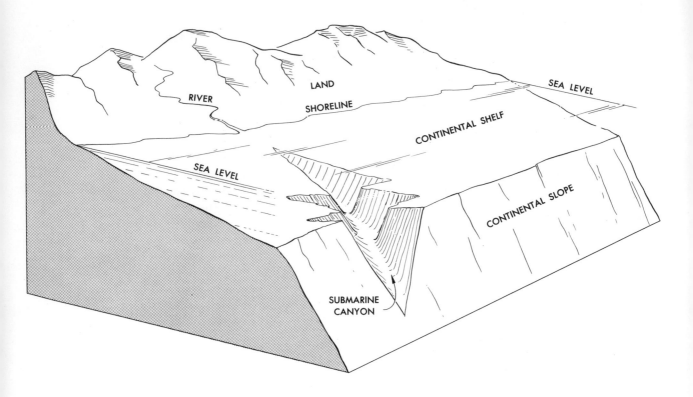

Fig. 9–5. *Position of a submarine canyon on the continental shelf (highly diagrammatic). Such canyons may be over a mile in depth and are often situated immediately opposite the mouth of a river.*

ered sea level during fairly recent times to a much greater depth than many researchers are willing to accept. These people talk in terms of turbidity currents or heavy mud-saturated currents impelled by gravity down the steep wall at the outer edge of the continental slope, scouring and cutting the canyon contours. Whatever the cause, the canyons of the shelf are a major and highly dramatic feature.

The Continental Slope

Where the continental shelf sharply falls away to the great depths of the ocean proper, there occurs the most imposing escarpment in all the world. It is called the *Continental Slope*. Varying in height from place to place, it probably averages 12,000 feet, which is in itself impressive as a single steep slope. But when continental slopes of almost 30,000 feet may be encountered in a number of places, we begin to realize the enormity of this undersea feature. Undoubtedly, the south wall of the Himalayas is the greatest single slope visible to us on the land, but if we combine the continental slope, which begins almost at the beach off the Peruvian coast, with the Andean heights immediately inland, we find what is virtually a continuous slope of about 42,000 feet or almost double that of the Himalayas. This is where the ocean begins. These deep basins beyond the continental slope have always contained the sea, in sharp contrast to their shallow and transitory extensions onto the margins of the continents.

Oceanic Ridges (Fig. 9–6) (Map V, pp. 414–15)

Apparently the bottom of the sea has been subject to all of the tectonic forces that have affected the rest of the earth's crust. No longer do we regard the ocean floor as essentially a vast level plain with only occasional ridges or deeps, for as soundings and samplings have become more frequent, they have disclosed evidences of a very rugged bottom topography indeed, resulting from folding, faulting, and vulcanism on a scale comparable to that of the continents. It now appears that extensive plains, such as one discovered in 1947 by a Swedish expedition southeast of Ceylon in the Indian Ocean, are very much an exception. The remarkable thing is that the deep-sea topography is not even more rugged since the compensatory erosional forces of the land are lacking. Only when an oceanic mountain rears itself

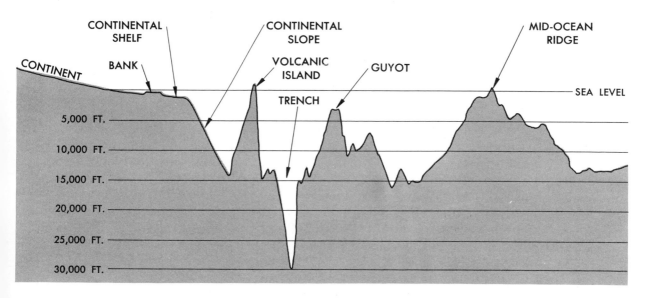

Fig. 9–6. *Idealized sea bottom configuration (great vertical exaggeration).*

Fig. 9–7. In the distance, the highest point on Pico Island in the Azores. It is also the highest point of the Atlantic Ridge, over 7,000 feet above sea level and 27,000 feet above the ocean floor. The volcanic origin of the island is evident in the use of broken lava fragments for the building of walls in the foreground. (Courtesy of Casa de Portugal.)

above the surface do waves, rain, and wind attack it, and because of this it is generally believed that many undersea landforms are of extreme age.

The earliest of the major undersea topographic features to be studied and plotted was the Atlantic Ridge, for it was directly athwart the trans-Atlantic cable route between Europe and North America. Subsequent investigation has revealed the outlines of a substantial mountain range running the full length of the Atlantic (with only one narrow break near the equator called the *Romanche Trench*) from Iceland in the north to roughly 50°S latitude from where it veers off to the east to pass south of Africa. This great cordillera, several times as wide as the Appalachians, reaches its greatest height of 27,000 feet above the sea floor in the Azores, one of only a few places where it breaks the surface. (Fig. 9–7.) Ascension Island, Tristan da Cunha Island, and St. Paul's Rocks are also emergent peaks, but for the most part the Ridge is submerged a mile or more even though it averages

5,000–10,000 feet in elevation. Rachel Carson's description of the Atlantic Ridge in her classic little volume *The Sea Around Us* is almost poetic.

. . . most of the Ridge lies forever hidden from human eyes. Its contours have been made out only indirectly by the marvelous probings of sound waves; bits of its substance have been brought up to us by corers and dredges; and some details of its landscape have been photographed with deep-sea cameras. With these aids our imaginations can picture the grandeur of the undersea mountains, with their sheer cliffs and rocky terraces, their deep valleys and towering peaks. If we are to compare the ocean's mountains with anything on the continents, we must think of terrestrial mountains far above the timber line, with their silent snow-filled valleys and their naked rocks swept by the winds. For the sea, too, has its inverted "timber line" or plant line, below which no vegetation can grow. The slopes of the undersea mountains are far beyond the reach of the sun's rays, and there are only the bare rocks, and, in the valleys, the deep drifts of sediments that have been silently piling up through the millions upon millions of years.[1]

Other seas have ridges too, but none are as extensive as that of the Atlantic. In the Indian Ocean, there is a broad ridge of moderate height pushing southward from India to Antarctica, and the Arctic Ocean may have a northerly extension of the Atlantic Ridge, although constant thick ice has so far limited research to only a few preliminary soundings. No comparable transoceanic ridges exist in the Pacific; however, there is a broad plateau involving much of the eastern South Pacific, and the Hawaiian, Gilbert-Marshall, and other island archipelagos mark the courses of volcanic uplifts. (Fig. 9–8.)

Trenches (Map V, pp. 414–15)

Much more prominent in the Pacific than its limited mid-ocean ridges are its "deeps." These long trenches are a great deal deeper than the general ocean floor, and by far the largest number of them and those with greatest depth are found in the Pacific. Curiously, they are ranged around the margin of the ocean basin rather than in its center and always in conjunction with active vulcanism and frequent seismic activity. Thus it follows, virtually without question, that they are related to the very faulting and vulcanism that raises the high mountains along their margins. In the western Pacific where the chains of mountain peaks form island arcs along offshore fault lines, the trenches align themselves parallel and immediately adjacent to the convex side of most arcs. These are the greatest known depths anywhere on earth.

[1] Rachel Carson, *The Sea Around Us* (Fair Lawn, N.J.: Oxford University Press, 1951), pp. 68–69. Quoted by permission, Oxford University Press.

Fig. 9–8. Aoba Island, New Hebrides, is the emergent part of a volcanic ridge in the South Pacific; immediately adjacent is a linear trench. Both are evidence of the deep-seated faulting that is so typical of much of the Pacific Basin. (Courtesy of U.S. Navy.)

Until just a very few years ago, it was thought that Mindanao Deep in the Philippine Trench was the deepest of all at 34,428 feet below sea level, but the British found Challenger Deep in the Mariana Trench to be 35,800 feet deep, and a further sounding just a few miles away by the Russians led to a claim of a 36,000-foot depth. Simply measuring these depths has proved to be a very difficult operation through the years, even with specially equipped ships and trained personnel, yet the U.S. Navy astounded the world in 1961 when two men in a bathyscaph were successfully lowered to the bottom of the Mariana Trench and brought back alive and well. (Fig. 9–9.) It may

Fig. 9–9. (A) The U.S.S. "Trieste," Navy bathyscaph (Official U.S. Navy photo.)

be difficult to comprehend just how far down 36,000 feet is unless we compare it with; say, the elevation of Mt. Everest, the highest known point above sea level at 29,028 feet, or visualize Mt. Rainier on top of Mt. Whitney, the two together failing by over a mile to equal the depth of several of these oceanic trenches. (Fig. 9–10.) Others of similar depth include the Kurile Trench, 34,020 feet; Ramapo Deep off Japan, 33,000 feet; and the Tonga Trench, 34,860 feet.

Although the total area of ocean bottom involved in these narrow deeps is minuscule, some of them extend for great distances. Off the west coast of South America, for example, where the volcanic activity is on the mainland and there is virtually no continental shelf, the 25,000-foot deep Chile-Peru Trench parallels the coast for over 2,000 miles. And the Aleutian Trench on the south side of that island chain is almost as long. In the other oceans, marginal trenches are present but in limited numbers; however, they once again occur adjacent to volcanic-seismic regions. The West Indies and the island archipelago south of Cape Horn are accompanied by great deeps, as are the south coasts of Java and Sumatra in the Indian Ocean.

Sea Mounts and Coral

Charles Darwin on the celebrated voyage of the "Beagle" in 1835 was the first to suggest that the Pacific *atoll,* with its ringing coral reef and shallow enclosed lagoon, might be related to undersea volcanic mountains. (Fig. 9–11.) He envisioned a slowly sinking volcanic peak with coral growing upward around the rim of the crater at a rate rapid enough to match subsidence. At that time, not enough was known about either coral or Pacific vulcanism to prove or disprove such a theory, but today it appears that Darwin was essentially correct. The Pacific floor is liberally peppered with steep-sided volcanic cones or *sea mounts,* usually arranged along fault lines. And there is a considerable body of evidence pointing to a sinking of the sea floor or a rise in sea level or both. Recently discovered flat-topped sea mounts or *guyots,* chiefly in the Pacific but also in the other oceans, suggest wave planation of the tops of volcanoes once at sea level but now drowned. And the thousands of atolls, so typical of the tropical Pacific, are evidence in themselves, once the peculiarities of coral growth are understood. (Fig. 9–12.)

The coral polyp is a living creature that forms about itself a calcium carbonate cell from which it can reach out and feed off the zooplankton in seawater. Although there are many different kinds of coral growing under a wide variety of conditions, the several types of colony-dwelling corals, whose calcium dwellings become cemented together to form reefs, require a fairly limited set of physical circum-

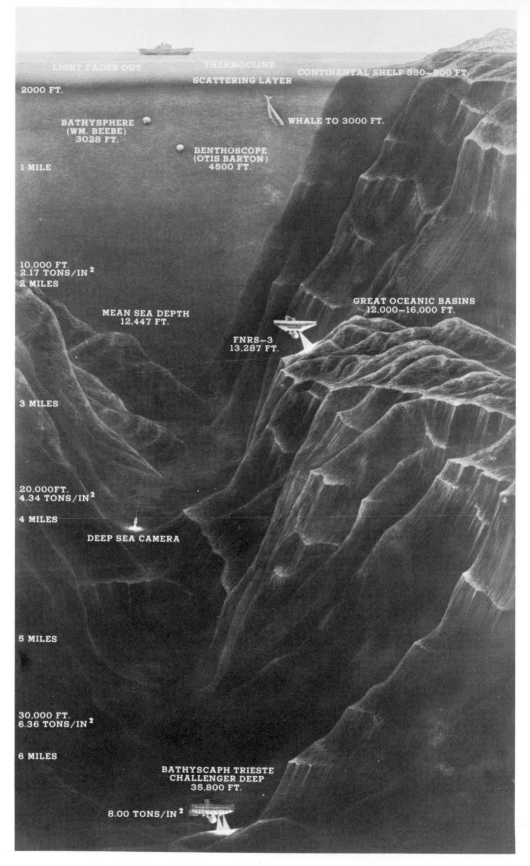

Fig. 9–10. *An appreciation of the great depths involved in the Pacific trenches may be gained from this artist's sketch.* (Official U.S. Navy photo.)

Fig. 9–11. *Is it an amoeba? No, it happens to be Swain's Island, a U.S. owned coral atoll north of Samoa. The dark granular circle is dry land, a few feet above sea level and studded with coconuts. The mottled area in the center is the lagoon. Surf foams over the outer edge of the reef, while white sand beaches fringe the shore. A small break in the reef is visible opposite the village at the left.*

In one respect, this atoll is atypical, as most atolls feature fragments of land ringing the lagoon, with channels between them, allowing ships access to the lagoon. Possibly there has been a slight uplift here following the original atoll development. (Courtesy of U.S. Coast & Geodetic Survey.)

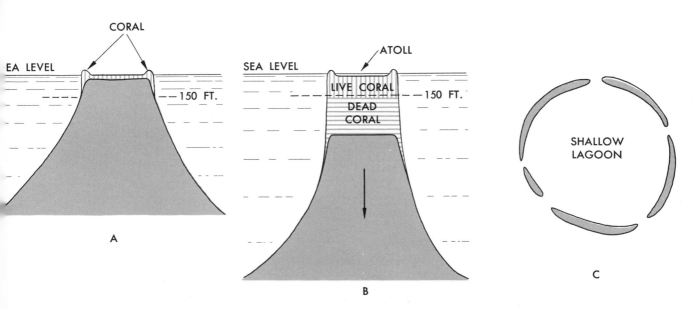

Fig. 9–12. *The development of an atoll. (A) An oceanic mountain peak in cross-section, the top beveled by wave action, and the beginnings of coral formation. (B) Again in cross-section, the continued development of coral at and near the surface as the mountain slowly sinks to form an atoll. (C) A plan view of a typical circular atoll with its shallow lagoon, marking the dimensions of the sunken peak.*

stances in order to flourish. First, they cannot survive if water temperatures fall below 65°–70°, so that if we draw a set of lines across the world's oceans at about 30°N and S, we will have for the most part enclosed all those tropical seas that will permit their growth.[2] Second, coral requires a reasonably saline water and does not do well, for instance, where rivers discharge large quantities of fresh water into the sea. Third, the muddy turbid waters of many beaches and river mouths have a deleterious effect on coral. And finally, coral requires light and feeds on plankton with the same requirement so there is a depth limit, generally described as about 150 feet, below which reefs cannot form.

With respect to this last condition, borings of several thousand feet on atolls have demonstrated that coralline rock is present at these depths with volcanic rock below, thus making virtually mandatory an explanation of sinking sea mounts. The reef below 150 feet is, of course, no longer living, but atop this base, coral has been able to maintain itself, suggesting that the sinking was a slow process. The outer edge of the reef, supplied with fresh seawater and the food within it, grows most vigorously and may rise above sea level if waves constantly break over it. We see this same sort of development in the offshore or *barrier reefs*. The Great Barrier Reef off the east coast of tropical Australia is 1,500 miles long and occupies the outer edge of the continental shelf which has been depressed slowly. (Fig. 9–13.) *Fringing reefs* are found immediately adjacent to many tropical coasts, but slow sinking can cause a fringing reef to become a barrier reef as the land is inundated and the former beach line, marked by growing coral, remains visible some distance offshore. (Fig. 9–14.) Coralline limestone frequently encountered at some distance up a mountain slope or a former atoll with its lagoon high and dry is evidence that uplift may occur as well as subsidence.

So we can see that the sea bottom is far from uniform. At least the gross outline is known to us today, although we should expect constant new discoveries and refinements of theories. The shallow continental shelf with its minor irregularities and spectacular canyons is quite a different world from the tremendous continental slopes and deep ocean basins featuring whole mountain ranges, abysmal deeps, and isolated sea mounts.

---

[2] Warm currents moving poleward may push this limit somewhat beyond 30° in places, and conversely cold currents moving equatorward may inhibit reef development at rather low latitudes. Also, temperatures much above 90°, such as are experienced in the enclosed Red Sea and Persian Gulf, often affect coral growth.

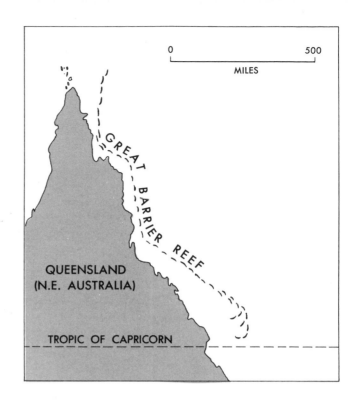

Fig. 9–13. *Australia's Great Barrier Reef. The most extensive barrier reef in the world faithfully follows the outer margin of the drowned continental shelf.*

Fig. 9–14. *The outer line of surf marks a barrier reef at Avarua, Rarotonga, in the Cook Archipelago. Tidal currents maintain an opening in the reef opposite the wharf, allowing shipping to approach the island. (Courtesy of New Zealand Government Travel Commissioner.)*

OCEAN CURRENTS

Basic ocean current circulation was introduced in Chapter 4 in order to help explain the peculiarities of several coastal climates, so that the typical clockwise character of each Northern Hemisphere *gyral* and the counterclockwise gyral in the Southern Hemisphere should be familiar. Once the surface currents are set in motion (the chief causes probably being prevailing winds and salinity variations), they immediately begin to react to Coriolis force and display their respective curvatures, aided and abetted by the easterly trade winds in the tropics and the Westerlies in the middle latitudes whose directions are themselves a result of this same Coriolis force. It will be recalled that in every major ocean basin, there is a warm current flowing poleward along the east coast and a cold current flowing equatorward along the west coast (below 35–40 degrees of latitude). (Fig. 9–15.) (See Map V, pp. 414–15.)

By all odds, the most powerful of the poleward flowing warm currents is the Atlantic Gulf Stream, a veritable river in the sea, carrying huge volumes of indigo blue tropical water far to the north at speeds of up to 3 knots. Because of its distinctive color, it is readily visible to the observer crossing it off the coast of the United States, and the balmy temperatures and occasional storms associated with it are reminiscent of the tropics. But even this great current must respond to the influence of the earth's rotation, and as it moves past Cape Hatteras, it begins to pull away from the coast toward the northeast. The result is a suction, pulling cold water southward from the Arctic along the New England shore in an eddy current called the *Labrador Current*. As these two, the brilliant blue tropical waters and the icy green current from the Arctic, merge over the Outer Banks, the cold runs under the warm. Virtually permanent fog results at this juncture, as warm air is abruptly cooled and the roiling waters mix oceanic ingredients ideal for propagation of plankton and fish life.

Now the Gulf Stream trends eastward, impelled by the Westerlies, losing some of its vigor as it widens out, spilling minor eddy currents both north and south as it goes. Upon reaching the coast of Western Europe in the vicinity of the British Isles, once again the tendency to curve to the right is instinctive, and the bulk of the *West Wind Drift* flows southward much cooler and more subdued. But a lesser branch, split off by Ireland, swings northward, hugging the Norwegian coast past North Cape and eventually fading out along the Russian north coast. Cool as it has become by now, this branch exerts a warming influence at these high latitudes and is responsible for ice-free harbors far north of the Arctic Circle.

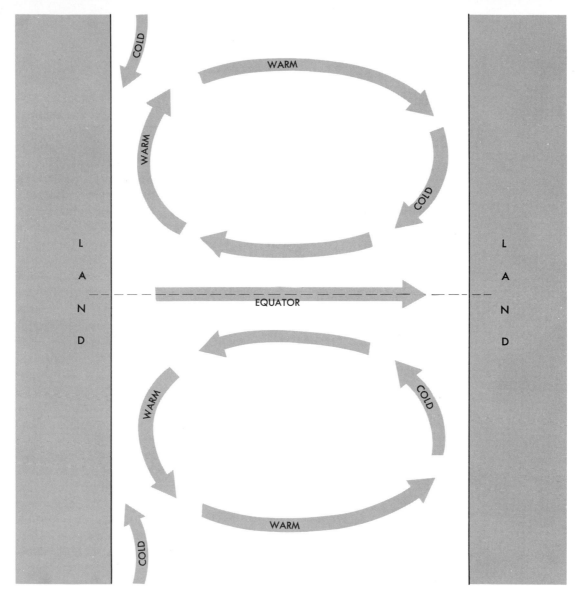

Fig. 9–15. *Basic ocean current circulation. This standard pattern is recognizable in every major ocean except the North Indian.*

The main current, cool now as it moves to the south and into tropical waters off the coasts of Portugal and Morocco, is called the *Canaries Current*. Its generally low temperature is reinforced by the upwelling of cold waters inshore as the prevailing winds from off the land blow the surface water away from the coast. Once again the mixing of cold and warm water sets up conditions highly favorable for oceanic microorganisms which are basic fish food, and important sardine fisheries have been developed in this region. As the southerly reach is concluded, the *Canaries Current* again becomes tropical and, warming rapidly, swings right to flow due west north of the equator and is here termed the *North Atlantic Equatorial Current*.

At the center of this great North Atlantic whirlpool is a region peculiar unto itself in all the world; this is the *Sargasso Sea*. Each ocean has the identical gyral characteristics, and in every case its center coincides with the generally calm Horse Latitudes' permanent high-pressure cell. But only the North Atlantic combines this quiet, currentless, windless sea with the great accumulation of sargassum weed. Seemingly endless miles of ocean contain the weed brought in originally by the Gulf Stream from the West Indies where storms have torn it loose from its rocky coastal habitat. And through countless thousands of years, it has evolved the ability to maintain and reproduce itself here in mid-ocean. The old legend of the Sargasso Sea as a graveyard of ships has some small basis of fact in that, given enough time, any floating debris is likely to find its way into the heart of the spiraling current circulation. And the Bermuda High is a permanent area of calms that makes sailing difficult. But the sargassum is scarcely thick enough to entrap any seaworthy craft, and the actual facts of the matter have been greatly exaggerated and embroidered upon through the years.

In the South Atlantic, virtually a mirror image of the North Atlantic current circulation prevails: the poleward flowing *Brazilian Current,* following the South American coast, is warm; the broad and still warm *West Wind Drift* flows to the east; the large and vigorous *Benguela Current,* with its associated upwelling, draws Antarctic water equatorward off of West Africa; and finally, the westward-moving *South Atlantic Equatorial Current* completes the circulation. Even the cold Labrador eddy current finds a counterpart in the *Falkland Current* of the South Atlantic

Between the two equatorial currents running to the west is an apparently out-of-place *Equatorial Countercurrent* exhibiting a diametrically opposed course. This is explained by the piling up of surface water on the west side of the Atlantic by the constantly blowing Trades. It is common knowledge that the water level at the Atlantic end of the Panama Canal is several feet higher than at the Pacific end—this despite the fact that sea level is supposed to be the same the world over. But the winds are onshore on the east side of the isthmus and offshore on the west. This is the phenomenon that causes the Equatorial Countercurrent. As the major warm currents of each hemisphere curve away to flow poleward taking some of this water surplus with them, the remainder flow "downhill" to the east in the windless Doldrums. This same situation is supposedly accountable for the high current velocities of the *Florida Current* and other elements contributing to the Gulf Stream as they flow east-northeast through the restricted channels of the West Indies.

The Pacific displays essentially the same basic pattern as the Atlantic. The *North Pacific Equatorial Current* curves northward off the coast of Southeast Asia and becomes the Japanese Current (*Kuro Shio* or Black Current because of its dark blue coloration). This warm flow in turn curves right when it reaches central Japan to become the *West Wind Drift,* and in so doing sucks in behind it a southward-probing finger of cold water from the Arctic called the *Okhotsk Current (Oya Shio).* Here again the cold current under-runs the warm, developing a region of fog and often turbulent seas. Unlike the North Atlantic, the Aleutian chain and Gulf of Alaska do not allow more than a very minor part of the *West Wind Drift* to invade Arctic seas, and essentially the entire current turns south to parallel the North American coast and become the cold *California Current.*

In the eastern Pacific, the *South Equatorial Current* is a powerful stream as is the *Equatorial Countercurrent* to the north of it, but although the *Countercurrent* maintains itself across the entire ocean basin, the *South Equatorial Current* runs into difficulties as it moves westward into the island world of the East Indies and Australia. The general tendency is to curve south, but each island group and narrow strait forces adjustments and deflection of some part of the stream, and in the absence of a definitive continental wall to force its pole-ward curvature, it tends to become badly disorganized. One fraction, called the *East Australia Current,* moves along the coast of the southern continent and is eventually picked up by the Westerlies and swung east. And here, under the influence of these strong winds that roar around the world uninterrupted by land, a sizable *West Wind Drift* is established. Upon reaching the far tip of South America, this current turns northward, pulling with it large quantities of Antarctic water, and the world's greatest cold current comes into being. This is the *Humboldt Current,* which, constantly maintaining its low temperature through massive upwelling, flows along the coast of South America to the equator. Here again, but on a larger scale than in other oceans, the exchange of salts through overturning and the invasion of tropical seas by icy water stimulates the active growth of zooplankton and in turn a great concentration of fish. No wonder Ecuador and Peru have attempted to claim sovereignty over the navigable waters for 100–300 miles offshore rather than the traditional 3–12 miles, and in so doing have found themselves in continual conflict with the deep-sea fishermen of many nations.

The Indian Ocean is somewhat different from the others. South of the equator, a reasonably typical gyral exists, but the limited sea of the Northern Hemisphere is strongly affected by the seasonal monsoon winds so that no permanent currents exist, and the surface waters tend to move in opposite directions in winter and summer.

These many currents of the various oceans that have been described so far are all surface currents, propelled in large part by winds. On occasion, over continental shelves, they scour the bottom, but at most they only represent the movement of surface waters to a depth of a few hundred fathoms. What about the great mass of the sea? Does it move in any sort of a coordinated predictable manner? Very little is known of the ocean depths, but in theory the warm and thus lighter waters of the tropics should drift poleward at the surface, while cold Arctic and Antarctic waters subside and move equatorward along the bottom. A few experimental testings beneath the Gulf Stream have indicated that there is indeed a current of cold water moving in opposition to that at the surface, but no widespread definable pattern has yet been found.

The tides, of course, activate all the ocean waters in their daily rhythms, and there is some cause to believe that deep waves, quite unlike the normal surface waves, are widely occurring phenomena.[3] But at the moment, we have only the sketchiest hints concerning deep-sea movement, and it will undoubtedly require many years of work before these riddles are solved.

TIDES

Theoretically, the oceanic tides are a simple and highly predictable phenomenon. We know their basic cause—the gravitational attraction of the moon and sun, but the moon, although many times smaller than the sun, is so much nearer to the earth that it exerts roughly double the force of the sun. Even the ancients were aware of something of this relationship between the moon and the tides, for in most places on the earth, the time of high and low tide progresses by 50 minutes each day as the moon rises 50 minutes later. And the height of each tide varies regularly each month as the moon waxes and wanes. (Fig. 9–16.) When the moon is new (dark), it is between the sun and the earth, and the combined forces of both act to pull the mobile waters away from the earth into a bulge. At the same time, a similar oceanic bulge appears exactly opposite as a result of centrifugal force. Now, as the earth rotates on its axis, every coastline is exposed to each bulge 12 hours apart. A roughly comparable

---

[3] Surface waves are described briefly in Chapter 7 dealing with shoreline features, and tidal waves or tsunamis, which are a type of deep-ocean wave, are treated in the same chapter relative to sea bottom faulting and vulcanism.

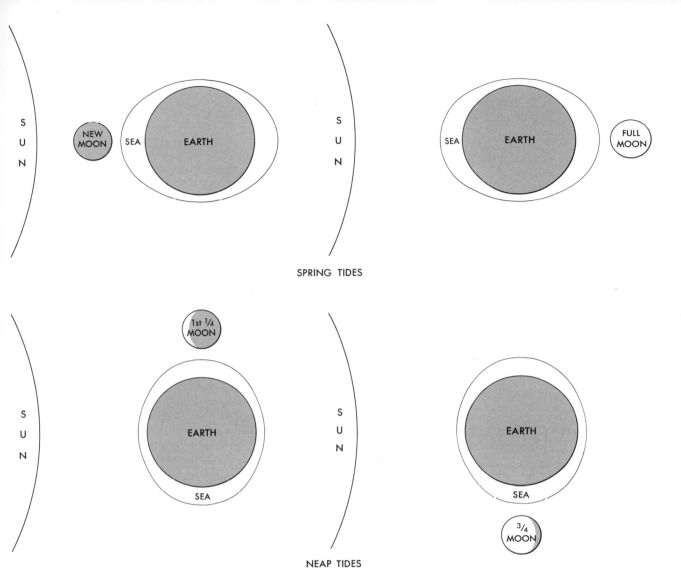

Fig. 9–16. *Idealized relationship of tides to the phases of the moon. The fundamental cause of tides everywhere is illustrated here, although variations are infinite because of myriad local factors.*

situation occurs once again during the full moon when the earth, moon, and sun are all in line, but this time the earth is between moon and sun. Two sizable oceanic bulges are once more in evidence and each location experiences two high tides. These are the highest tides of each month, a result of moon and sun acting in concert, and are called *spring tides* (an unfortunate term for they have nothing to do with season). Subsequent tides exhibit the same sequence of daily occurrence, but the high tides become progressively lower until at the quarter phases of the moon, the relative positions of sun and moon

Fig. 9–17. High and low tides at Eastport, Maine, where an 18-foot differential is normal. (Courtesy of U.S. Army Corps of Engineers.)

are at right angles and their forces oppose one another. Now the tidal bulges are much less exaggerated and the mildest high tides, or *neap tides,* occur. So each day there are two high tides and two low tides six hours apart, but the greatest of these are at the new and full moon every month and the least at the quarter. (Fig. 9–17.)

Once again, however, it should be emphasized that this is theoretical, for, although the attractive force of moon and sun are most certainly the basic motive force, the actual character of the tides at any given place varies widely. Puget Sound has 12-foot spring tides; Tahiti only 1-foot, and parts of Korea, Alaska, and the Siberian Pacific coast have 30–40 foot tides. Yet all face out on the same ocean. The tides at opposite ends of the Panama Canal vary over 15 feet. Furthermore, the classic cycle of two high and two low tides advancing 50 minutes each day is found to occur something less than unanimously. The Gulf of Mexico has only one rise and fall; the Pacific Coast of the United States has two but of differing heights; and Tahiti does not have the 50-minute advance each day of its mild but otherwise normal tides.

These great variations, sometimes occurring only a few miles from each other, are the result of both bottom topography and local coastline configuration. The head of the Bay of Fundy in Canada's Maritime Provinces has, at 50 feet, the greatest tidal variation known. (Fig. 9–18.) But it is only partially explainable by its long funnel shape and shallowing bottom—surely some peculiarity of the continental shelf contributes to this phenomenal tidal range that is not shared by other similarly shaped bays.

Fig. 9–18. Passamaquoddy Bay, Maine, a part of the Bay of Fundy. The dams in the photo date from 1936 and are a portion of the proposed Passamaquoddy project that aims at harnessing the world's highest tides to produce power. (Courtesy of U.S. Army Corps of Engineers.)

Fig. 9–19. *Narrow defiles such as Deception Pass between Whidby Island and the mainland on Puget Sound often channel tidal waters into swift currents. Here, twice a day, the tides, which reach a maximum of 12 feet, roar through the pass, and shipping can be accommodated only at slack water. (Courtesy of Washington State Department of Commerce & Economic Development.)*

In inshore waters, tidal currents may commonly reach high velocities, and shipping is advised to shun certain restricted channels during flood tides. (Fig. 9–19). The Norwegian Maelstrom in the Lofoten Islands creates devastating whirlpools. And much-used Seymour Narrows between Vancouver Island and the mainland, a part of the Inside Passage to Alaska, has proved to be so dangerous that demolition of shoal rocks has been carried out in an attempt to tame the fury of its tidal currents. (Fig. 9–20.) Tide rips too along a broken coastline where retreating tides from opposite shores meet in frothing eddies are both common and dangerous.

Fig. 9–20. *A break in a Dutch dike illustrates the difficulties of repair in the face of the rushing tidal currents through the confined channel. (Courtesy of Netherlands Information Service.)*

Many river ports, such as Calcutta on the Hooghly, are dependent on tidal bores to keep their deep-sea channels open, but here and there a bore becomes so exaggerated that all navigation must be suspended. A virtual wall of water rushes up the river channel sometimes for many miles. To produce a bore, a river mouth must not only experience a high tidal range, but some sort of obstruction such as a bar or spit that functions to hold the rising water back until finally it is overcome with almost explosive force. Then, if the estuary is funnel shaped, as is the case at Hanchow Bay, China, where perhaps the world's best known bore is encountered, the height of the advancing wave builds up rapidly. Most rivers discharging into the sea do not experience a bore, but nearly all are troubled by tides backing up normal stream flow, causing upstream flooding and allowing saline water to invade irrigation outlets and the like.

World Maps

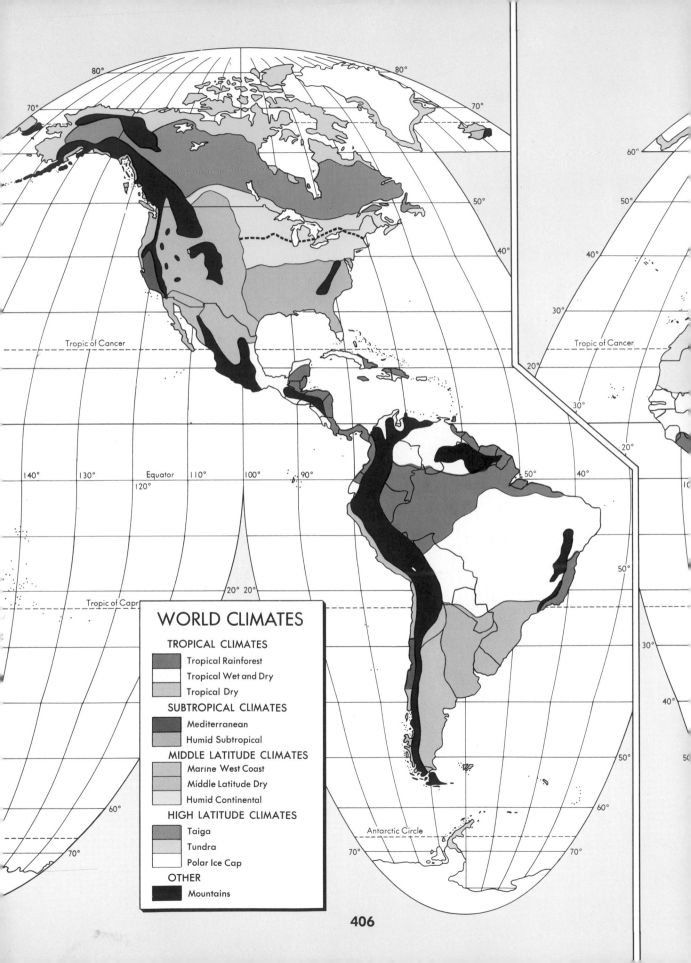

WORLD CLIMATES

TROPICAL CLIMATES
Tropical Rainforest
Tropical Wet and Dry
Tropical Dry

SUBTROPICAL CLIMATES
Mediterranean
Humid Subtropical

MIDDLE LATITUDE CLIMATES
Marine West Coast
Middle Latitude Dry
Humid Continental

HIGH LATITUDE CLIMATES
Taiga
Tundra
Polar Ice Cap

OTHER
Mountains

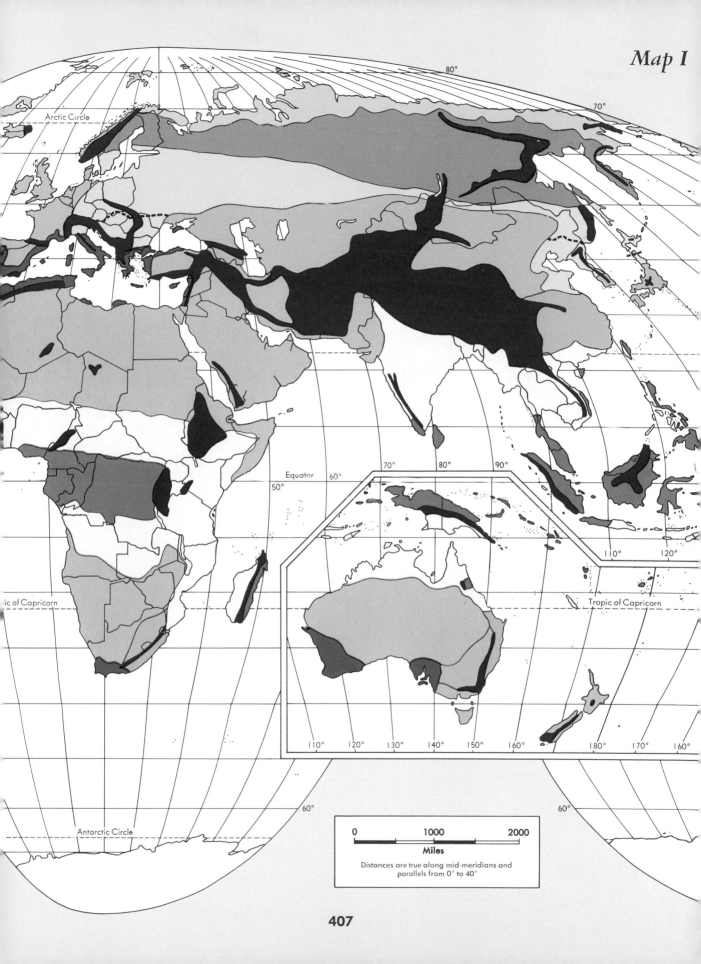

Map I

80°

70°

Arctic Circle

Equator 60°
50°

70° 80° 90°

110° 120°

Tropic of Capricorn

ic of Capricorn

110° 120° 130° 140° 150° 160° 180° 170° 160°

60° 60°

Antarctic Circle

0	1000	2000

Miles

Distances are true along mid-meridians and
parallels from 0° to 40°

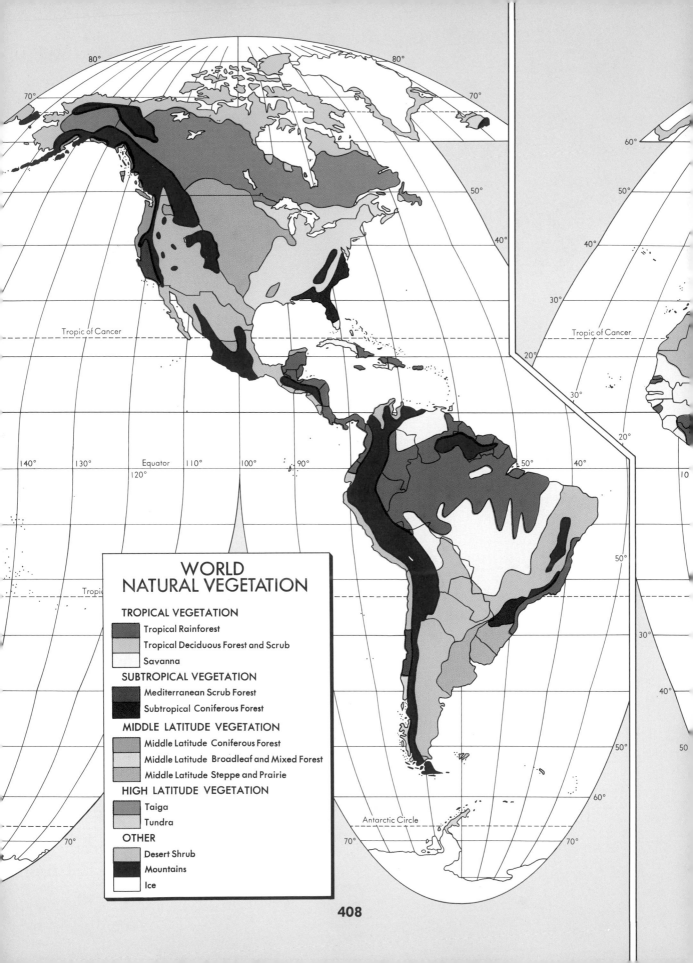

WORLD
NATURAL VEGETATION

TROPICAL VEGETATION

- Tropical Rainforest
- Tropical Deciduous Forest and Scrub
- Savanna

SUBTROPICAL VEGETATION

- Mediterranean Scrub Forest
- Subtropical Coniferous Forest

MIDDLE LATITUDE VEGETATION

- Middle Latitude Coniferous Forest
- Middle Latitude Broadleaf and Mixed Forest
- Middle Latitude Steppe and Prairie

HIGH LATITUDE VEGETATION

- Taiga
- Tundra

OTHER

- Desert Shrub
- Mountains
- Ice

408

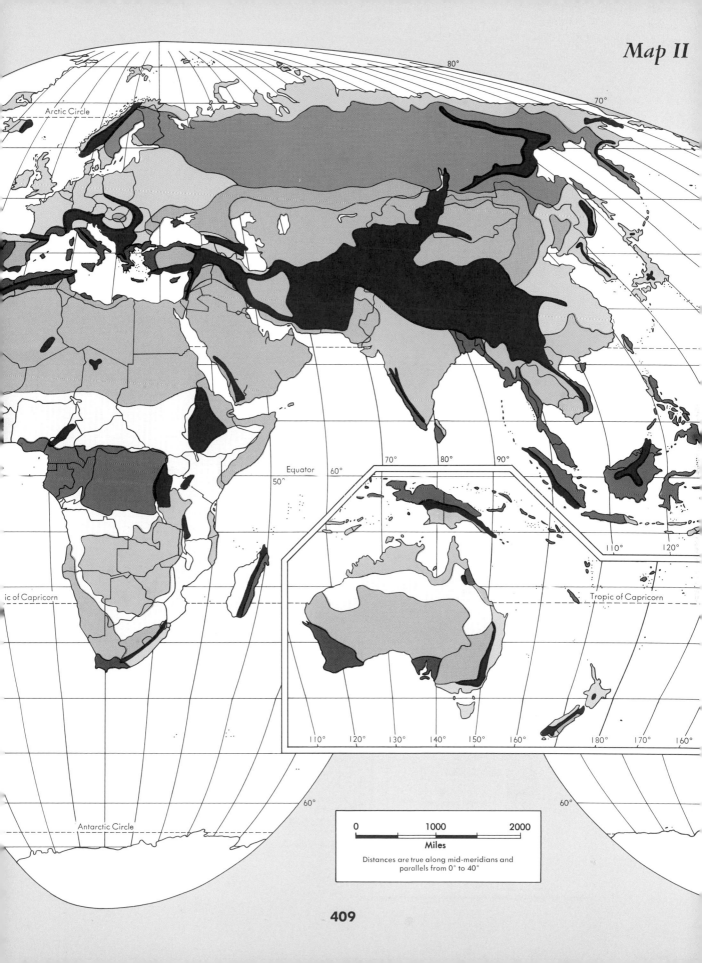

Map II

Arctic Circle

80°

70°

Equator
50°
60°

70°   80°   90°

110°   120°

ic of Capricorn

Tropic of Capricorn

110°   120°   130°   140°   150°   160°   180°   170°   160°

60°

60°

Antarctic Circle

0		1000		2000

Miles

Distances are true along mid-meridians and
parallels from 0° to 40°

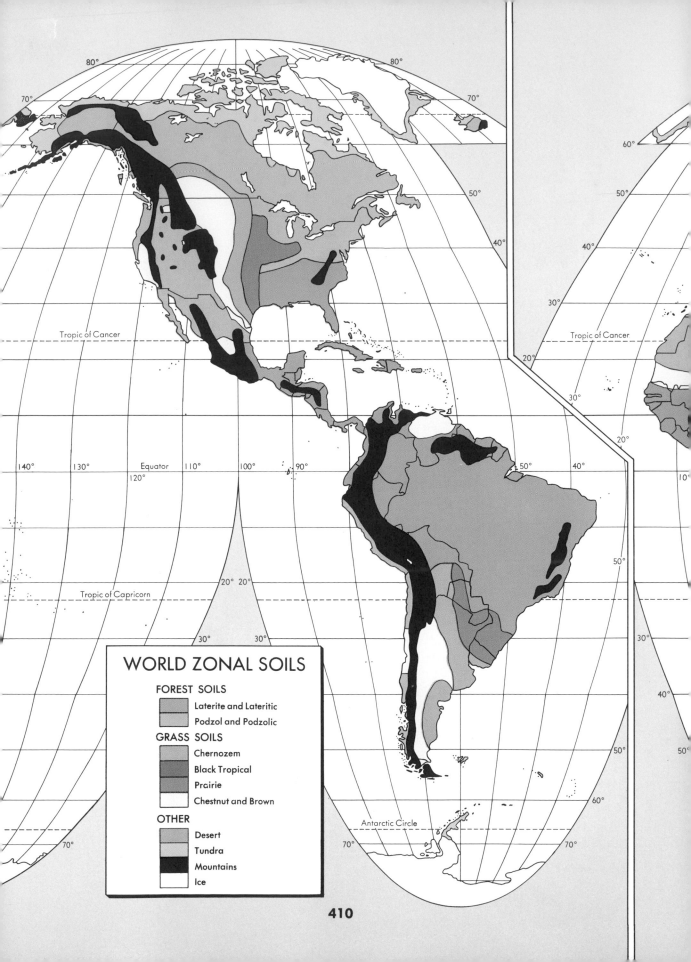

WORLD ZONAL SOILS

FOREST SOILS
- Laterite and Lateritic
- Podzol and Podzolic

GRASS SOILS
- Chernozem
- Black Tropical
- Prairie
- Chestnut and Brown

OTHER
- Desert
- Tundra
- Mountains
- Ice

410

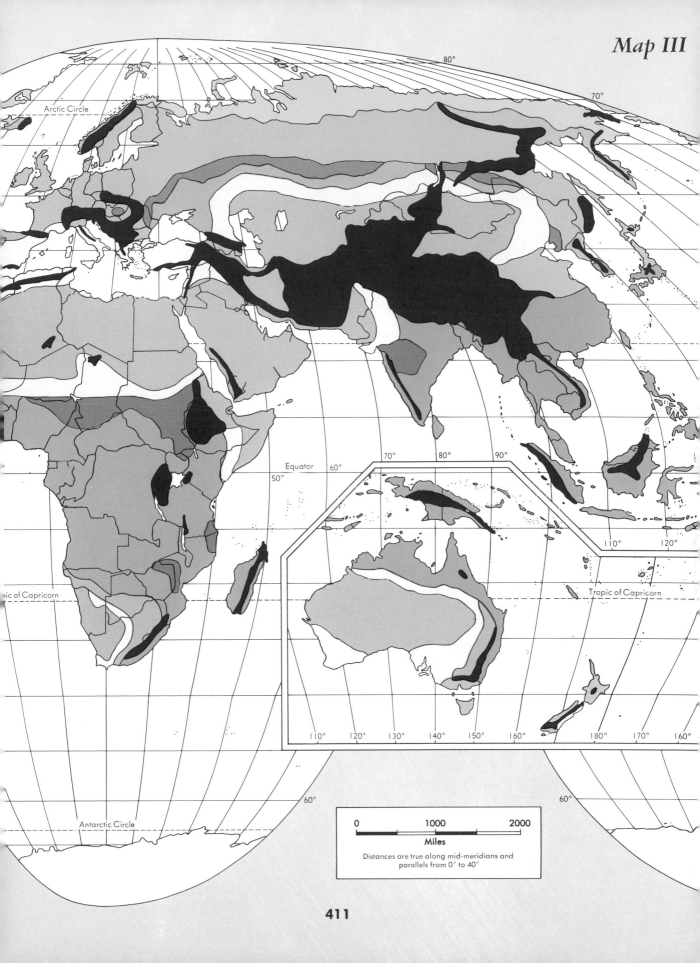

Map III

Equator

Arctic Circle

70°

80°

Tropic of Capricorn

Antarctic Circle

60°

60°

| 0 | 1000 | 2000 |

Miles

Distances are true along mid-meridians and
parallels from 0° to 40°

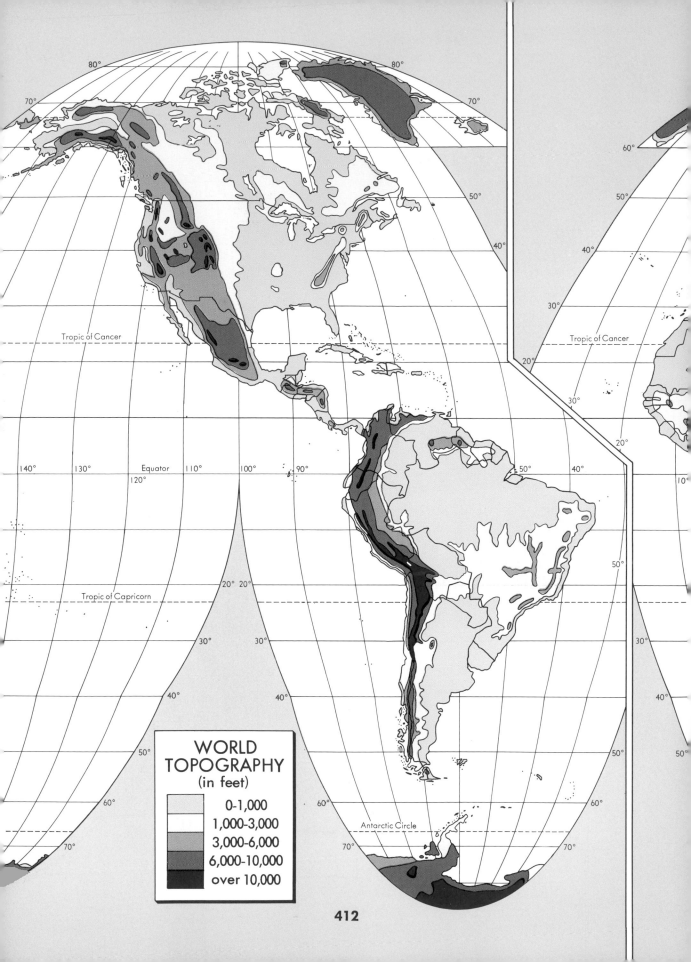

WORLD
TOPOGRAPHY
(in feet)

0-1,000
1,000-3,000
3,000-6,000
6,000-10,000
over 10,000

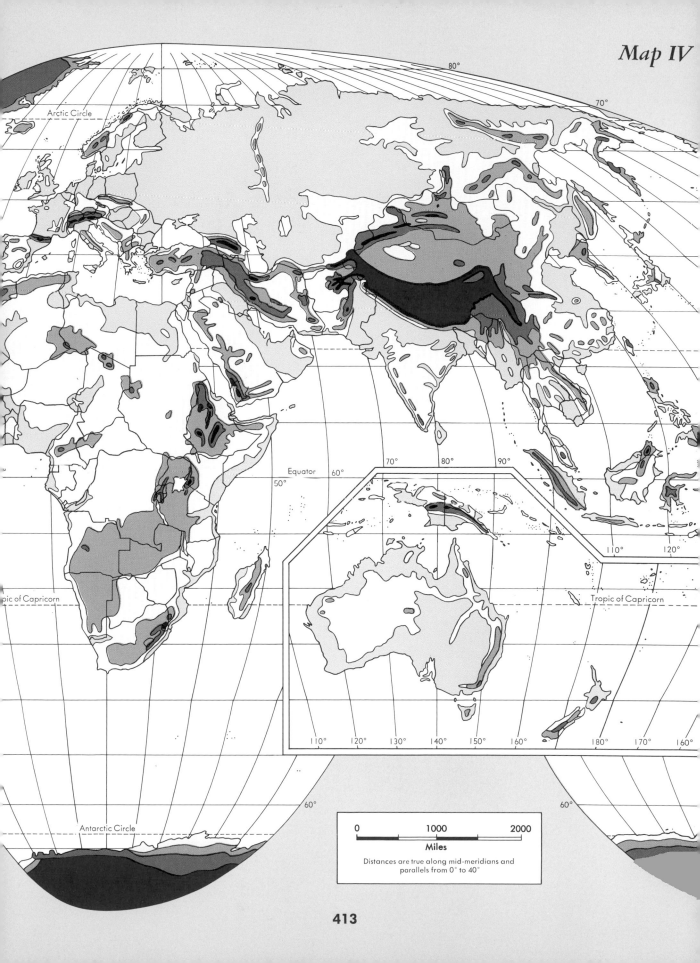

Map IV

Arctic Circle

80°

70°

Equator

70°   80°   90°

60°
50°

110°   120°

Tropic of Capricorn

Tropic of Capricorn

110°   120°   130°   140°   150°   160°   180°   170°   160°

60°

60°

Antarctic Circle

0   1000   2000
Miles
Distances are true along mid-meridians and
parallels from 0° to 40°

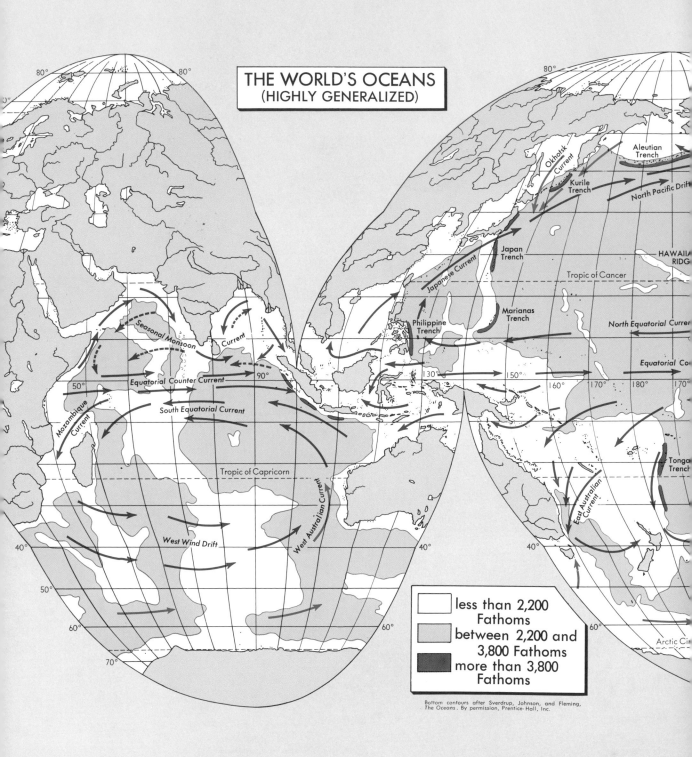

THE WORLD'S OCEANS
(HIGHLY GENERALIZED)

80° 80°

Aleutian Trench

Okhotsk Current

Kurile Trench

North Pacific Drift

Japan Trench

HAWAIIA RIDG

Tropic of Cancer

Japanese Current

Marianas Trench

Philippine Trench

North Equatorial Curren

Equatorial Co

130 150° 160° 170° 180° 170°

Seasonal Monsoon

Current

Equatorial Counter Current

90°

South Equatorial Current

Mozambique Current

Tonga Trench

Tropic of Capricorn

West Australian Current

East Australian Current

West Wind Drift

40° 40°

50° 50°

60° 60°

70°

Arctic Cir

	less than 2,200 Fathoms
	between 2,200 and 3,800 Fathoms
	more than 3,800 Fathoms

Bottom contours after Sverdrup, Johnson, and Fleming,
The Oceans. By permission, Prentice-Hall, Inc.

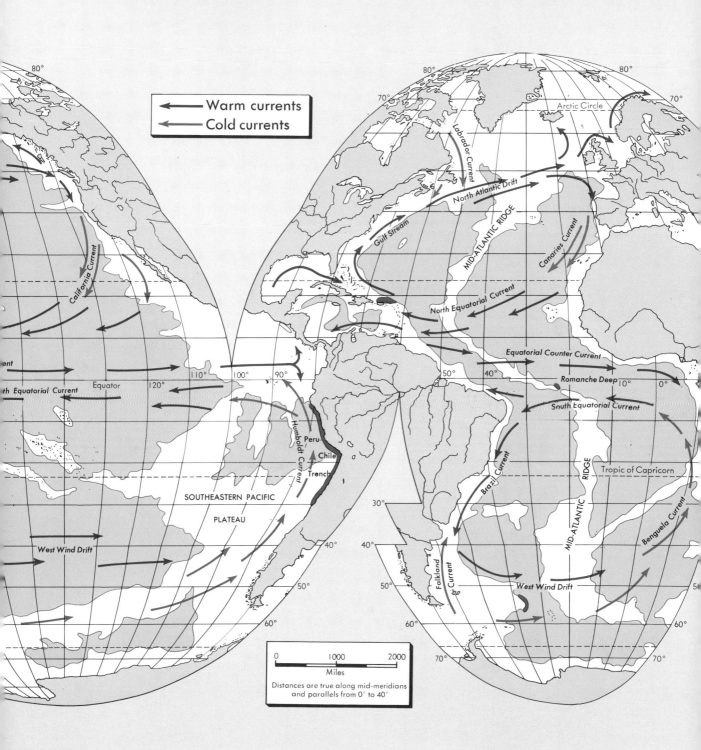

Map V

Warm currents
Cold currents

80° 70° 80° 80° 70°

Arctic Circle

Labrador Current

North Atlantic Drift

Gulf Stream

MID-ATLANTIC RIDGE

Canaries Current

California Current

North Equatorial Current

Equatorial Counter Current

Equator 110° 100° 90° 50° 40° Romanche Deep 10° 0°

120°

th Equatorial Current

South Equatorial Current

Peru-
Chile
Trench

Humboldt Current

Brazil Current

MID-ATLANTIC RIDGE

Tropic of Capricorn

Benguela Current

SOUTHEASTERN PACIFIC

PLATEAU

30°

West Wind Drift 40° 40°

Falkland Current West Wind Drift 50°

50° 50°

60° 60° 60°

70° 70°

0   1000   2000
Miles
Distances are true along mid-meridians
and parallels from 0° to 40°

415

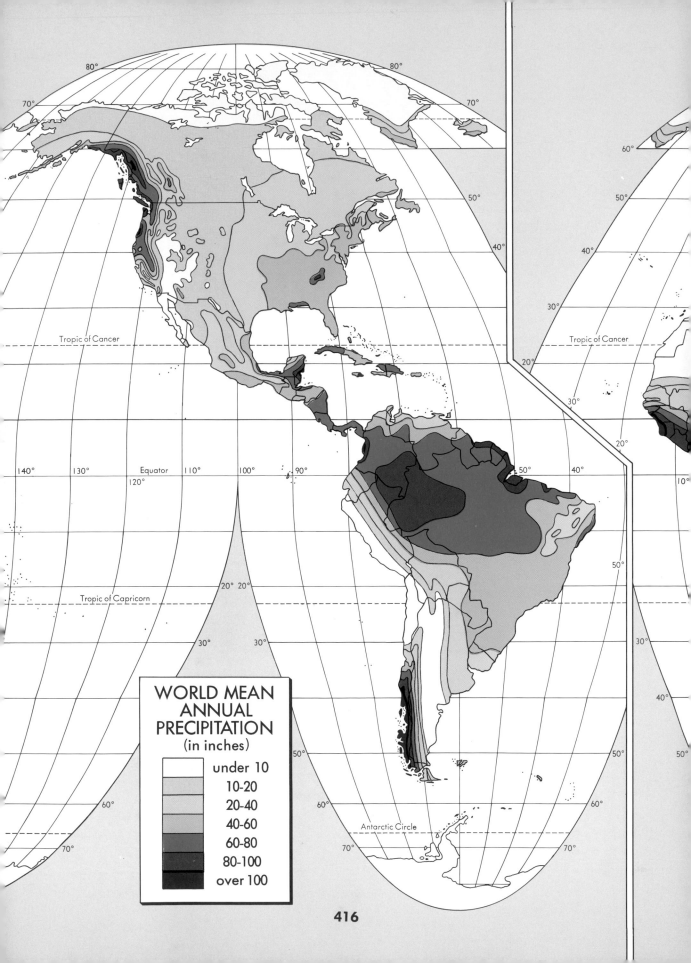

WORLD MEAN
ANNUAL
PRECIPITATION
(in inches)

under 10
10-20
20-40
40-60
60-80
80-100
over 100

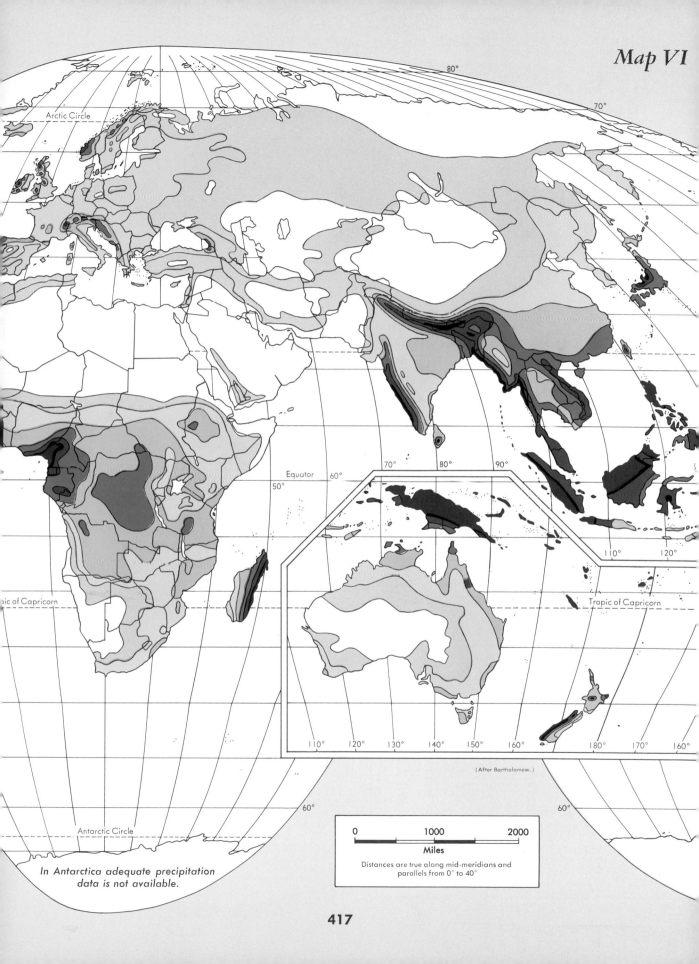

Map VI

Arctic Circle

80°

70°

Equator

50°

60°

70°

80°

90°

110°

120°

Tropic of Capricorn

Tropic of Capricorn

110°

120°

130°

140°

150°

160°

180°

170°

160°

60°

60°

Antarctic Circle

*In Antarctica adequate precipitation
data is not available.*

(After Bartholomew.)

0   1000   2000
Miles

Distances are true along mid-meridians and
parallels from 0° to 40°

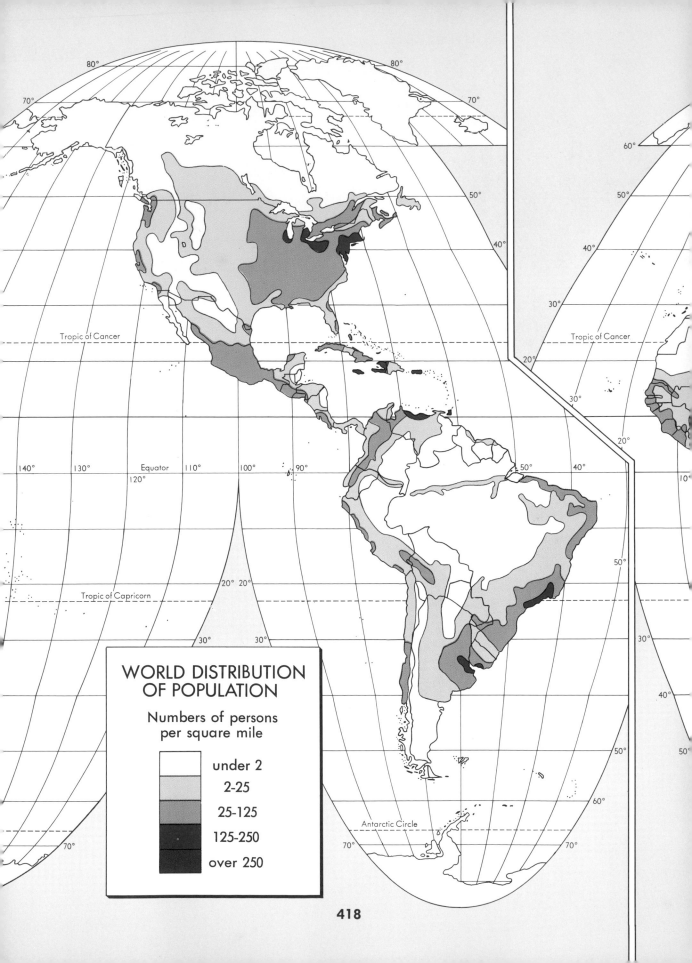

WORLD DISTRIBUTION
OF POPULATION

Numbers of persons
per square mile

under 2

2-25

25-125

125-250

over 250

418

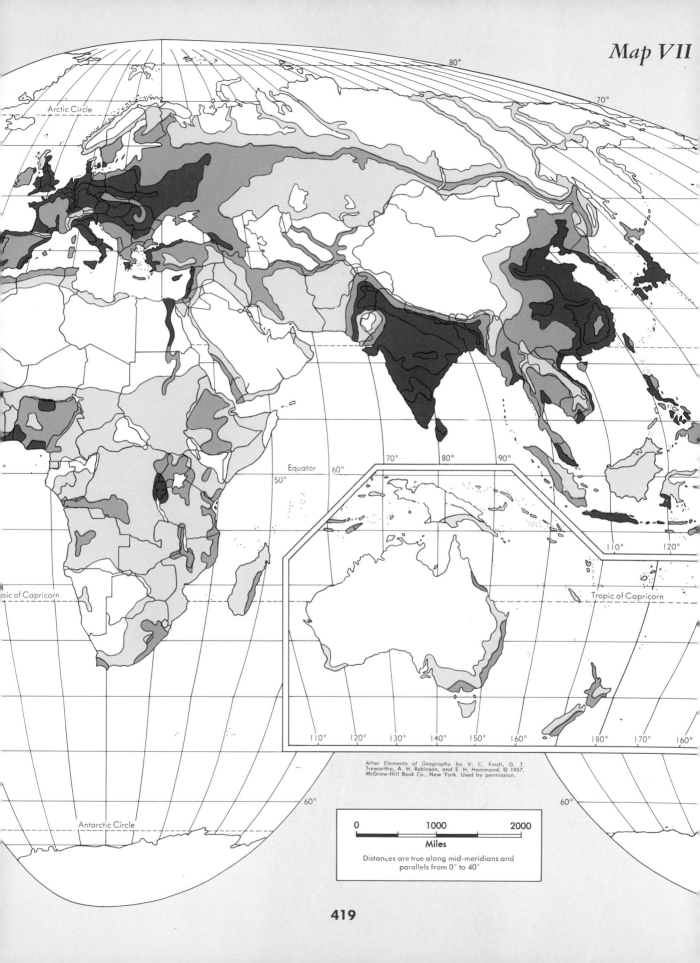

Map VII

Arctic Circle

80°

70°

Equator

Tropic of Capricorn

Antarctic Circle

60°

60°

60°

50°

60°

70°

80°

90°

110°

120°

110°

120°

130°

140°

150°

160°

180°

170°

160°

Tropic of Capricorn

After *Elements of Geography* by V. C. Finch, G. T.
Trewartha, A. H. Robinson, and E. H. Hammond. © 1957,
McGraw-Hill Book Co., New York. Used by permission.

0   1000   2000

Miles

Distances are true along mid-meridians and
parallels from 0° to 40°

Map VIII

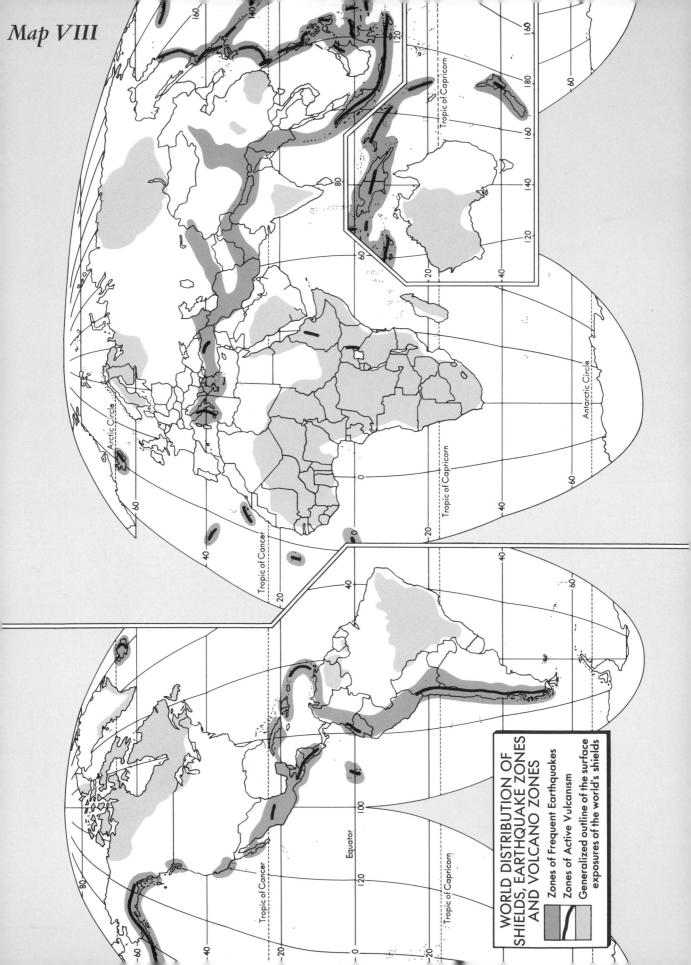

WORLD DISTRIBUTION OF
SHIELDS, EARTHQUAKE ZONES
AND VOLCANO ZONES

Zones of Frequent Earthquakes

Zones of Active Vulcanism

Generalized outline of the surface
exposures of the world's shields

Arctic Circle

Tropic of Cancer

Tropic of Capricorn

Antarctic Circle

Equator

Tropic of Cancer

Tropic of Capricorn

The Köppen Climatic Classification

There are five basic climatic categories in the Köppen system, symbolized as A, B, C, D, and E. These are further subdivided by adding lower-case letters to indicate lesser variations of temperature and moisture within the major groupings.

A—*Tropical Humid Climates*

Coolest month must be above 18° C. (64.4° F.).

Af—Tropical Rain Forest (f—feucht or moist)
No dry season. Driest month must attain at least 6 cm. (2.4 in.) of rainfall.
Aw—Tropical Savanna (w—winter)
Winter dry season. At least one month must attain less than 6 cm. (2.4 in.) of rainfall.

The following lower-case letters may be added for clarification in special situations.

m (monsoon)—despite a dry season, total rainfall is so heavy that rain forest vegetation is not impeded.
w'—autumn rainfall maximum.
w"—two dry seasons during a single year.
s (summer)—summer dry season.
i—annual temperature range must be less than 5° C. (9° F.).
g (Ganges)—hottest month occurs prior to summer solstice.

421

B—*Dry Climates*

No specific amount of moisture makes a climate dry. Rather, the
rate of evaporation (determined by temperature) relative to the
amount of precipitation dictates how dry a climate is in terms
of its ability to support plant growth. This is reckoned through
the use of formulas that are not included here. See Selected
Bibliography, Chapters 3 and 4, Köppen and Geiger.

BW (W—wuste or wasteland)—desert.
BS (S—steppe)—semiarid.

*The following lower-case letters may be added for clarification
in special situations.*

h (heiss or hot)—average annual temperature must be above
18° C. (64.4° F.).
k (kalt or cold)—average annual temperature must be under
18° C. (64.4° F.).
k'—temperature of warmest month must be under 18° C.
(64.4° F.).
s—summer dry season. At least three times as much precipitation
in the wettest month as in the driest.
w—winter dry season. At least ten times as much precipitation
in the wettest month as in the driest.
n (nebel or fog)—frequent fog.

C—*Temperate Humid Climates*

Coldest month average must be below 18° C. (64.4° F.), but above
−3° C. (26.6° F.). Warmest month average must be above 10° C.
(50° F.).
Cf—no dry season. Driest month must attain at least 3 cm. (1.2 in.)
of precipitation.
Cw—winter dry season. At least ten times as much rain in the wettest
month as in the driest.
Cs—summer dry season. At least three times as much rain in the
wettest month as in the driest. Driest month must receive less
than 3 cm. (1.2 in.) of rainfall.

*The following lower-case letters may be added for clarification
in special situations.*

a—hot summer. Warmest month must average above 22° C.
(71.6° F.).
b—cool summer. Warmest month must average below 22° C.
(71.6° F.).
c—short cool summer. Less than four months over 10° C. (50° F.).
i—see A climate.
g—see A climate.
n—see B climate.
x—maximum precipitation in late spring or early summer.

D—*Cold Humid Climates*

Coldest month average must be below −3° C. (26.6° F.). Warmest month average must be above 10° C. (50° F.).

Df—no dry season.
Dw—winter dry season.

> *The following lower-case letters may be added for clarification in special situations.*

a—see C climate.
b—see C climate.
c—see C climate.
d—coldest month average must be below −38° C. (−36.4° F.).
f—see A climate.
s—see A climate.
w—see A climate.

E—*Polar Climates*

Warmest month average must be below 10° C. (50° F.).

ET (T—tundra)—Warmest month average must be above 0° C. (32° F.).
EF—All months must average below 0° C. (32° F.).

The Geologic Time Scale

Eras				Beginning of Each Period
CENOZOIC	EPOCHS	Quaternary {	Recent (holcene)	15,000 years ago
			Pleistocene (ice age)	1,500,000 years ago
		Tertiary {	Pliocene	15,000,000 years ago
			Miocene	30,000,000 years ago
			Oligocene	40,000,000 years ago
			Eocene	50,000,000 years ago
			Paleocene	60,000,000 years ago
MESOZOIC			Cretaceous	120,000,000 years ago
			Jurassic	160,000,000 years ago
			Triassic	180,000,000 years ago
PALEOZOIC			Permian	225,000,000 years ago
			Pennsylvanian } Carboniferous	270,000,000 years ago
			Mississippian	300,000,000 years ago
			Devonian	345,000,000 years ago
			Silurian	375,000,000 years ago
			Ordovician	435,000,000 years ago
			Cambrian	540,000,000 years ago
PRECAM-BRIAN (CRYPTO-ZOIC)	PROTEROZOIC		Keweenawan	
			Huronian	1,000,000,000 years ago
	ARCHEOZOIC			Possibly 3,350,000,000 years ago to 5,000,000,000 years ago
			Unknown	

425

Selected Bibliography

Chapter 1

BOWDITCH, NATHANIAL. *American Practical Navigator.* Washington, D.C.: Government Printing Office. (Issued irregularly as U.S. Hydrographic Office Publication No. 9 since 1802.)

BROWN, LLOYD A. *The Story of Maps.* Boston: Little, Brown & Co., 1950.

DUTTON, BENJAMIN. *Navigation and Nautical Astronomy.* 8th ed. Annapolis: U.S. Naval Institute, 1943.

GREENHOOD, DAVID. *Mapping.* Chicago: University of Chicago Press, 1964.

HARRIS, RUBY M. *The Rand McNally Handbook of Map and Globe Usage.* 3d ed. Chicago: Rand McNally & Co., 1960.

HARRISON, LUCIA C. *Sun, Earth, Time and Man.* Chicago: Rand McNally & Co., 1960.

JOHNSON, W. E. *Mathematical Geography.* Cincinnati: American Book Co., 1907.

KUIPER, G. P., *et al. The Solar System.* Vol. II, *The Earth as a Planet.* Chicago: University of Chicago Press, 1954.

PYNE, T. E. *Standard Time.* Washington, D.C.: Interstate Commerce Commission, Government Printing Office, 1958.

RAISZ, ERWIN. *General Cartography.* 2d ed. New York: McGraw-Hill Book Co., Inc., 1948.

ROBINSON, ARTHUR H. *Elements of Cartography.* 2d ed. New York: John Wiley & Sons, Inc., 1960.

Chapter 2

BROWN, LLOYD A. *The Story of Maps.* Boston: Little, Brown & Co., 1950.

CHAMBERLIN, WELLMAN. *The Round Earth on Flat Paper.* Washington, D.C.: National Geographic Society, 1947.

DEETZ, CHARLES A., and ADAMS, OSCAR S. *Elements of Map Projection.* 5th ed. Special Publication No. 68. Washington, D.C.: U.S. Coast and Geodetic Survey, Government Printing Office, 1945.

GREENHOOD, DAVID. *Mapping.* Chicago: University of Chicago Press, 1964.

HARRIS, RUBY M. *The Rand McNally Handbook of Map and Globe Usage.* 3d ed. Chicago: Rand McNally & Co., 1960.

LOBECK, ARMIN K. *Block Diagrams.* New York: John Wiley & Sons, Inc., 1924.

———. *Things Maps Don't Tell Us.* New York: The Macmillan Co., 1957.

RAISZ, ERWIN. *General Cartography.* 2d ed. New York: McGraw-Hill Book Co., Inc., 1948.

ROBINSON, ARTHUR H. *Elements of Cartography.* 2d ed. New York: John Wiley & Sons, Inc., 1960.

TANNENBAUM, BEULAH, and STILLMAN, MYRA. *Understanding Maps.* New York: Whittlesey House, 1957.

UNITED STATES DEPARTMENT OF THE ARMY. *Map Reading.* Technical Manual F M 21–26. Washington, D.C.: Government Printing Office, 1956.

Chapters 3 and 4

BLAIR, THOMAS A. *Climatology, General and Regional.* Englewood Cliffs, N.J.: Prentice-Hall, Inc., 1942.

BLAIR, THOMAS A., and FITE, ROBERT C. *Weather Elements.* 5th ed. Englewood Cliffs, N.J.: Prentice-Hall, Inc., 1965.

BRUNT, D. *Weather Study.* New York: The Ronald Press Co., 1942.

CLAYTON, H. HELM. *World Weather Records.* Smithsonian Misc. Collection, Vol. LXXIX. Washington, D.C.: Smithsonian Institution, 1944.

CRITCHFIELD, HOWARD J. *General Climatology.* Englewood Cliffs, N.J.: Prentice-Hall, Inc., 1960.

FLORA, S. D. *Tornadoes of the United States.* Norman: University of Oklahoma Press, 1954.

HAURWITZ, BERNHARD, and AUSTIN, JAMES M. *Climatology.* New York: McGraw-Hill Book Co., Inc., 1944.

HUNTINGTON, ELLSWORTH. *Civilization and Climate.* New Haven: Yale University Press, 1924.

KOEPPE, C. E., and DE LONG, G. C. *Weather and Climate.* New York: McGraw-Hill Book Co., Inc., 1958.

KÖPPEN, W., and GEIGER, R. *Handbuch der Klimatologie.* 5 Vols. Berlin: Verlagsbuchhandlung Gebrüder Borntaeger, 1930.

MILLER, A. AUSTIN. *Climatology.* 3d ed. New York: E. P. Dutton & Co., Inc., 1953.

RIEHL, H. *Tropical Meteorology.* New York: McGraw-Hill Book Co., Inc., 1954.

——————. *Introduction to the Atmosphere.* New York: McGraw-Hill Book Co., Inc., 1965.

TANNEHILL, I. R. *Hurricanes.* Princeton: Princeton University Press, 1956.

TREWARTHA, GLENN T. *An Introduction to Climate.* 3d ed. New York: McGraw-Hill Book Co., Inc., 1954.

UNITED STATES DEPARTMENT OF AGRICULTURE. *Climate and Man.* The Yearbook of Agriculture, 1941. Washington, D.C.: Government Printing Office, 1941.

WENSTROM, W. H. *Weather and the Ocean of Air.* Boston: Houghton Mifflin Co., 1942.

Chapter 5

HADDEN-GUEST, STEPHEN, WRIGHT, JOHN K., and TECLAFF, EILEEN M. *A World Geography of Forest Resources.* New York: The Ronald Press Co., 1956.

HILL, ALBERT F. *Economic Botany.* 2d ed. New York: McGraw-Hill Book Co., Inc., 1952.

KLAGES, KARL H. S. *Ecological Crop Geography.* New York: The Macmillan Co., 1949.

NEWBIGIN, MARION I. *Plant and Animal Geography.* London: Methuen & Co., Ltd., 1936.

OOSTING, HENRY J. *The Study of Plant Communities.* 2d ed. San Francisco: W. H. Freeman & Co., 1956.

POLUNIN, N. *Introduction to Plant Geography.* New York: McGraw-Hill Book Co., Inc., 1960.

TRANSEAU, EDGAR N., SAMPSON, H. C., and TIFFANY, L. H. *Textbook of Botany.* Rev. ed. New York: Harper & Row, 1953.

UNITED STATES DEPARTMENT OF AGRICULTURE. *Grass.* The Yearbook of Agriculture, 1948. Washington, D.C.: Government Printing Office, 1948.

————. *Trees.* The Yearbook of Agriculture, 1949. Washington, D.C.: Government Printing Office, 1949.

WEAVER, JOHN E., and CLEMENTS, F. E. *Plant Ecology.* 2d ed. New York: McGraw-Hill Book Co., Inc., 1938.

WILSON, CHARLES MORROW. *Grass and People.* Gainesville: University of Florida Press, 1963.

Chapter 6

BENNETT, HUGH H. *Soil Conservation.* New York: McGraw-Hill Book Co., Inc., 1939.

GLINKA, K. D. *The Great Soil Groups of the World and Their Development.* Ann Arbor: J. W. Edwards, Inc., 1927.

JENNY, HANS. *Factors of Soil Formation.* New York: McGraw-Hill Book Co., Inc., 1941.

JOFFE, JACOB S. *Pedology.* 2d ed. New Brunswick: Rutgers University Press, 1949.

KELLOG, C. E. *The Soils That Support Us.* New York: The Macmillan Co., 1940.

LUTZ, HAROLD J., and CHANDLER, ROBERT F., JR. *Forest Soils.* New York: John Wiley & Sons, Inc., 1946.

ROBINSON, GILBERT W. *Soils: Their Origin, Constitution and Classification.* 3d ed. New York: John Wiley & Sons, Inc., 1950.

UNITED STATES DEPARTMENT OF AGRICULTURE. *Soils.* The Yearbook of Agriculture, 1957. Washington, D.C.: Government Printing Office, 1957.

————. *Soils and Men.* The Yearbook of Agriculture, 1938. Washington, D.C.: Government Printing Office, 1938.

WOLFANGER, L. A. *The Major Soil Divisions of the United States.* New York: John Wiley & Sons, Inc., 1930.

Chapter 7

BASCOM, WILLARD. *A Hole in the Bottom of the Sea: The Story of the Mohole Project.* Garden City, N.Y.: Doubleday & Co., Inc., 1961.

BULLARD, FRED M., *Volcanoes: In History, In Theory, and In Eruption.* Austin: University of Texas Press, 1963.

COTTON, C. A. *Landscape as Developed by Processes of Normal Erosion.* Cambridge: Cambridge University Press, 1941.

FLINT, RICHARD F. *Glacial and Pleistocene Geology.* 2d ed. New York: John Wiley & Sons, Inc., 1957.

IACOPI, ROBERT. *Earthquake Country: How, Why and Where Earthquakes Strike in California.* Menlo Park, Calif.: Lane Book Co., 1963.

JEFFERIES, H. *Earthquakes and Mountains.* London: Methuen & Co., Ltd., 1950.

JOHNSON, DOUGLAS W. *Shore Processes and Shoreline Development.* New York: John Wiley & Sons, Inc., 1919.

JOHNSTONE, DON, and CROSS, WILLIAM P. *Elements of Applied Hydrology.* New York: The Ronald Press Co., 1949.

KING, CUCHLAINE A. *Beaches and Coasts.* London: E. Arnold & Co., 1959.

KUIPER, G. P., *et al.* *The Solar System.* Vol. II, *The Earth as a Planet.* Chicago: University of Chicago Press, 1954.

LEET, L. D., and JUDSON, S. *Physical Geology.* Englewood Cliffs, N.J.: Prentice-Hall, Inc., 1954.

LEOPOLD, LUNA B., and MADDOCK, THOMAS, JR. *The Flood Control Controversy—Big Dams, Little Dams, and Land Management.* New York: The Ronald Press Co., 1954.

LOBECK, ARMIN K. *Geomorphology.* New York: McGraw-Hill Book Co., Inc., 1939.

LONGWELL, CHESTER R., and FLINT, RICHARD F. *Introduction to Physical Geology.* 2d ed. New York: John Wiley & Sons, Inc., 1962.

LOOMIS, F. B. *Field Book of Common Rocks and Minerals.* New York: G. P. Putnam's Sons, Inc., 1948.

MATTHES, F. E. *The Incomparable Valley; A Geological Interpretation of the Yosemite.* Edited by F. FRYXELL. Berkeley: University of California Press, 1950.

PUTNAM, WILLIAM C. *Geology.* Fair Lawn, N.J.: Oxford University Press, 1964.

THORNBURY, W. D. *Principles of Geomorphology.* New York: John Wiley & Sons, Inc., 1954.

THWAITES, F. T. *Outlines of Glacial Geology.* Ann Arbor: J. W. Edwards, Inc., 1934.

UNITED STATES DEPARTMENT OF AGRICULTURE. *Water.* The Yearbook of Agriculture, 1955. Washington, D.C.: Government Printing Office, 1955.

VON ENGELN, O. D. *Geomorphology, Systematic and Regional.* New York: The Macmillan Co., 1942.

WISLER, CHESTER O., and BRATER, E. F. *Hydrology.* 2d ed. New York: John Wiley & Sons, Inc., 1959.

Chapter 8

BENNISON, E. E. *Ground Water: Its Development, Uses and Conservation.* St. Paul: Edward E. Johnson Co., 1947.

JOHNSTONE, DON, and CROSS, WILLIAM P. *Elements of Applied Hydrology.* New York: The Ronald Press Co., 1949.

LEET, L. D., and JUDSON, S. *Physical Geology.* Englewood Cliffs, N.J.: Prentice-Hall, Inc., 1954.

LOBECK, ARMIN K. *Geomorphology.* New York: McGraw-Hill Book Co., Inc., 1939.

LONGWELL, CHESTER R., and FLINT, RICHARD F. *Introduction to Physical Geology.* 2d ed. New York: John Wiley & Sons, Inc., 1962.

THOMAS, H. F. *The Conservation of Ground Water.* New York: McGraw-Hill Book Co., Inc., 1951.

THORNBURY, W. D. *Principles of Geomorphology.* New York: John Wiley & Sons, Inc., 1954.

TODD, D. K. *Ground Water Hydrology.* New York: John Wiley & Sons, Inc., 1959.

TOLMAN, C. F. *Ground Water.* New York: McGraw-Hill Book Co., Inc., 1937.

UNITED STATES DEPARTMENT OF AGRICULTURE. *Water.* The Yearbook of Agriculture, 1955. Washington, D.C.: Government Printing Office, 1955.

UNITED STATES OFFICE OF SALINE WATER. *Demineralization of Saline Water.* Research and Development Progress Report, 1952–60. Washington, D.C.: Government Printing Office, 1960.

VON ENGELN, O. D. *Geomorphology, Systematic and Regional.* New York: The Macmillan Co., 1942.

WISLER, CHESTER O., and BRATER, E. F. *Hydrology.* 2d ed. New York: John Wiley & Sons, Inc., 1959.

Chapter 9

CARSON, RACHEL L. *The Sea Around Us.* Fair Lawn, N.J.: Oxford University Press, 1951.

COKER, R. E. *This Great and Wide Sea.* Chapel Hill: University of North Carolina Press, 1947.

DARWIN, CHARLES. *The Structure and Distribution of Coral Reefs.* 3d ed. New York: Appleton-Century-Crofts, Inc., 1898.

ELLIS, CECIL B. *Fresh Water from the Ocean—For Cities, Industry, and Irrigation.* New York: The Ronald Press Co., 1954.

ENGLE, LEONARD. *The Sea.* Life Nature Library. New York: Time, Inc., 1961.

KING, CUCHLAINE A. *An Introduction to Oceanography.* New York: McGraw-Hill Book Co., Inc., 1962.

———. *Oceanography for Geographers.* London: E. Arnold & Co., 1962.

KUENEN, P. *Marine Geology.* New York: John Wiley & Sons, Inc., 1950.

MARMER, H. A. *The Tide.* New York: Appleton-Century-Crofts, Inc., 1926.

RUSSELL, R. C. H., and MACMILLAN, D. H. *Waves and Tides.* London: Hutchinson's Scientific and Technical Publications, 1954.

SHEPARD, FRANCIS P. *Submarine Geology.* 2d ed. New York: Harper & Row, 1963.

———. *The Earth Beneath the Sea.* Baltimore: Johns Hopkins Press, 1959.

SVERDRUP, H. U., JOHNSON, MARTIN W., and FLEMING, RICHARD H. *The Oceans: Their Physics, Chemistry and General Biology.* Englewood Cliffs, N.J.: Prentice-Hall, Inc., 1942.

UNITED STATES OFFICE OF SALINE WATER. *Demineralization of Saline Water.* Research and Development Progress Report, 1952–60. Washington, D.C.: Government Printing Office, 1960.

Index